INTERNATIONAL SERIES OF MONOGRAPHS ON
ELECTRONICS AND INSTRUMENTATION
GENERAL EDITORS: D. W. FRY and W. HIGINBOTHAM

VOLUME 22

OTHER TITLES IN THE SERIES

(FORMERLY PERGAMON SCIENCE SERIES ELECTRONICS AND WAVES)

Vol. 1 *Signal, Noise and Resolution in Nuclear Counter Amplifiers*
by A. B. GILLESPIE

Vol. 2 *Scintillation Counters*
by J. B. BIRKS

Vol. 3 *Probability and Information Theory with Applications to Radar*
by P. M. WOODWARD

Vol. 4 *Physics and Applications of Secondary Electron Emission*
by H. BRUINING

Vol. 5 *Millimicrosecond Pulse Techniques* (2nd edition)
by I. A. D. LEWIS and F. H. WELLS

Vol. 6 *Introduction to Electronic Analogue Computers*
by C. A. A. WASS

Vol. 7 *Scattering and Diffraction of Radio Waves*
by J. R. MENTZER

Vol. 8 *Space-Charge Waves and Slow Electromagnetic Waves*
by A. H. W. BECK

Vol. 9 *Statistical Theory of Signal Detection*
by C. W. HELSTROM

Vol. 10 *Laplace Transforms for Electronic Engineers*
by J. G. HOLBROOK

Vol. 11 *Frequency Modulation Theory—Application to Microwave Links*
by J. FAGOT and P. MAGNE

Vol. 12 *Theory of Microwave Valves*
by S. D. GVOZDOVER

Vol. 13 *Electronic Computers*
by A. I. KIROV and N. A. KRINITSKII

Vol. 14 *Topics in Engineering Logic*
by M. NADLER

Vol. 15 *Environmental Testing Techniques*
by G. W. A. DUMMER and N. B. GRIFFIN

Vol. 16 *Fundamentals of Microwave Electronics*
by V. N. SHEVCHIK

Vol. 17 *Static Electromagnetic Frequency Changers*
by L. L. ROZHANSKII

Vol. 18 *Problems in the Design and Development of 750 MW Turbogenerators*
by V. P. ANEMPODISTOV, E. G. KASHARSKII and I. D. URUSOV

Vol. 19 *Controlled-Delay Devices*
by S. A. DOGANOVSKII and V. A. IVANOV

Vol. 20 *High Sensitivity Counting Techniques*
by D. E. WATT and D. RAMSDEN

Vol. 21 *Asynchronized Synchronous Machines*
by M. M. BOTVINNIK

SAMPLING SYSTEMS THEORY

AND ITS APPLICATION

Volume 1

Sampling Systems Theory
and its Application
Volume 1

YA. Z. TSYPKIN
Institute of Automatics and Telemechanics
Academy of Sciences of the U.S.S.R.

TRANSLATED FROM THE RUSSIAN BY

R. C. HUTCHISON

TRANSLATION EDITED BY

I. COCHRANE
Electronics Laboratory
Department of Electrical Engineering
Royal College of Science and
Technology, Glasgow

A Pergamon Press Book

THE MACMILLAN COMPANY
NEW YORK
1964

THE MACMILLAN COMPANY
60 Fifth Avenue
New York 11, N.Y.

This book is distributed by
THE MACMILLAN COMPANY
pursuant to a special arrangement with
PERGAMON PRESS LIMITED
Oxford, England

Library of Congress Catalog Card Number 62-9190

Translated from the original Russian volume entitled
Teoriya impul'snykh sistem, published by Fizmatgiz,
Moscow, 1958

MADE IN GREAT BRITAIN

CONTENTS

VOLUME I

Preface ix

Introduction xiii

Chapter I — Pulse Systems and Their Applications

1.1 Introduction to Pulse Systems 1
1.2 Open-Loop Pulse Systems 8
1.3 Closed-Loop Pulse Systems 35

Chapter II — Fundamentals of the Discrete Laplace Transformation and Difference Equations

2.1 Lattice Functions and Difference Equations 93
2.2 Definition of the Discrete Laplace Transformation 104
2.3 Fundamental Rules and Theorems 109
2.4 Solution of the Simplest Difference Equations 132
2.5 Solution of Linear Difference Equations of Arbitrary Order 144
2.6 Inverse Discrete Laplace Transformation 150
2.7 Relationship between the Discrete Laplace Transformation, Fourier Series and Laurent Series 163
2.8 Relationship between the Image of a Continuous Function and the Image of the Corresponding Lattice Function 168
2.9 Random Lattice Functions 183

Chapter III — Fundamentals of the Theory of Open-Loop Pulse Systems

3.1 Reduction of a Pulse System to the Simplest Form 193
3.2 Equations and Transfer Functions of Open-Loop Pulse Systems 203
3.3 Equation and Transfer Functions of Open-Loop Pulse Systems with Several Pulse Elements 226
3.4 Equation and Transfer Functions of Open-Loop Pulse Systems with Variable Parameters 236
3.5 Response of Open-Loop Pulse Systems to Typical Excitations 248
3.6 Pulse and Frequency Characteristics of Open-Loop Pulse Systems 260
3.7 Response of Open-Loop Pulse Systems to Arbitrary Non-Periodic and Periodic Excitations 272
3.8 Open-Loop Pulse Systems with Stationary Random Excitations 280
3.9 Comparison of Open-Loop Pulse Systems and Open-Loop Continuous Systems 290

CHAPTER IV — INVESTIGATION AND ANALYSIS OF OPEN-LOOP PULSE SYSTEMS

4.1 Thermal Behaviour of a Device under Intermittent Operation .. 297
4.2 The Peak Detector 302
4.3 Clamping Circuit 306
4.4 Pulse Control of Motor Speed 309
4.5 The Inverter 319
4.6 Oscillations of Mechanical Systems under the Action of Impulsive Forces 327
4.7 A Wide-Band Video Amplifier 335
4.8 Mutual Interference in Multichannel Pulse Systems 348
4.9 The Synchronous Filter 357
4.10 Device for Determining System Characteristics from Data Obtained under Normal Operating Conditions 364
4.11 A Communications System Using Prediction 369

VOLUME II

CHAPTER V — FUNDAMENTALS OF CLOSED PULSE SYSTEMS

5.1 Reduction of Closed Pulse Systems to the Simplest Form 377
5.2 Equations and Transfer Functions of Closed Pulse Systems 383
5.3 Equations and Transfer Functions of Closed Pulse Systems with Several Pulse Elements 391
5.4 Stability and Stabilisation of Closed Pulse Systems 401
5.5 Frequency and Pulse Characteristics of Closed Pulse Systems 448
5.6 Transient and Steady-state Processes in Closed Pulse Systems and their Evaluation 466
5.7 Closed Pulse Systems with Stationary Random Influences 493
5.8 Closed Pulse System with Extrapolators 513
5.9 Synthesis of Closed Pulse Systems 527
5.10 The Processes in Closed Non-linear Pulsed Systems 538

CHAPTER VI — INVESTIGATION AND COMPUTATION OF CLOSED PULSE SYSTEMS

6.1 Automatic Temperature Control System 555
6.2 Automatic Control System of Mixture Concentration 575
6.3 Noncontact Servo-System 586
6.4 Automatic Frequency Control System 598
6.5 System of Automatic Gain Control 608
6.6 Automatic Ranging System 622
6.7 The Digital Computer as a Converter of Discrete Data 641
6.8 Smoothing and Prediction of Discrete Data in Digital Computers 657
6.9 Pulse System for Converting Discrete Data into Continuous 664

APPENDIXES 677
BIBLIOGRAPHY 711
INDEX 737

PREFACE

THE rapid advance in pulse techniques, radar, digital computing techniques and automation has led in recent years to the intensive development and application of pulse systems, i.e. systems whose operation is associated with the generation, transmission and transformation of a train of pulses.

The simplest open-loop pulse systems include motors and electromagnetic devices operating under pulse conditions, and the electrical circuits and video-amplifiers used in phototelegraphy and television. Telemetry pulse systems and multichannel pulse communication systems are further examples of open-loop pulse systems.

Pulse servo-systems and intermittent control systems are examples of a more complex type of pulse system, namely, closed-loop pulse systems. Automatic systems with digital computers as constituent elements also come under the category of closed-loop pulse systems.

The extent to which pulse systems, or sampling systems, are used in modern technology is obvious even from this short list.

All pulse systems, irrespective of field of application and individual differences, can be considered from a single point of view and investigated by a common method that enables us to obtain the required results directly and in a simple form suitable for engineering purposes.

In the present volumes the author has attempted to develop the theory and methods of analysing pulse systems, together with, as far as is possible, the theory and methods of analysing conventional continuous systems. That this is possible is due to the nature of the mathematical apparatus, the discrete Laplace transformation, which enables us to introduce for pulse systems the concepts of transfer function, frequency and time characteristics, and to define clearly the transient and steady-state response.

The analogy between the methods of analysing continuous systems and pulse systems is important not only because it permits the methods of continuous-system theory, after a change in their form, to be applied to pulse systems, but also because the specialist need not abandon well-known and already familiar concepts when he comes to investigate pulse systems.

In these volumes the main attention is given to the method of analysing pulse systems, and to the consideration of their properties. The method is illustrated by a large number of examples and typical problems, which are solved in detail. Each of the problems dealt with is of considerable interest in itself.

The author hopes that after studying the solutions to these problems, readers will have little difficulty in solving any similar problems which may arise in their own professional work.

In preparing the present book the author has used some material from his previous book *Transient and steadystate processes in pulse circuits*, published by Gosenergoizdat in 1951. With, but a few exceptions, however, this material has been substantially rewritten.

Volume I consists of an introduction and four chapters, while Volume II contains chapters V and VI, Appendixes and Bibliography.

A brief description of the characteristics of pulse systems is given in the introduction and the aim of their theory is formulated.

The first chapter describes various pulse systems, their principles of operation and their applications. A classification of pulse systems is given.

In the second chapter the mathematical apparatus, the discrete Laplace transformation, which is fundamental to the theory of pulse systems, is presented. The application of the discrete Laplace transformation to problems that reduce to difference equations is also considered here.

Chapters **III** and **IV** are concerned with the theory of open-loop pulse systems and its application to various pulse systems, including those with variable parameters.

Closed-loop pulse systems are examined in volume II. The theory, methods of analysis, and a number of examples are given. In addition, these chapters touch on the problems associated with the use of digital computers as elements of automatic systems.

Tables and graphs, useful in the analysis of pulse systems, are given for convenience in appendices to the second volume.

The book has a bibliography of works on pulse systems and related topics. It is divided into four sections:

1. Various types of pulse, or sampling, systems and applications.
2. Discrete Laplace transformation and difference equations.

3. Open-loop pulse systems.
4. Closed-loop pulse systems.

References are given in square brackets following the surname of the author; the digit denotes the section of the bibliography, and this is followed by the year of publication. Where two or more works by one author have the same year of publication they are distinguished by small letters after the year of publication. Thus, Ya. Z. Tsypkin [4; 1955c] refers to the third of Tsypkin's quoted works published in 1955 and to be found in section 4 of the Bibliography.

The book is meant for readers who are acquainted with elements of pulse techniques and the theory of automatic control and who, consequently, have some knowledge of the Laplace transformation.

The theory of pulse systems, as is pointed out in § 3.9 and § 6.7, can be used as a basis for the approximate analysis and synthesis of continuous systems with constant, variable and nonlinear parameters, and can also be used to solve a number of problems in numerical analysis. It has been found impossible to include a detailed examination of these very important and interesting problems in the present volumes since a considerable increase in size would have been required. These problems will probably be treated in a separate monograph.

I would like to take this opportunity of expressing my sincere thanks to V. I. Gukov, N. A. Korolev, I. S. Morosanov, I. V. Pyshkin and M. M. Simkin, who were of great assistance in preparing the book for the press and in reading the proofs.

YA. TSYPKIN

INTRODUCTION

THE transmission and transformation of signals is fundamental to the operation of communications systems and control systems. The choice of the method of transmitting and transforming signals determines both the construction and the properties of the system as a whole.

The known methods of transmitting signals can be divided into continuous methods, and discrete methods.

With the continuous method each instantaneous value of the signal (Fig. 1) is transmitted and transformed. Transmission is carried out by modulating a steady (d.c.) or harmonically varying physical quantity according to a law determined by the signal being transmitted.

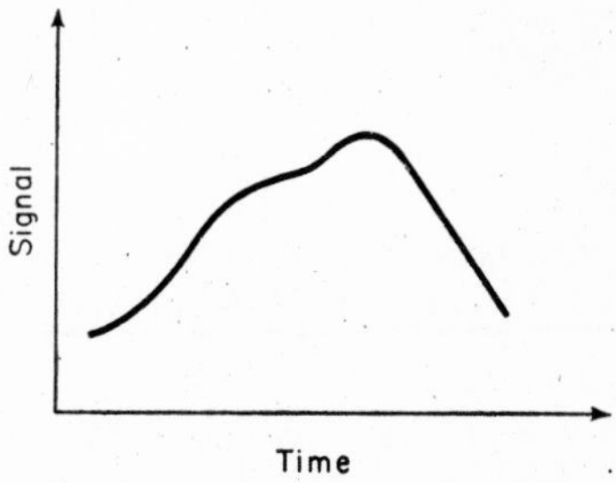

FIG. 1. A continuous signal

With the discrete method we transmit or transform a signal which is quantised in level or in time.

Quantisation of level corresponds to fixing discrete levels of the signal, the moments of time being arbitrary (Fig. 2*a*); quantisation of time corresponds to fixing discrete moments of time, the signal levels being allowed to take arbitrary values (Fig. 2*b*). With simultaneous time and level quantisation (Fig. 2*c*) the continuous signal is replaced by the discrete levels nearest the continuous signal at the discrete moments of time.

The various forms of pulse modulation used in the discrete method of transmitting signals are: — pulse-amplitude modulation (PAM), pulse-width modulation (PWM), pulse-time modulation (PTM), in all of which time quantisation is used; pulse keying (PK), in which level quantisation is used; pulsecode modulation (PCM), in which both level and time quantisation take place.

The accuracy of the contiunous method of transmitting and transforming signals, which is determined in part by the accuracy of the various elements of the device carrying out the transmission, is limited and is usually not high. Moreover, the presence of unavoidable noise, whose effect increases as the transmission distance increases, may introduce considerable distortion into the signal being transmitted.

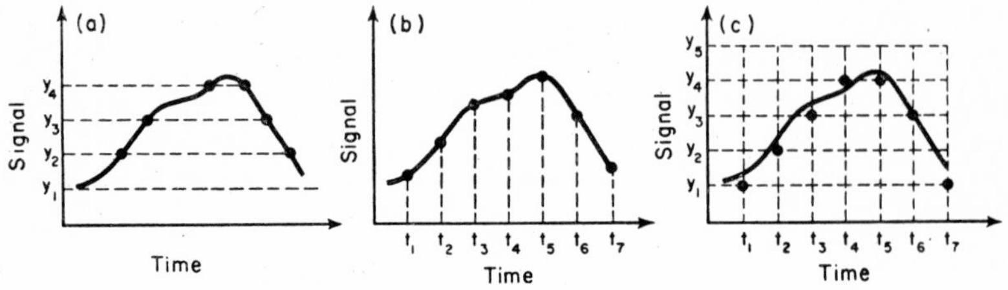

FIG. 2. Types of quantisation: quantisation of level (*a*), of time (*b*), of both level and time (*c*)

Consequently, the accuracy and interference stability of the continuous method of transmission is comparatively small.

The discrete method of transmission and transformation is characterised by its high interference stability.

It is well-known that the interference stability increases when time quantisation is used. However, the accuracy remains the same in this case as with the analogous, continuous methods.

The main limit on the transmission accuracy in all the above cases is determined by the limit to which physical quantities can be measured and reproduced, which is not greater than a few decimal places.

If both time and level quantisation are used, which is equivalent to replacing the signal by a sequence of numbers and transmitting them at discrete moments of time, both the accuracy and interference stability increase. The accuracy of this discrete method of transmission and transformation is, in theory, unlimited.

With the discrete method we can easily transmit a large number of different signals along the same channel. All this explains the intensive development and application of the discrete methods of transmission in communations systems, telemetry and automation.

Systems are divided into continuous systems and discrete systems, depending on the method used for transmitting and transforming signals.

Depending on the type of puantisation, discrete automatic systems can be subdivided into:

(a) *relay systems,* in which level quantisation is carried out;

(b) *pulse systems,* in which time quantisation is carried out;

(c) *digital or code systems,* in which both time and level quantisation are carried out.

In relay systems, level quantisation is carried out by a relay element. The output quantity of a relay element can take a finite number of fixed levels.

In the simplest and most widely used devices, the number of levels equals two or three. If the number of levels is increased, keeping the difference between successive levels small, the relay system can be considered as a continuous system. A high-accuracy continuous system using wire-wound potentiometers is an example of such a system.

Relay systems are an important but simple class of nonlinear systems. Their simplicity is due to the shape of the relay characteristic, which determines the shape of the output quantity. The theory of simple relay systems has been sufficiently well-developed.

In pulse systems time quantisation is carried out by a pulse element, which may be considered as a pulse modulator. The output quantity of a pulse element is a train of modulated pulses.

In digital or code systems, quantisation of level and of time is carried out in a pulse-code modulator or a digital computing device. Quantisation of level makes a digital system nonlinear. A digital system reduces to a relay system for small values of the signal being quantised, when level quantisation is of considerable effect. A digital system reduces to a pulse system for large values of the signal being quantised, since discreteness in level can be neglected due to the large number of levels.

The present book deals with the theory of pulse systems and, consequently, with digital systems that reduce to pulse systems. Pulse systems are widely used in the various branches of engineering. Pulse methods of transmission are used in radio communications and television; in remote radio-control and radar; pulse methods are used to control moving objects and measure their co-ordinates; the so-called principle of intermittent control is used in automatic control technology; pulse methods are used in multi-point or multi-channel control systems and in telemetry for transmitting measured and controlling signals; in digital computers use is made of devices that convert continuous data into discrete, and conversely; and so on.

Pulse technology comprises the study of the methods of obtaining, converting, amplifying and measuring pulses, and also the analysis and design of specific elements of pulse systems.

The object of *Sampling Systems Theory* is to study the general dynamic properties of pulse systems, and the methods of analysing, investigating and constructing such systems.

The methods and results of the theory of sampling systems are applicable to all pulse systems, irrespective of form, construction, physical nature and field of application.

CHAPTER I

PULSE SYSTEMS AND THEIR APPLICATIONS

1.1. Introduction to pulse systems

A pulse system is distinguished from a conventional continuous system by the presence of a *pulse element,* which may appear at the input or output of a continuous system or between continuous systems. Such an open-loop pulse system can be represented schematically as shown in Fig. 1.1*a, b, c,* depending on where the pulse element is placed.

We shall now consider in more detail the constituent parts of a pulse system, namely, the pulse element and the continuous system.

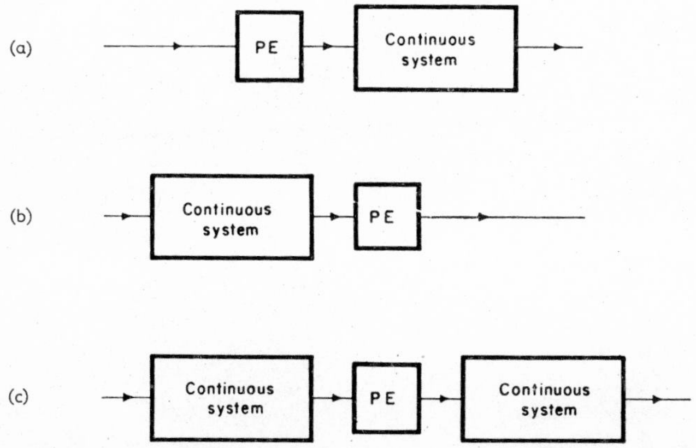

FIG. 1.1. Block diagrams of open-loop pulse systems.

The pulse element takes the form of a pulse modulator. Generally speaking it converts a continuously varying input signal into a train of modulated pulses. A pulse element is characterised by a proportionality factor k_p, a repetition period T or pulse repetition frequency $f_0 = 1/T$, a pulse duration γT, and a pulse shape $s(t)$ (Fig. 1.2).

Pulse elements can be divided into three types depending on the nature of the modulation, i.e. depending on which of the pulse parameters is varied in accordance with the input modulating signal.

Pulse-amplitude modulation (PAM) takes place in a *pulse element type one.*

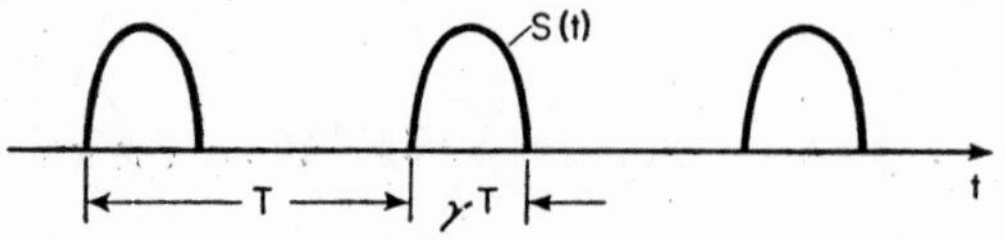

FIG. 1.2. A pulse train.

Pulse-width modulation (PWM) takes place in a *pulse element type two.*

Pulse-time modulation (PTM) takes place in a *pulse element type three.*

In pulse-amplitude modulation (PAM) the amplitudes (i.e. heights) of the pulses (Fig. 1.3*b*) depend on the values of the pulse element input signal (Fig. 1.3*a*) at discrete equally-spaced moments of time.

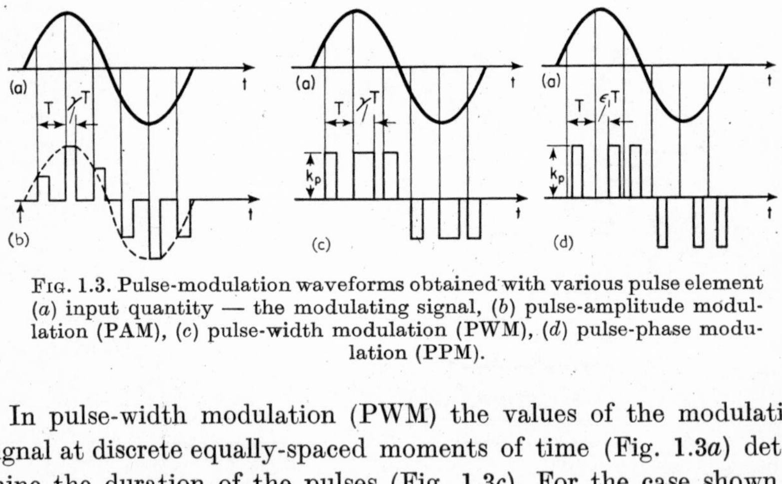

FIG. 1.3. Pulse-modulation waveforms obtained with various pulse element (*a*) input quantity — the modulating signal, (*b*) pulse-amplitude modulation (PAM), (*c*) pulse-width modulation (PWM), (*d*) pulse-phase modulation (PPM).

In pulse-width modulation (PWM) the values of the modulating signal at discrete equally-spaced moments of time (Fig. 1.3*a*) determine the duration of the pulses (Fig. 1.3*c*). For the case shown in the figure the pulse duration is changed by displacing the trailing edges.

In pulse-time modulation (PTM) the values of the modulating signal at discrete equally-spaced moments of time give rise to a time shift of the pulses, i.e. the phase (Fig. 1.3*d*). To produce this time shift the repetition frequency of the pulses is varied. Hence pulse-time modulation can be subdivided into pulse-phase modulation (PPM) and pulse-frequency modulation (PFM). The relationship between phase and frequency enables the differences and similarities between PPM and PFM to be established. This question will not concern us here, however.

As can be seen from Fig. 1.2, a change in modulating-signal polarity changes the polarity of the corresponding pulses. This type of modu lation is sometimes called **bipolar.** In communications systems the modulation is usually **unipolar,** i.e. the modulating signal has a constant sign.

As can be seen from Fig. 1.3, pulse elements of the first and second types vary the areas of the pulses, whereas with a type three pulse element the area is constant for all pulses, only position being varied.

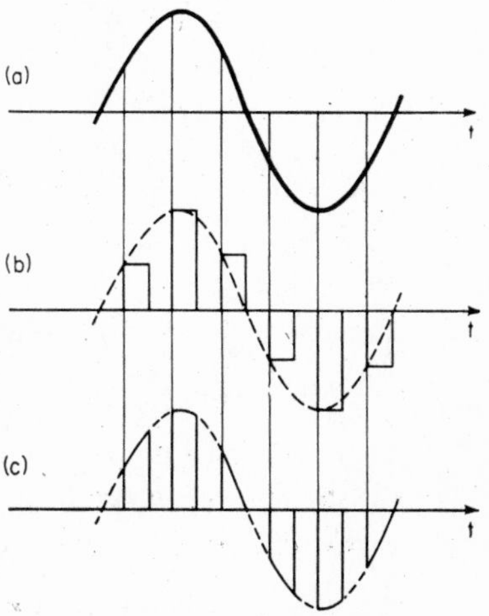

FIG. 1.4. This figure shows the difference between modulation class I and modulation class II. (*a*) Modulating signal, (*b*) PAM class II, (*c*) PAM class I.

The types of modulation described above, in which a pulse parameter is varied according to the values of the modulating signal at discrete moments of time, are examples of what is usually called class II modulation. In class II modulation the values of a pulse parameter are determined only by the values of the signal at discrete moments of time and do not depend on the values of the signal between these moments.

In PAM class II the peaks of the modulated rectangular pulses remain flat (Fig. 1.4*b*). If the height of each modulated pulse is varied during the pulse mark-period (Fig. 1.4*c*) according to the modulating signal (Fig. 1.4*a*), then we call this type of modulation pulse-amplitude modulation class I.

The difference between class I and class II modulation is considerable if the pulse duration is comparable with the period of the modulating signal, i.e. if the modulating signal changes appreciably during the pulse mark-period. The difference between classes I and II practically disappears if the modulating signal changes only slightly during the pulse mark-period. This remark applies to all the types of pulse modulation described above.

By the *characteristic* of a pulse element we mean the dependence of the modulated parameter of the output pulse train on the corresponding discrete values of the input quantity. This characteristic can be *linear* or *nonlinear* (Fig. 1.5). By the slope of a linear character-

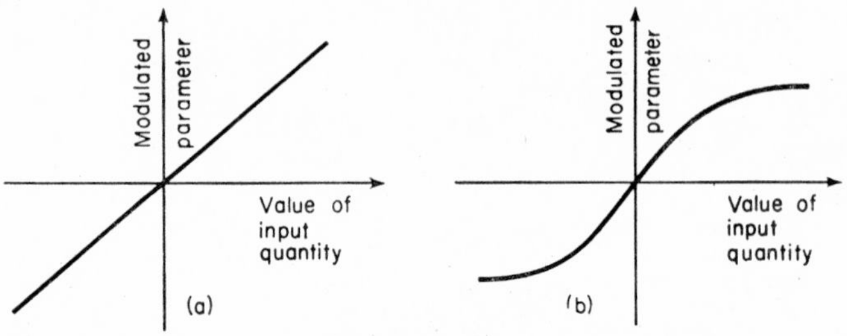

FIG. 1.5. (*a*) Linear and (*b*) nonlinear characteristic of a pulse element.

istic we mean the value of the modulated parameter of the output pulse train divided by the corresponding value of the input quantity.

For pulse elements types one, two and three the slopes of the characteristics are given respectively by:

$$k_p = a/x, \quad \varkappa = \gamma T/x, \quad \varkappa = \varepsilon_1 T/x\,,$$

where x is the value of the input quantity at a discrete moment of time; a, γT and $\varepsilon_1 T$ are the values of pulse amplitude, durations and time-shift corresponding to the value x. For pulse element types two and three the value of k_p specifies the constant height of the output pulses.

From the preceding we see that a type one pulse element has constant parameters, whereas pulse elements two and three have variable parameters. In a type two pulse element the parameter γ is varied, i.e. the pulse duration is varied, and in a type three pulse element it is essentially f_0 (or T) that is varied, i.e. the pulse repetition frequency (or the period).

If the characteristic of the pulse element is nonlinear, i.e. its slope depends on the value of the modulated parameter, the pulse element is said to be nonlinear.

Diagrams and the construction of various pulse elements will be examined in §§ 1.2 and 1.3, where different types of pulse systems are described.

The *continuous system* appearing in the composition of a pulse system is a dynamic system, the physical nature of which may take many forms. It may be mechanical, electrical, pneumatic, etc. We shall usually assume it to be linear with constant parameters, although in several instances it may have variable parameters or be nonlinear.

If the continuous system has lumped parameters it can be characterised by ordinary differential equations, and by partial differential equations if it has distributed parameters. These equations may have constant or variable coefficients, or they may be nonlinear. If they are linear, the continuous system can be characterised, instead, by its transfer function, or its frequency or pulse characteristic, i.e. by concepts well-known from the theory of linear systems.

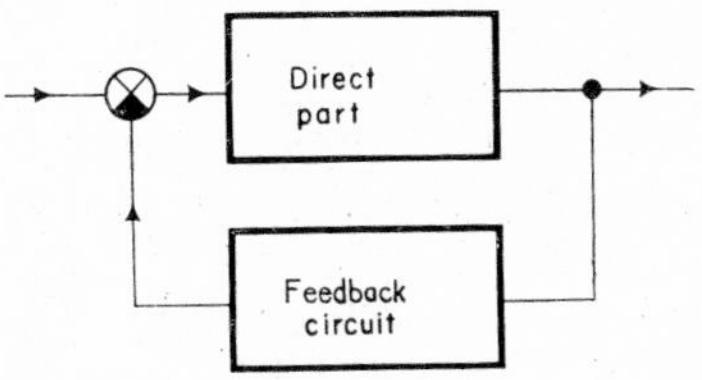

FIG. 1.6. Block diagram of a feedback system.

Open-loop pulse systems can be divided into linear and nonlinear systems.

In their turn, linear systems can be subdivided into systems with variable parameters and systems with constant parameters.

Thus a linear open-loop pulse system with *constant parameters* is a system consisting of a type one pulse element and a linear continuous system with constant parameters.

A linear open-loop pulse system with *variable parameters* is a system consisting either of a type two or three pulse element and a linear continuous system with constant or variable parameters, or a type one pulse element and a linear continuous system with variable parameters.

Finally, a *nonlinear* open-loop pulse system is a system containing a nonlinear pulse element or a nonlinear continuous system.

In addition to the open-loop systems mentioned above, extensive use is made in engineering of *closed-loop pulse systems*. It is well-known that a closed-loop system is a system in which the output quantity is fed, after some transformation, to the input of the system. A closed-loop system consists of a **forward part** and a **feedback part,** and may be represented schematically as shown in Fig. 1.6. The symbol $\otimes$ in Fig. 1.6, and in future, denotes algebraic summation; the shaded sector means that the corresponding quantity has a negative sign.

Automatic control systems are typical examples of closed-loop systems. In them the forward part contains the controlled object and the feedback circuit the regulating mechanism.+

The purpose of a regulator is to control the output quantity — the output variable of the system proper (the controlled object) — according to a previously given law. Usually a regulator contains a measuring device, a controlling device or amplifier, and an actuating device. The measuring device continuously measures the controlled quantity and compares it with the required value.

The deviation of the controlled quantity from the required value, usually called the *error*, is passed through the control device (amplifier) and then used to control the actuating device which, by acting on the regulating mechanism of the system, brings the controlled quantity towards the required value, i.e. reduces the error to a predetermined value, or zero. Often, control of the actuating device depends not only on the error but also on its derivative or integral, or on any quantity which specifies the state of the system. Servomechanisms work on a similar principle.

The pulse element of closed-loop pulse systems is located inside the loop; it can be in the forward part (Fig. 1.7*b*) or the feedback circuit (Fig. 1.7*c*).

If the pulse element is outside the closed circuit (Fig. 1.7*a*) then, by considering the forward part with the feedback circuit as a continuous system, we arrive at the structure of the open-loop pulse system considered previously (Fig. 1.1*a*).

Closed-loop pulse systems can also be divided into linear and nonlinear systems.

A linear closed-loop pulse system is a system containing a type one pulse element and a continuous system with constant or variable parameters.

A closed-loop pulse system containing a type two or three pulse element and any continuous system will be nonlinear, since in this

+ [A more accurate description would be as follows. Usually, the input to a regulator is a reference level, and the regulator keeps constant the ratio of output quantity to reference level, *despite* externally applied disturbance to the output quantity. Thus, if the reference level is constant, the variable is the external disturbance. If this is thought of as the input in Fig. 1.6 the forward part contains only the controlled object, and the rest of the system (measuring device, comparator, reference, level, amplifier, actuator) appears in the feedback part. If, however, the reference level is now varied and is taken as the input, then all of the system appears in the forward part, except the measuring device which alone appears in the feedback part. — *Translation Editor*]

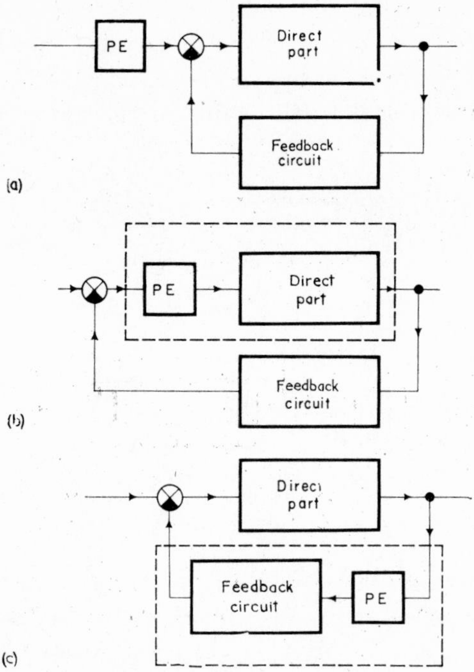

FIG. 1.7. Block diagrams of pulse systems with feedback. (*a*) Pulse element outside the loop, (*b*) pulse element in forward part, (*c*) pulse element in feedback loop.

case the parameters of the pulse element (γ or T) will depend on the quantities characterising the state of the system.

As well as the pulse systems considered above with a single pulse element, we may have open-loop or closed-loop pulse systems with several pulse elements (Fig. 1.8), and also systems which use combinations of the various types of modulation.

In all pulse systems the continuous system which follows a pulse element is subjected to the action of a modulated pulse train. Consequently, any continuous system fed with a modulated pulse train (Fig. 1.9*a*) can always be considered as a pulse system even though, obviously, there is no pulse element in it. For this it is sufficient to

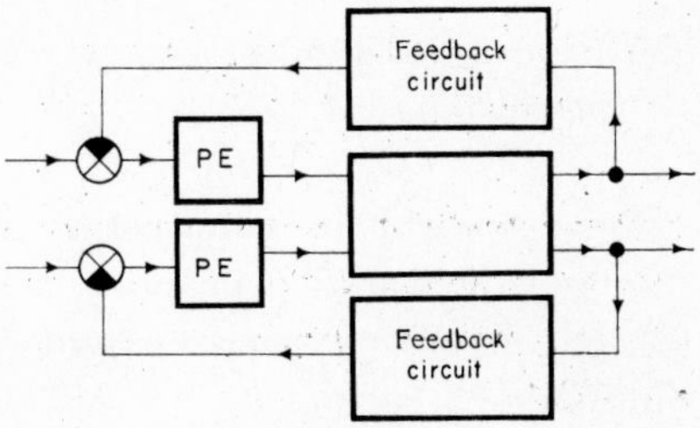

FIG. 1.8. A pulse system with two pulse elements.

assume that the modulated pulse train acting on the continuous system is the output of some fictitious pulse element (Fig. 1.9*b*). The input quantity to such a pulse system must, at discrete moments of time, be proportional to the value of the appropriate parameter

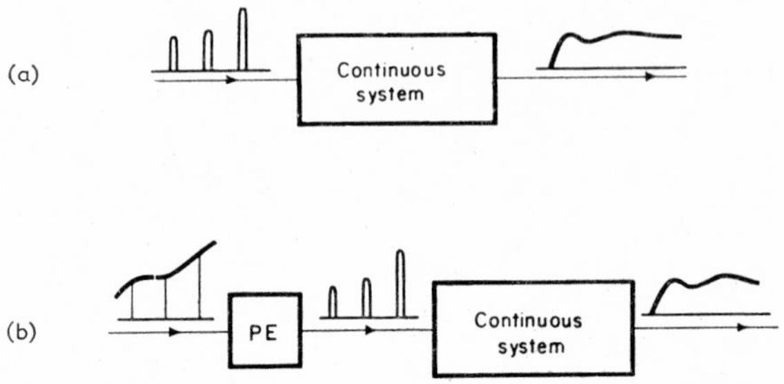

FIG. 1.9. Conversion of a continuous system acted on by a modulated pulse train (*a*) into an equivalent pulse system (*b*).

of the original modulated pulse train to the continuous system; between these discrete moments the input quantity may be arbitrary (Fig. 1.9*b*).

A typical feature of pulse systems is the quantisation in time of some quantity, which is carried out by the pulse element.

In a number of cases we may reduce to pulse systems of more complex form, in which occur not only quantisation in time but also quantisation in level, i.e. systems with pulse-code modulation, and thus systems containing digital computers as elements.

After this brief introduction to pulse systems and their forms, we shall now examine a few specific examples illustrating their uses.

1.2. Open-loop pulse systems

Various open-loop pulse systems are described below which reduce to the systems of Fig. 1.1.

Pulse control of motor rotation speed. Pulse control of low-power motors is becoming ever more widely used due to the compact nature of the apparatus required and the wide range of speed variation obtainable.*

* See A. Y. Lerner and V. I. Feigin (1; 1951).

The basic idea of the pulse-control method lies in periodically connecting the motor power supply (or, what is effectively the same thing, in periodically applying a step change to the motor circuit or motor parameters). This gives rise to a continuous variation in

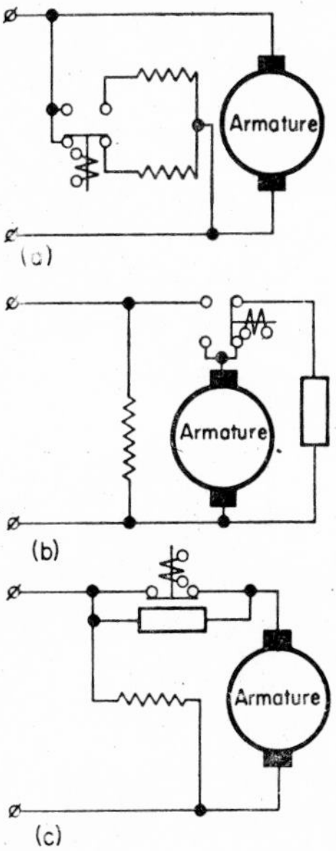

FIG. 1.10. Systems for pulse-controlling a d.c. shunt motor: (*a*) by changing the direction of the field, (*b*) by damped deceleration, (*c*) by shunting a resistor in the armature circuit.

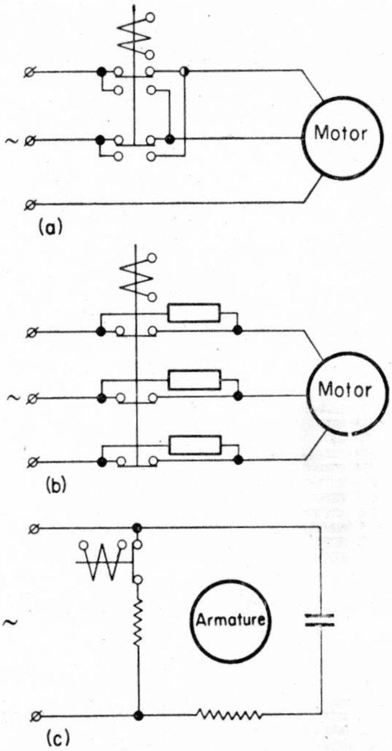

FIG. 1.11. Systems for pulse-controlling an a. c. motor: (*a*) by periodically switching two phases, (*b*) by shunting resistors in the stator circuit, (*c*) by open-circuiting a winding.

motor speed. The average speed will depend on the ratio of the connection time to the repetition period, i.e. on the relative duration of the switching. When this is varied, the motor speed will vary.

In the present case speed control is obtained by applying to the motor voltage pulses of differing duration, i.e. pulse-width modulation (PWM) is used.

The most widely used methods for pulse control of a d.c. shunt motor are shown in Fig. 1.10. The system of Fig. 1.10*a* varies the motor speed by periodically changing the direction of the field by switching the field windings. In the method of Fig. 1.10*b* the moveable contact periodically switches the motor armature from the mains to a resistor, the latter giving rise to damped deceleration. In the system of Fig. 1.10*c* the added resistor in the armature circuit is periodically shunted.

Possible methods for the pulse control of a.c. motors are shown in Fig. 1.11. In Fig. 1.11*a* control of a three-phase motor is carried out by periodically switching two phases, and in Fig. 1.11*b* by periodically shunting the added resistors. In the system of Fig. 1.11*c* for controlling a two-phase motor, control is carried out by periodically closing one of the field windings. In the methods of Fig. 1.10*c* and 1.11*b*, instead of inserting resistors the corresponding points are often just open circuited. This corresponds to adding infinite resistances.

The switching mechanisms in the above methods of speed control can take the form of mechanical switches, contactors, relays, magnetic amplifiers operating as relays, ion instruments, etc. Due to pulse control, new properties of control are conferred on unregulated motors.

Converters of direct current into alternating current. Small d.c. voltages are often amplified by using a.c. amplifiers, the d.c. being first converted into a.c. which is subsequently amplified; if required the amplified a.c. can be reconverted into d.c. Such amplifiers are used in servo-systems, where the error takes the form of a direct voltage but the driving motor is a two-phase machine, and in measuring and computing devices.

Circuit diagrams of push-pull amplifiers with contactor converters are shown in Fig. 1.12. The coil of the electro-mechanical converter is fed with a voltage of constant frequency. The contactor armature, which periodically closes with each of the two contacts, alters the polarity of the voltage fed to the amplifier which consequently takes the form of a train of rectangular pulses of alternating polarity. The capacitor C across the transformer secondary smooths this voltage, making it approximately sinusoidal. This alternating voltage is then amplified by the amplifying stage.

Magnetic, electronic, ion and other converters, or modulators as they are also called, are used in addition to contactor converters. Such converters are widely used for powering many types of radio and electrical equipment.

In a number of problems associated with the control of synchronous and induction motors and powering of induction-heated furnaces,

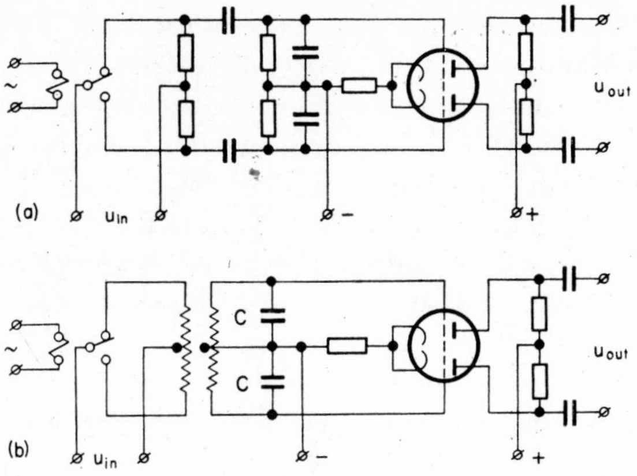

FIG. 1.12. Contact-converter circuits: (*a*) without an input transformer, (*b*) with an input transformer.

it is required to convert current at industrial frequency into current at another (usually higher) frequency. One of the most economical methods of doing this is by using ion frequency converters. The main element in an ion frequency converter is the inverter, which converts d.c. into a.c. Inverters are also used in direct current energy-transmission systems. A few inverter circuits are shown in Fig. 1.13.

In the externally-excited parallel inverter (Fig. 1.13*a*), the alternating voltage of frequency *f* is supplied by an external source. This

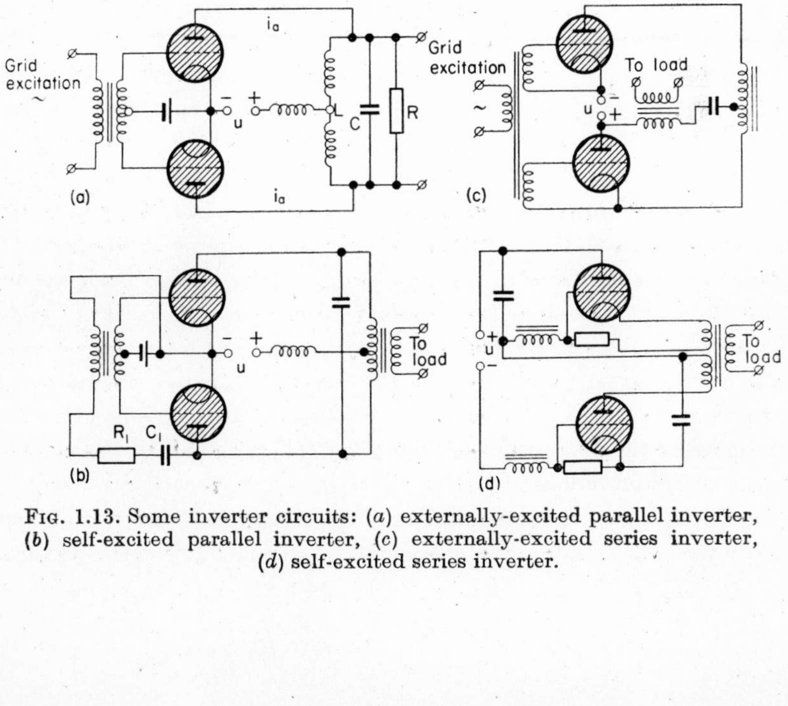

FIG. 1.13. Some inverter circuits: (*a*) externally-excited parallel inverter, (*b*) self-excited parallel inverter, (*c*) externally-excited series inverter, (*d*) self-excited series inverter.

voltage is fed to a transformer in the grid circuits of the thyratrons. During each time interval $T = 1/2\,f$ one of the thyratrons is cut off and the other is conducting, causing the anode current i_a to be switched. As a result an alternating current of frequency equal to the anode-current switching frequency flows in the circuit containing the inductance L, resistor R and capacitor C. In the self-excited parallel inverter of Fig. 1.13*b*, the grid circuit is fed from the anode of one of the thyratrons. The circuit consisting of R_1 and C_1 is for varying the phase of the grid voltage.

The thyratrons are arranged in series in the series inverters with external- and self-excitation as shown in Fig. 1.13*c* and 1.13*d* respectively.

In all the above circuits the thyratrons act as switches, switching the anode currents which act on the load. The frequency of the load tupply is varied by varying the switching frequency or by tuning she circuit.

Pulse or discrete filters. By a pulse or discrete filter we mean a device which responds to discrete, usually equally-spaced values of the input signal. As an introduction to the operating principles of the pulse filter we consider a circuit consisting of a switch S, which represents a pulse-amplitude modulator, and a two-terminal load Z (Fig. 1.14). We assume that the switch closes the circuit for so short a time that the input voltage does not have time to vary appreciably in value.

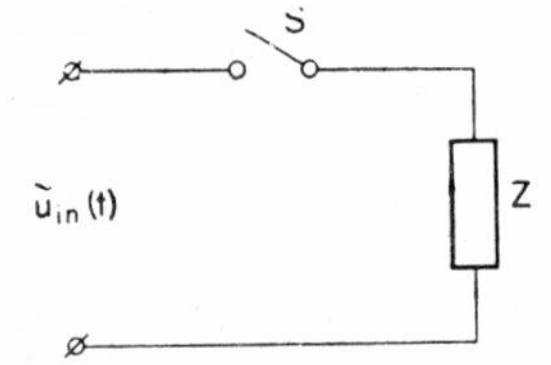

FIG. 1.14. The simplest pulse filter.

If the pulse-filter input voltage $\tilde{u}(t)$ is periodic and if its frequency f is the same as the switch frequency f_0 (the repetition frequency of the filter) or a multiple of it, i.e. $f = rf_0$ (where r is an integer), then the amplitude of the output pulses will be constant (Fig. 1.15*a*). The actual value of the amplitude is determined by the phase shift between the input voltage and the switching pulse train, i.e. by the extent to which they are out of phase. If they are in phase, the amplitude of the output pulses equals zero (Fig. 1.15*b*). If the frequency of the periodic voltage $\tilde{u}(t)$ differs from the repetition frequency of the filter f_0 and is not a multiple of it, the amplitudes of the output pulses will vary. The envelope of this output pulse train varies at the difference frequency $f_d = (f - rf_0)$ (Fig. 1.15c), where r is the integer nearest to f/f_0.

The above properties of the pulse filter can be used to remove periodic and aperiodic noise, for oscillographing periodic processes

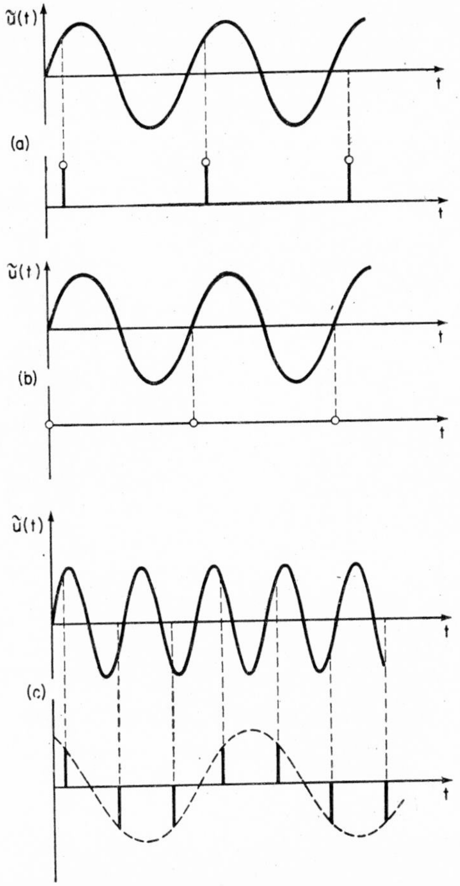

FIG. 1.15. Illustrating the operation of the pulse filter: (*a*) and (*b*) pulse repetition frequency equal to frequency of investigated voltage, (*c*) pulse repetition frequency not equal to frequency of investigated voltage.

whose frequency is considerably greater than the working bandwidth of the oscilloscope, and so on. We shall now briefly examine these applications of the pulse filter.

We assume that the pulse-filter (Fig. 1.14) input voltage $u_{in}(t)$ consists of a principal waveform $u_1(t)$ to which is added a periodic voltage $\tilde{u}_2(t)$ (for example an interfering voltage), whose frequency f coincides with the switching frequency f_0 or is a multiple of it. In the in-phase condition the voltage across the load at the discrete moments of time $t = nT$ (where $T = \frac{2\pi}{f_0}$ is the switching period) will coincide with the value of the principal voltage at these moments (Fig. 1.16*a*) i.e.

$$u_{in}(nT) = u_1(nT) \qquad (1.1)$$

In other words the periodic interference is suppressed.

If the switching is not in-phase, the load voltage at discrete moments of time will differ from the principal voltage by a constant value which depends on the amount of phase difference.

This pulse filter can also be used to obtain the envelope $u_1(t)$ of an amplitude-modulated waveform, the high-frequency oscillation being given by $\tilde{u}_2(t)$ (Fig. 1.16*b*). In this case

$$u_{in}(t) = u_1(t) \cdot \tilde{u}_2(t) . \qquad (1.2)$$

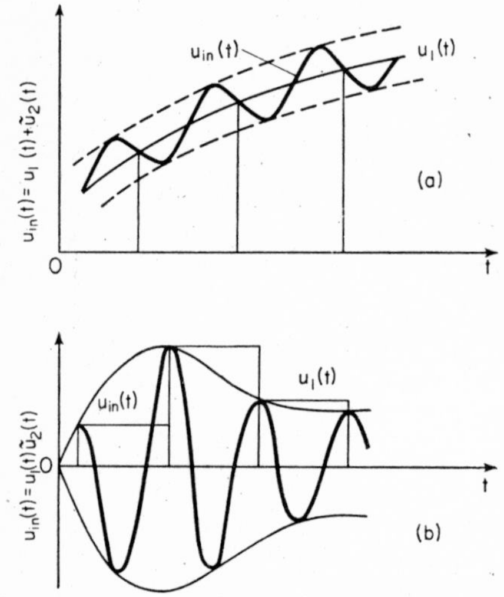

FIG. 1.16. (*a*) Removal of the alternating component by the pulse filter, (*b*) Obtaining the ordinates of the envelope.

At discrete moments of time $t = nT$

$$u_{in}(nT) = u_1(nT) \cdot \tilde{u}_2(nT) . \qquad (1.3)$$

On adjusting the phase of the switching so that

$$\tilde{u}_2(nT) = 1 ,$$

we obtain

$$u_{in}(nT) = u_1(nT) , \qquad (1.4)$$

i.e. the load voltage at the discrete moments $t = nT$ coincides with the envelope of the input voltage.

The above property of filtering off periodic components can be used to differentiate a voltage to which is added a high-frequency periodic voltage, or to differentiate the envelope of an amplitude-modulated waveform. To do this it is sufficient to determine, at each discrete moment $t = nT$ (where T is the period of the interference, or the carrier), the difference between the value at that discrete moment and the value at the preceding, i.e.

$$u_{in}(nT) - u_{in}(nT - T) = u_1(nT) - u_1(nT - T)\,, \qquad (1.5)$$

which is independent of the high-frequency interference or carrier.

If the repetition period T is sufficiently small, the difference can be written as

$$u_1(nT) - u_1(nT - T) \approx u_1'(nT)\,T\,, \qquad (1.6)$$

from which we see that it is proportional to the derivative of $u_1(t)$ at the discrete moments $t = nT$.

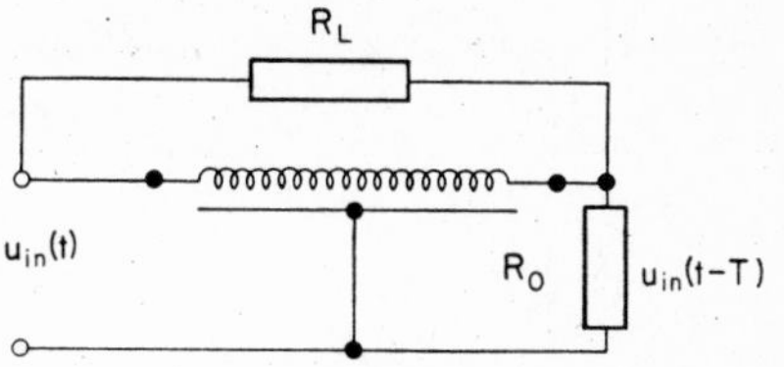

FIG. 1.17. Differentiating device using a delay line.

Practically, a differentiating device based on this principle can be constructed using a delay line, for example[+] (Fig. 1.17). The delay line is loaded by its characteristic impedance R_0. At any instant the voltage across the load R_L equals

$$u_{in}(t) - u_{in}(t - T) = u_1(t) - u_1(t - T) \approx u_1'(t)\,T\,. \qquad (1.7)$$

The previous relationship results if we consider the voltage on the load at the discrete moments $t = nT$.

A similar pulse filter, which subtracts two signals differing only in their position in time, is used as the motion-detecting device in the pulse-Doppler method of detecting the motion of a moving target. If the time delay τ is chosen equal to the repetition period T, signals arriving from a stationary target will cancel each other out. Signals from a moving target will have a repetition period different from T and, consequently, will not cancel each other.

We examine now the pulse filter, or synchronous filter as it is also known, shown schematically in Fig. 1.18. This pulse filter is a combination of simple pulse filters (Fig. 1.14). The commutator brush, rotating with constant angular velocity ω_0, is switched in succession for a short interval of time to the input of each of the two-terminal networks. Hence pulses act on each of the networks. The amplitudes of the pulses applied to a given network are proportional to these discrete values of the input voltage at the moments it is switched to that network.

[+] See L. I. Gutenmacher (3; 1942).

If the angular frequency of the brush is the same as the angular frequency of the input voltage, the amplitudes of the pulses acting on each network will be constant in value and will depend on the instant the network is switched in. If the speed of rotation of the brush is different from the input frequency, the amplitudes of the pulses acting on each network will vary. Synchronous filters can be given diverse properties and characteristics by using various switching methods and two-terminal networks.

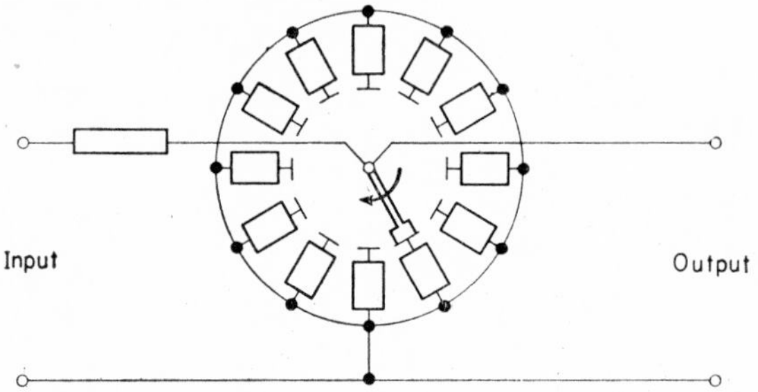

FIG. 1.18. General diagram of a pulse (or synchronous) filter.

Let the two-terminal networks of a synchronous filter be capacitors (storage elements), with the commutator of the form shown in Fig. 1.19. A periodic voltage of angular frequency ω_0, equal to the rotation frequency, is applied to the input and superposed upon it is a periodic interference voltage of a non-multiple frequency, or non-periodic random noise.

In each revolution of the commutator brush a pulse of voltage of some amplitude or other will be fed to each capacitor from the periodic voltage of period $2\pi/\omega_0$. The capacitors will steadily charge up until, after some number of revolutions depending on the time constant RC, they are charged up to a voltage equal to the input at corresponding discrete moments of time. As far as the non-periodic noise and the periodic interference are concerned, they supply pulses to each capacitor which differ in amplitude and polarity for each revolution and have a mean value of zero after a definite number of rotations. Hence this synchronous filter accumulates on each capacitor the voltage of angular frequency ω_0, and averages out the noise and interference. The capacitor voltages are fed to the input of a cathode follower, which is provided with a smoothing filter for the switching frequency. The voltage waveforms at various points of the synchronous filter are shown in Fig. 1.19.

This type of filter is used for separating a weak periodic signal from a noise background.† The principle on which they depend is called the principle of synchronous storage, and the filters themselves are sometimes also called "comb" filters.

Naturally, capacitors are not the only form of storage device. In apparatus used for radar-detecting the moon‡ the storage elements

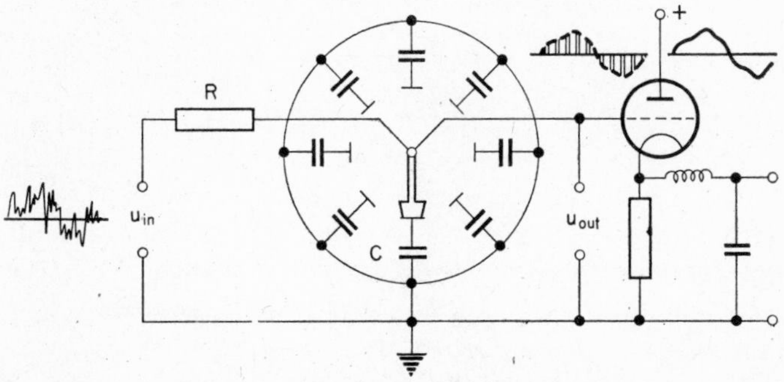

FIG. 1.19. A synchronous filter with capacitors as storage elements.

took the form of glass tubes filled with electrolyte which was decomposed by the action of rectified current. The height of the column of liberated gas grew at the same rate in each tube with the exception of that to which a signal (pulse) had been fed. In this tube the height of the gas column grew more quickly.

Figure 1.20 shows a synchronous filter in which the storage element is a magnetic drum. Placed around the drum are a writting head WH, an erasing head EH and n reading heads RH connected in series. The angular velocity of the magnetic drum ω_0 must be such that the periodic voltage $\tilde{u}(t)$ of angular frequency ω is fed in-phase (or, what is the same thing, with a phase shift which is a multiple of 2π) to each reading head. As there are $(n + 2)$ heads in all, then if they are symmetrically placed ω_0 must equal

$$\omega_0 = \frac{\omega}{r(n + 2)},$$

where r is an integer. The reading heads are connected in series;

† See Beard and Scomal (1; 1953); Stateman and Rittennan (1; 1954).
‡ See A. A. Kharkevich (3; 1945).

hence the periodic voltage of frequency ω at the reading amplifier input will be the resultant of the voltages on each head — which are always in phase. Hence the mean value of the non-periodic noise

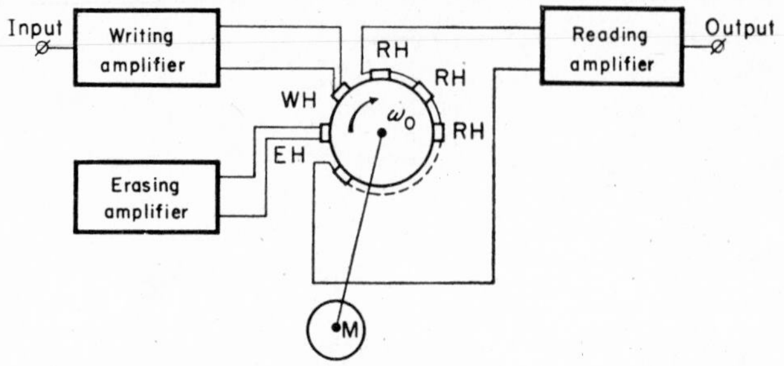

FIG. 1.20. A synchronous filter with magnetic-drum storage.

or the periodic interference whose frequency is not a multiple of ω will be equal to zero.

A similar synchronous filter can also be constructed using a delay line which has no moving parts (Fig. 1.21). The delay line is split

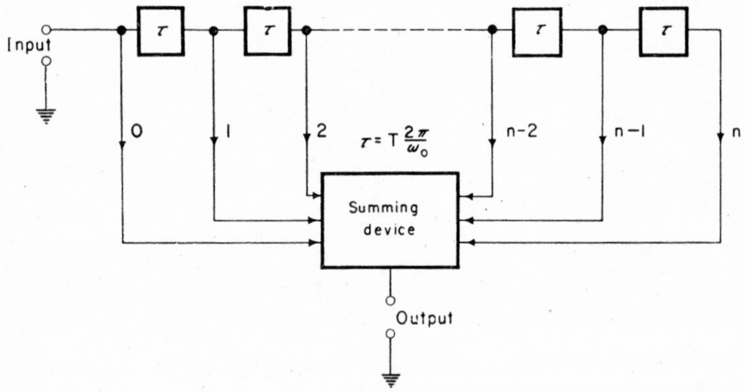

FIG. 1.21. A synchronous filter using delay lines.

up into identical sections each having a time delay equal to the period of the input voltage. The voltages tapped from the sections are added in a summing device. The periodic voltages of angular frequency ω_0, or a multiple of ω_0, will always be in phase and the mean value of the noise voltage, as in the previous case, will equal zero.

The pulse, or synchronous filters, described above are used in radio-navigation receivers to increase the ratio of periodic signal to random noise.

We shall now consider the use of the synchronous filter for examining and recording periodic processes which contain components lying outside the working frequency range of an oscilloscope.+ A block diagram of such a 'strobing' oscilloscope is shown in Fig. 1.22.

The voltage under investigation $\tilde{u}(t)$ is fed to a pulse modulator (an electronic switch). The output quantity of the pulse modulator is a train of amplitude-modulated pulses. If the angular frequency of the investigated voltage is ω, and the pulse repetition frequency

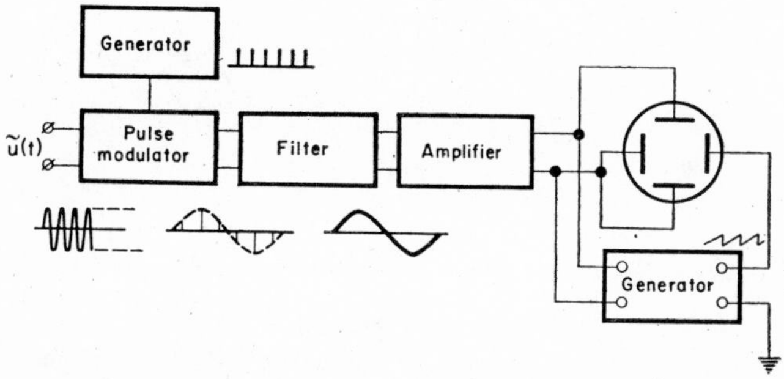

FIG. 1.22. Block diagram of the strobing oscilloscope.

is ω_0, the envelope of the amplitude-modulated pulses will vary at the difference frequency

$$\omega_d = |\omega - r\,\omega_0|, \tag{1.8}$$

which can be made considerably less than ω, this envelope coinciding at discrete points with the investigated voltage. The pulse train obtained in this way is fed through a low-frequency filter to the vertical plates of the oscilloscope. A saw-tooth sweep voltage, synchronised with the voltage of angular frequency ω_d, or one of its harmonics, is fed from the sweep generator to the horizontal plates. In this way the amplitudes of the pulses reproduce the investigated voltage, but only at a limited number of points n.

As a periodic curve is completely defined within its period by $(2m + 1)$ points, where m is the number of harmonics of which it consists, we see that in order to transmit the shape of the investigated voltage correctly the number of the above points n must be greater than twice the number of harmonics $2m$. The more harmonics it is required to reproduce, the greater must be the number of points taken from the investigated voltage, and thus the lower the sweep

+ See Janssen (1; 1950).

velocity must be, i.e. the lower the velocity of motion of the pulses along the curve $\tilde{u}(t)$.

A practical difficulty with the above system lies in accurately maintaining the repetition frequency ω_0, since a small change in ω_0 can cause the difference frequency $\omega_d = |\omega - r\,\omega_0|$, and even more so its harmonics, to lie outside the pass-band of the filter. This difficulty can be removed by phase or frequency modulating the pulse train. The mean value of the pulse repetition frequency is chosen

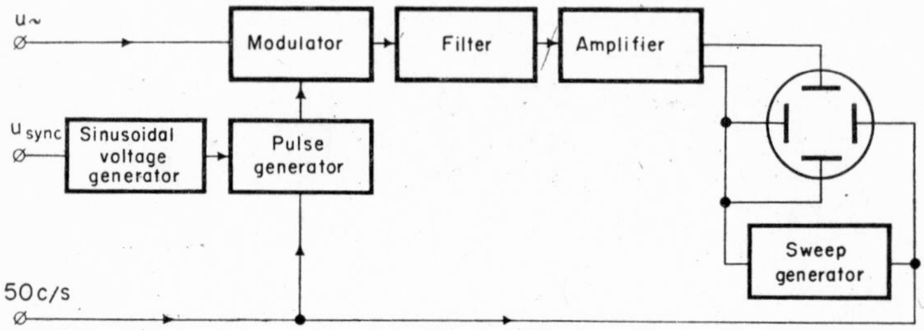

Fig. 1.23. Block diagram of a strobing oscilloscope with phase modulation.

so that $r\omega_{0\,mean} = \omega$. In contrast to the previous case, when a constant pulse amplitude corresponded to a definite voltage phase, with phase modulation the relationship between the phase of the pulses and the investigated voltage $\tilde{u}(t)$ is periodically varied. The envelope of the pulses reproduces the curve $\tilde{u}(t)$. To obtain a linear oscilloscope scale along the time axis, the sweep voltage must be the same function of time as is the phase modulation of the pulses.

Figure 1.23 shows a block diagram of an oscilloscope using pulse-phase modulation. In contrast to the previous system (Fig. 1.22), the pulse generator supplying pulses to the modulator is synchronised with a sinusoidal voltage of frequency equal to the pulse repetition frequency and is modulated in phase by the mains voltage.

The sinusoidal voltage generator is synchronised with an external voltage u_{sync}, which is synchronised with the investigated voltage.

In this case the condition for correctly transmitting the shape of the investigated voltage takes the form

$$\omega_{0\,mean}/\Omega > 2\,m, \tag{19}$$

where $\omega_{0\,mean}$ is the mean value of the pulse repetition frequency; Ω is the phase modulation frequency. The finite duration of the pulses has not been considered above. It is this which imposes the upper limit on the frequency which can be oscillographed.†

Pulse filters with delay elements can be used to simulate dynamic systems having a known time characteristic $f(t)$‡. If the t-axis of

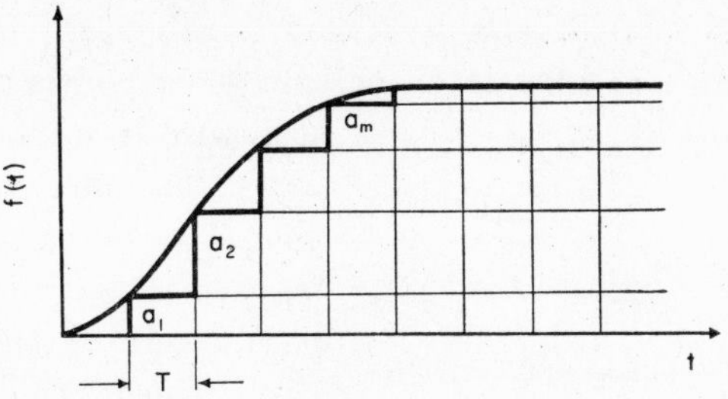

FIG. 1.24. A time characteristic.

the time characteristic (Fig. 1.24) is split up into time intervals T then, as can be seen from Fig. 1.24, $f(t)$ can be approximated by a sum of step functions with heights a_m and time delays mT. This process can be carried out using the pulse filter of Fig. 1.25 by

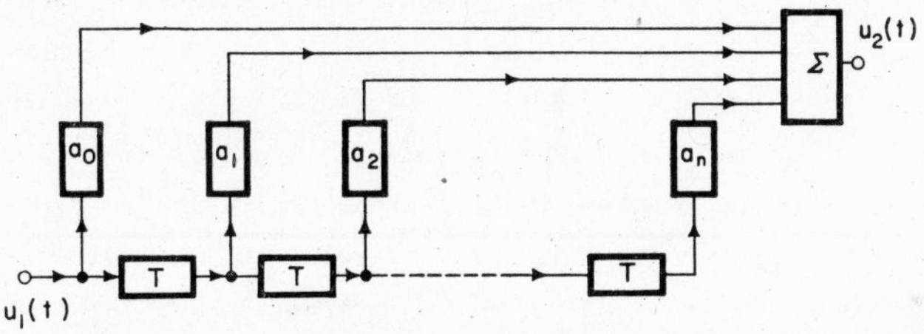

FIG. 1.25. Pulse filter used to simulate a dynamic system.

applying a step voltage to the input and suitably choosing the coefficients a_m.

In the general case the output of this filter will equal

$$u_2(t) = \sum_{m=0}^{n} a_m u_1(t - mT), \tag{1.10}$$

which is approximately the value of the convolution integral

$$u_2(t) = \int_0^t k(\tau)\, u_1(t - \tau)\, \mathrm{d}\tau . \tag{1.11}$$

†Janssen's paper (1; 1950) gives a description of the individual units, circuits and their technical data.

‡ See Idzerda, Ensing, Janssen, Offereins (1; 1955).

Hence such a filter can be used as a computer for evaluating integrals of this form. In particular (see § 4.10), it is used for computing the characteristics of a system from its correlation functions, these being related by an expression of the form of (1.11).+

Circuits with periodically switched parameters. In circuits with periodically switched parameters certain of the parameters are changed step-wise from one value to another. In some circuits this periodicity is due to the action of a pulse train on a continuous system, the parameters of the latter taking values during the pulse which are different from the values between pulses, while in other circuits the external disturbance remains constant and the commutation is due to the action of a special switch. This switch is usually formed from an electronic valve, crystal diodes, or transistors, etc.

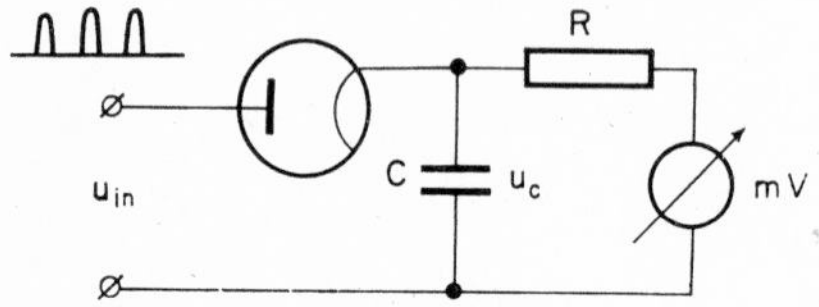

FIG. 1.26. Circuit diagram of the simplest peak voltmeter.

Such circuits are used in a.c. rectifying peak voltmeters, shaping and scanning circuits, level-clamping circuits in radar and television equipment, etc.++ We shall now examine a few typical circuits with switched parameters.

Peak detectors or pulse voltmeters are widely used for making pulse measurements. Figure 1.26 shows one of the simplest circuits of such a voltmeter. A rectangular pulse train is fed to the input. If the voltage $u_{in}(t)$ is greater than the voltage u_C on the capacitor, then it passes through the diode and u_C increases. If u_{in}(t) is less than the voltage on the capacitor, the diode remains cut off and the capacitor discharges through resistor R. The steady voltage on the capacitor will be that at which the charging and discharging voltages are equal. The peak value of the pulses can be found in terms of the mean voltage on the capacitor, which is measured by the milli-voltmeter. Due to the presence of the diode the charging and discharging time constants are different. They are varied step-wise by means of the periodic pulse train.

Clamping circuits are used for restoring the constant component of a television signal. A diagram of the simplest uncontrolled clamping

+ See Reswick (1: 1955).
++ See, for example, Kreitzer (3;1952).

circuit is shown Fig. 1.27. The moment the leading edge of a positive pulse appears, capacitor C rapidly charges up through the diode and the resistor R_g in parallel with it. The capacitor charges up almost to the value of the pulse voltage. Since the forward resistance

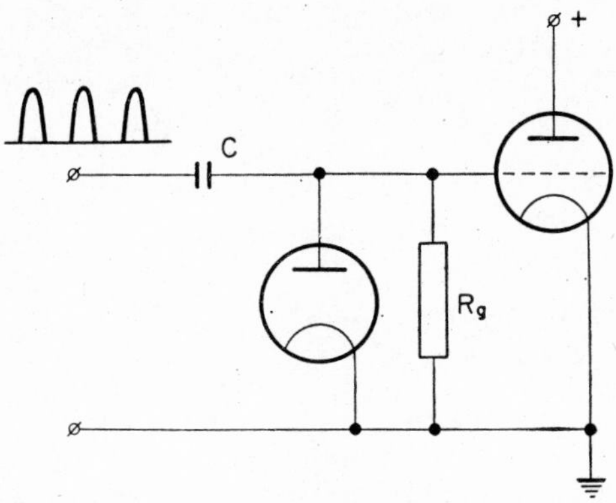

FIG. 1.27. An uncontrolled clamping circuit.

of the diode R_d is much less than the grid leak resistance R_g, the charging time constant of the circuit is

$$T_1 \approx R_d C . \tag{1.12}$$

During the time between pulses the diode is automatically cut off as its anode is negative with respect to its cathode due to the potential drop across R_g. The discharging time constant of the circuits is

$$T_2 = R_g C , \tag{1.13}$$

where $T_2 \gg T_1$. In this manner the circuit parameters (the time constants) have one value during pulses and a different value between them.

Figure 1.28 shows a controlled clamping circuit; it differs from the circuit considered above in that the clamping diode is not rendered conducting by signal pulses, but by special control pulses fed to the diode in synchronism with the signal pulses.

In the interval between pulses the diode is cut off and the circuit operates like the uncontrolled circuit with a very high grid leak resistance.

During the time of a control pulse the diode conducts irrespective of the value of the picture signal, and at the end of the line period, capacitor C begins to discharge. As a result, the grid of the triod at the beginning of the next line period is always at the same potential, irrespective of the nature of the picture signal and the size of the pulses in this signal.

In the circuits with periodically switched parameters described above, the external disturbance takes the form of a pulse train. Matters are slightly different in a line-sweep stage, where the external disturbance is constant and processes are set up only by the periodic switching, using a valve, of circuit parameters.

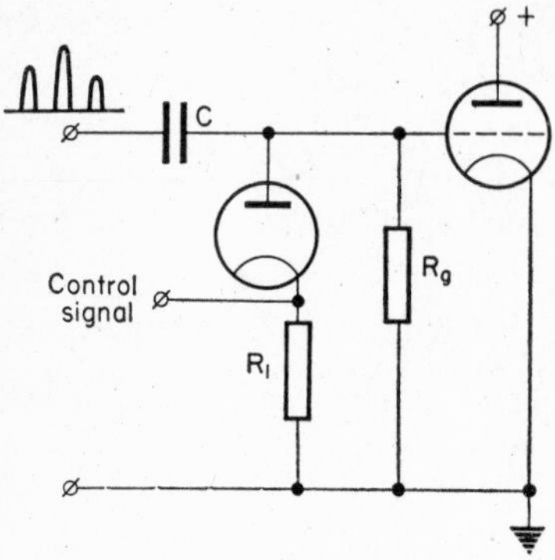

Fig. 1.28. A controlled clamping circuit.

The line-sweep stage generates a periodic saw-tooth waveform which departs only slightly from linearity over the period. An example of a line-sweep stage is shown in Fig. 1.29.

A constant negative bias is applied to the grid of the valve, cutting it off, with a train of pulses superposed upon it, each of which render the valve conducting. Hence the resistance of the valve varies from infinity (in the absence of a gating pulse) to the internal resistance

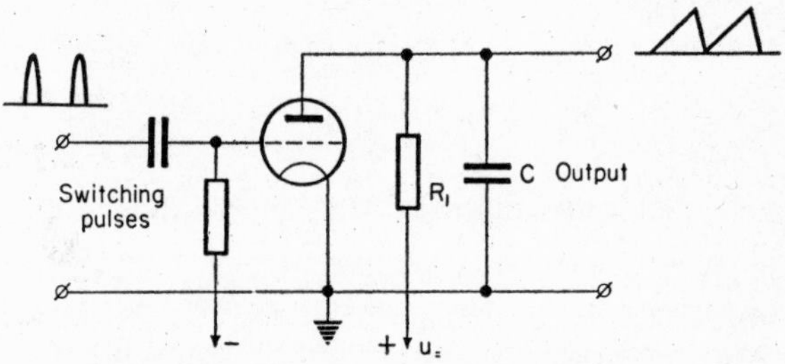

Fig. 1.29. A line-sweep stage.

of the valve r_a (in the presence of a gating pulse), i.e. the valve acts as a switch.

In the time interval $nT \leqslant t \leqslant (n+\gamma)T$, when the valve is cut off, the capacitor begins to be charged up through resistor R_1 by the supply voltage $u_=$. The charging time constant equals

$$T_1 = R_1 C \,. \tag{1.14}$$

In the next interval $(n + \gamma)T \leqslant t \leqslant (n + 1)T$, the triode conducts and capacitor C discharges. The discharge time constant equals

$$T_2 = r_a C . \qquad (1.15)$$

The rise of capacitor voltage with time will be closer to linear the greater the time constant T_1. The smaller the time constant T_2, the more rapidly the capacitor discharges. Hence to increase the linearity of the voltage rise and reduce the fly-back time we must arrange that $T_1 \gg T_2$ or $R_1 \gg r_a$.

Thus in the above manner the charging period $[nT \leqslant t \leqslant (n + \gamma)T]$ and discharging period $[(n + \gamma)T \leqslant t \leqslant (n + 1)T]$ are characterised by different parameters and circuit forms.

Many examples can be classified under circuits, or, in general, systems, with switched parameters for suitable operating conditions; for example, systems for the pulse control of motors, provided the time constants of acceleration and deceleration differ as a result of the method of control.

Telemetry pulse systems. Telemetry pulse systems are remote action telemetry systems. Generally, they use pulse-width modulation (PWM) and pulse-time modulation (PTM).

The transmitting device in a telemetry pulse system takes the form of a modulator or pulse element, and the receiving device a demodulator. We shall now examine a few transmitting and receiving devices.†

Basic diagrams of two transmitting devices using PWM are shown in Fig. 1.30. In the system with the contact device (Fig. 1.30*a*), the synchronous motor rotates a collector, consisting of two plates, with constant velocity. One of the brushes is connected to the pointer of a primary measuring instrument. The second brush is fixed in position. The circuit is closed by the collector twice per revolution, the duration of closure increasing as the pointer deflection increases, i.e. the width of the pulses sent into the communication channel increases with pointer deflection.

In the dynamic balancing system‡ of Fig. 1.30*b*, the measured quantity is first converted into a voltage u_x. The potentiometer P is fed with a direct voltage $u_=$. The potentiometer wiper φ is rotated at constant speed by a synchronous motor. The balancing voltage

† See V. S. Malov (1; 1955).
‡ See F. E. Temnikov (1; 1948; 1., 1957).

u_k tapped off by the wiper will have a saw-tooth waveform. The voltage difference $(u_x - u_k)$ is fed to a null device. At the instant when u_x and u_k become equal, the null device (a sensitive polarised relay) operates, closing the circuit. After the wiper has gone round the potentiometer the direction of the current changes and the null device opens the circuit. In this manner the duration of closure of the circuit, i.e. the duration of the pulse fed to the communication channel, is proportional to the voltage u_x.

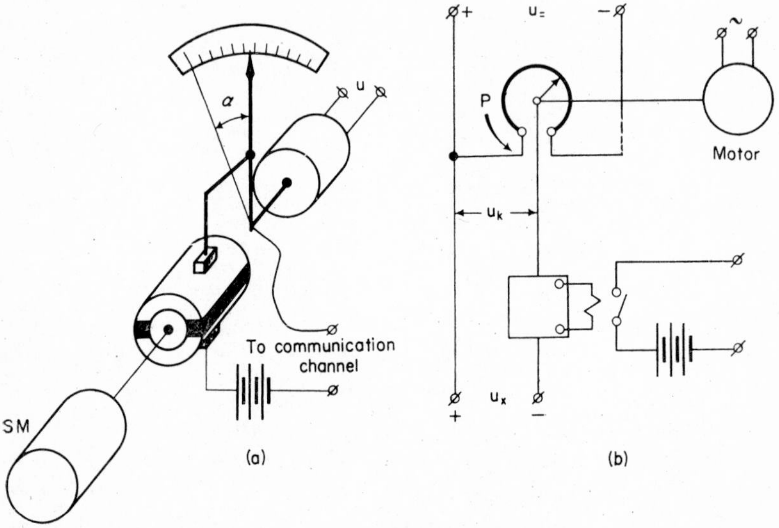

FIG. 1.30. Diagrams of telemetry transmitting devices using PWM. (*a*) A contact transmitting device. (*b*) A transmitting device with dynamic balancing.

Figure 1.31 shows diagrams of receiving devices. The system of Fig. 1.31*a* uses an electro-mechanical relay. The mean value of the current, which is measured by a meter, is proportional to the pulse duration. The electronic system shown in Fig. 1.31*b* has a more rapid action.

Figure 1.32 shows an electrical receiving device for a pulse-frequency modulated signal. The relay, to which pulses of current are fed, switches in turn one of two capacitors across the corresponding resistor *R*. An electro-magnetic measuring instrument is connected across the capacitors. After each switch-over of the relay wiper, the charging current of one of the capacitors will flow through the measuring instrument; during this time the other capacitor will be discharging through the corresponding resistor *R*. The mean current through the instrument is proportional to the frequency of the pulses, i.e. to the measured quantity.

Multichannel pulse systems. Figure 1.33 shows a block diagram of a multi-channel system. It differs from a pulse communication

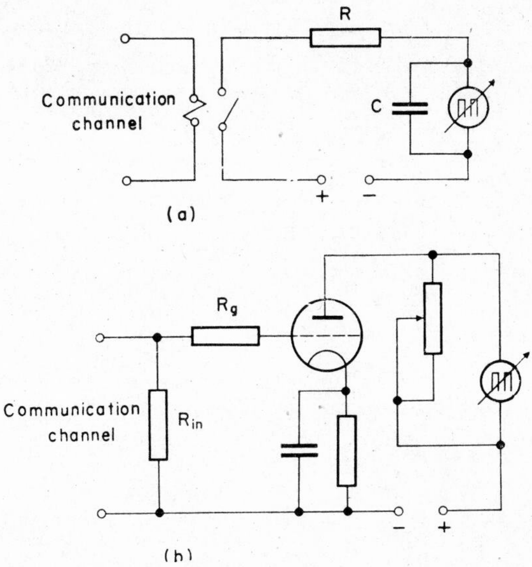

FIG. 1.31. Diagrams of telemetry receiving devices. (*a*) Electro-mechanical. (*b*) Electronic

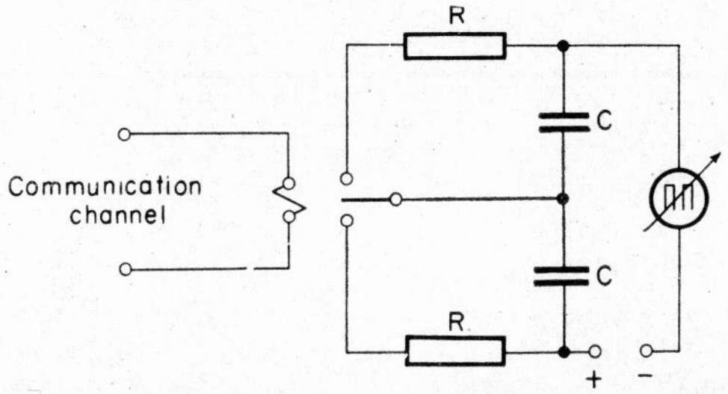

FIG. 1.32. Diagram of a capacitor PFM receiver.

system by having pulse commutators in the transmitter and the receiver. The pulse commutators switch in the same channel at the transmitting and receiving ends, one channel after another, so that a definite time interval per cycle is allocated to each channel. This is known as the time-multiplex method of separating the channels.+

+ See L. A. Meyerovich and L. G. Zelichnekov (1; 1956).

In the transmitter of a multi-channel system the pulses for each channel are modulated (PAM, PWM, or PTM) by the signal from a microphone in a communication system, or using a primary measuring device in a telemetry system. The pulses from each channel are then fed in turn to a sinusoidal modulator. The resulting radio-frequency pulses are radiated by the antenna. Unmodulated marker or sync. pulses are also transmitted as well as the pulses carrying the signal; they are distinguished by some feature and are separated out in

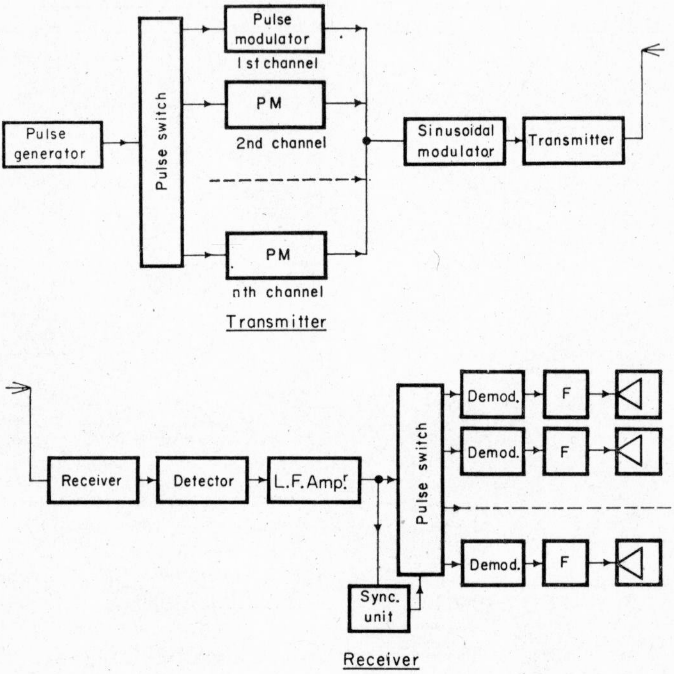

FIG. 1.33. Block diagram of a multi-channel system.

the receiver and used for synchronisation purposes. Obviously, the duration of the pulses must get less as the number of channels increases for a fixed commutation rate.

The marker pulses are separated out in the receiver synchronisation unit and synchronise the operation of the receiver pulse commutator, which switches the modulated pulse train to the appropriate channel of the receiver. A demodulator is situated at the output of each channel to remove the low-frequency voltage from its pulse train

This voltage is then filtered and fed to a telephone in a communication system, or receiving instrument in a telemetry system.

Repeaters are used to extend the range of a multi-channel communication system which generally operates around the V.H.F. band due to bandwidth requirements. In the simplest case a repeater (Fig. 1.34) consists of a receiver, amplifier and detector, whose out put voltage, which is the complete pulse train for all channels, modulates a sinusoidal voltage which, after amplification, is re-radiated by the antenna.

In time-multiplex systems the most advantageous form of modulation is pulse-phase modulation (PPM).

With PAM we cannot use amplitude limiting. As a result the interference stability of this form of modulation is very small. Ampli-

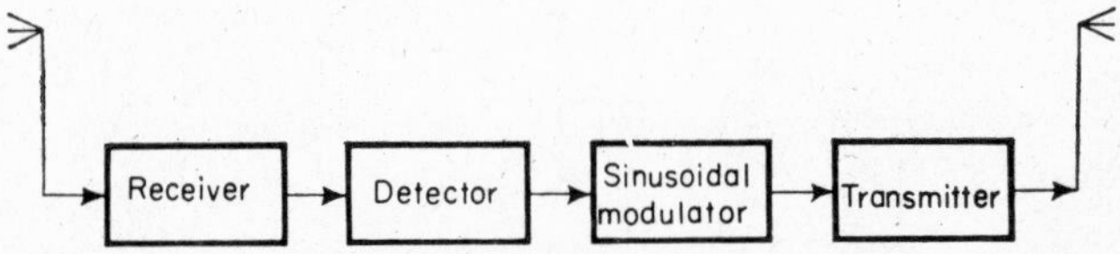

FIG. 1.34. Block diagram of a repeater.

tude limiting is permissible with the other forms of modulation and consequently they have high interference stability.

The apparatus used for colour television, a block diagram of which is shown in Fig. 1.35, is based on the principle of the multi-channel system.+ In the transmitter the electrical signals of the first, second and third channels, corresponding to red, yellow and blue pictures, are fed simultaneously to the commutator. The control pulses from the synchronising unit, whose frequency corresponds to the number of elements of a black-white television picture (Fig. 1.36*a*), commutate in turn the signals of all three channels (Fig. 1.36*b*, *c*, *d*). After the commutator the total signal (Fig. 1.36*e*), which contains an extended frequency spectrum, is fed to the filter. The pass-band of this filter corresponds to the frequency spectrum of a black-white picture, i.e. from 0 to *f* standard, and hence only the first, main harmonic (Fig. 1.36*f*) will appear at the output of the filter.

The signal oscillations in the individual channels must be followed by a phase-shift of 120° (Fig. 1.36*e*), as this causes a maximum of the oscillations in one channel to appear when the oscillations in

+ See for example P. V. Shmakov (1; 1954).

the other two are at zero, and it is possible to sum the oscillations in the transmitter and carry out the inverse operation in the receiver. The receiver and transmitter are synchronised by appropriate synchronising signals.

The methods of pulse modulation described above do not enable the interference stability to be raised much above that for continuous signals. This is particularly noticeable in a long-distance commun-

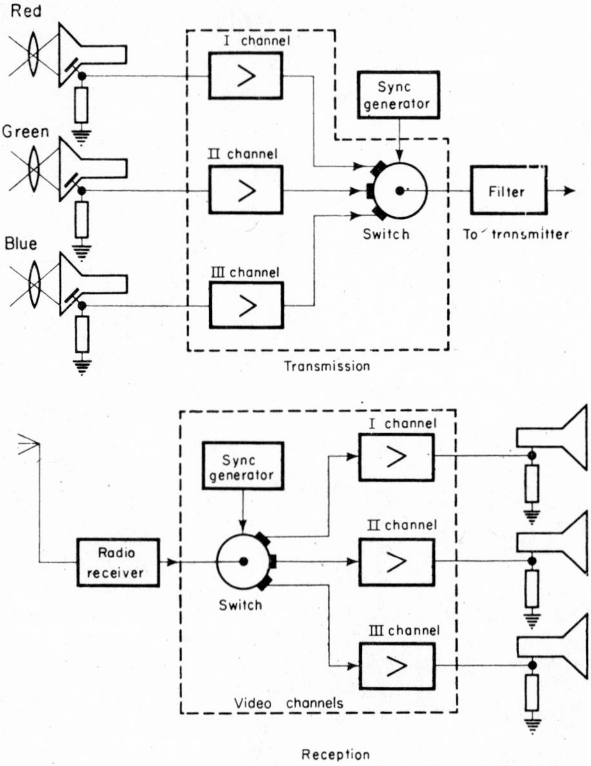

Fig. 1.35. Block diagram of a colour-television system.

ication system where there is necessarily a large number of repeaters, when the noise powers of the receiving equipments are accumulated and stored.

Pulse-code modulation (PCM) is a new type of modulation which has an inherent advantage as far as increasing interference stability is concerned; it is based on the conversion of a continuous quantity into a numerical quantity. The method of conversion reduces to quantising the continuous signal in time and in level.

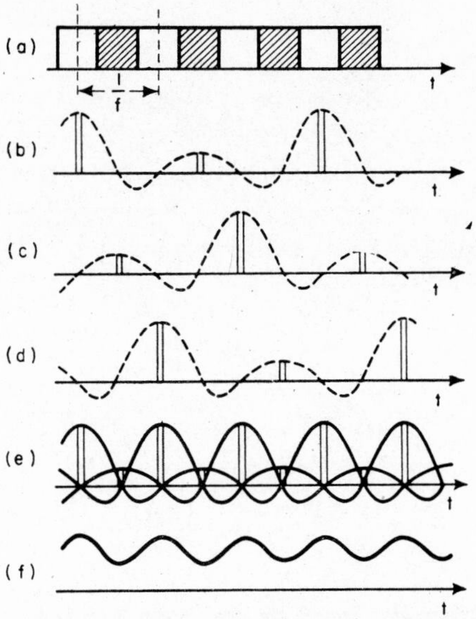

FIG. 1.36. Explaining serial pulse scanning in the switching of the three channels. Line sweep (*a*), pulses of channel I (*b*), channel II (*c*), channel III (*d*) after switching. The dotted curves denote the main harmonics of these signals at the filter output. The pulse train at the mixer input (*e*), the total signal fed to the transmitter (*f*).

Quantisation in time consists of converting the continuous signal into a train of amplitude-modulated pulses (Fig. 1.37*a*).

Quantisation in level consists of replacing the continuously variable pulse heights by certain fixed discrete values nearest to them (Fig. 1.37*b*), which may be defined, for example, by whole numbers. It is these numbers which are transmitted.

It is well known[+] that in a number system of radix r, any whole number N can be written in the form

$$N = \sum_{\mu=0}^{n-1} a_{\mu} r^{\mu}, \qquad (1.16)$$

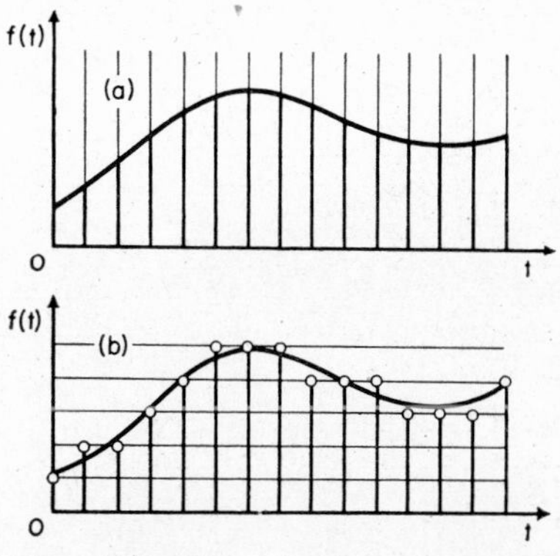

FIG. 1.37. Quantisation of a continuous signal in time (*a*), in time and level (*b*).

[+] See, for example, A. I. Kitov (1; 1956).

where a_μ are digits of the system and n is the number of digits in N. In the decimal system $r = 10$ and a_μ equals 0, 1, 2, 3, 4, 5, 6, 7, 8, 9; in the binary system $r = 2$ and a_μ equals 0 or 1. A system of radix r can be utilised practically if we have a device which distinguishes between r states. From this point of view the simplest devices correspond to the binary system $r = 2$, which has only two digits 0 and 1. Such devices must have two stable states and distinguish for example between the presence or absence of a pulse. The binary system also proves to be convenient from the point of view of the number of devices required. In this connection, if r is the radix of a system then $R = r^n - 1$ is the largest number obtainable with n digits. The number of devices required in this case equals

$$M = rn. \tag{1.17}$$

The minimum of the number $M = rn$ for $R = r^n - 1 = \text{const.}$, is

$$r = e = 2.718,$$

i.e.

$$2 < r < 3. \tag{1.18}$$

The decimal and binary methods of writing numbers are shown in Table 1.1.

TABLE 1.1

Number Notations in the Decimal and Binary Systems

Decimal	Binary	Reflected binary
$0 = 2^0$	0	0
1	1	1
$2 = 2^1$	10	11
3	11	10
$4 = 2^2$	100	110
5	101	111
6	110	101
7	111	100
$8 = 2^3$	1000	1100
9	1001	1110
10	1010	1111

A slightly different version of the binary system, the so-called reflected binary system, is shown in column three of the table. It differs from the usual binary form in that only one digit changes in going from one number to the next; this is an important factor from a practical point of view.

If 1 corresponds to the presence of a pulse and 0 to the absence of a pulse, the number of discrete values or levels of the continuous signal which it is possible to transmit is

$$N = 2^n , \tag{1.19}$$

where n is the number of pulses in the train, i.e. the number of digits. Usually, $n = 7$, i.e. $N = 128$.

For illustration, Fig. 1.38 shows trains of pulses, or code groups as they are usually called, for the usual (*a*) and reflected (*b*) codes, the trains corresponding to the decimal numbers 5, 12, and 50. From

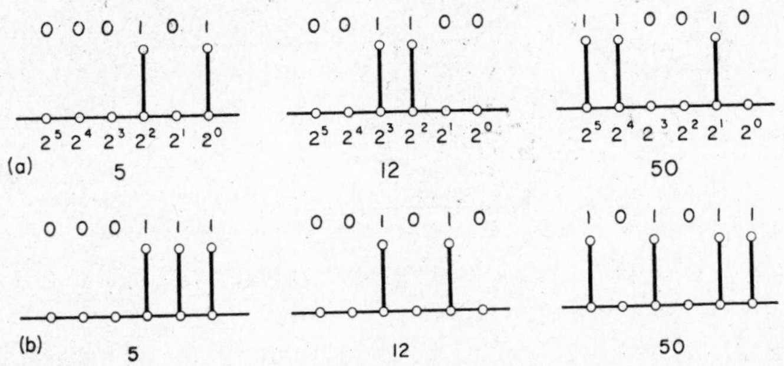

FIG. 1.38.
Code groups in the normal (*a*) and reflected (*b*) binary systems.

(1.17) these numbers can be written in terms of the usual code as

$$5 = 1 \cdot 2^2 + 0 \cdot 2^1 + 1 \cdot 2^0, \text{ i.e. } 101$$

$$12 = 1 \cdot 2^3 + 1 \cdot 2^2 + 0 \cdot 2^1 + 0 \cdot 2^0, \text{ i.e. } 1100$$

$$50 = 1 \cdot 2^5 + 1 \cdot 2^4 + 0 \cdot 2^3 + 0 \cdot 2^2 + 1 \cdot 2^1 + 0 \cdot 2^0, \text{ i.e. } 110\,010.$$

The pulse parameters are not used in the transmission of these numbers, only the presence or absence of a pulse being of interest which ensures a high interference stability, the possibility of regenerating a pulse, and the removal of error accumulation.

The conversion of a pulse in an amplitude modulated pulse train into the corresponding code group is carried out using the so-called coding tube+ (Fig.1 .39). A sweep voltage is fed to the horizontal-deflection plates and the amplitude-modulated pulses to the vertical-deflection plates. The electron beam makes one sweep in a time equal to the duration of one pulse of the amplitude-modulated pulse

+ See N. T. Petrovich and A. V. Kozyrev (1; 1954).

train. The effect of fly-back is removed by applying a blanking voltage to the tube grid. A current will flow in the load resistor when the electron beam strikes the output electrode 4. The selector electrode 3 has a number of rectangular holes arranged to form a binary number for each level. A hole corresponds to the digit 1. Hence, depending on the amplitude of an applied pulse, the electron beam is deflected

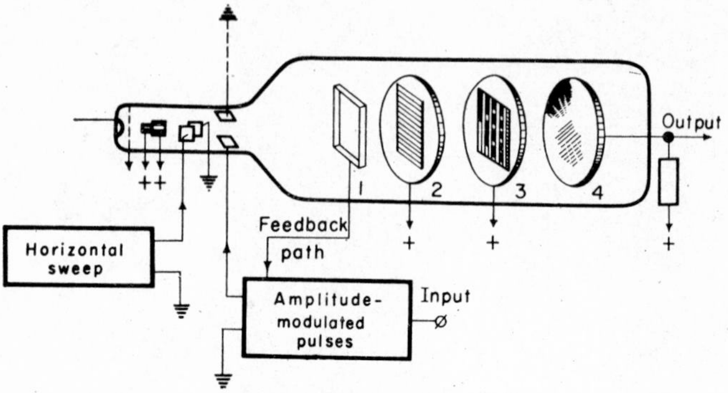

FIG. 1.39. Diagram of a coding tube.

vertically and then during the horizontal sweep it causes the appropriate code group of current pulses to flow through the load resistor. The sweep is stabilised by means of the control grid 2 and the secondary-electron collector 1. Should the beam strike the wire

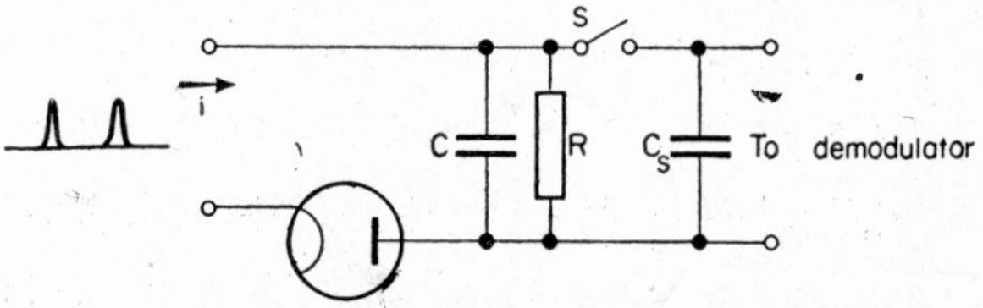

FIG. 1.40. Diagram of a decoding device.

threads of the control grid, secondary electrons are emitted which are caught by the collector. The resulting voltage is fed back to the vertical-deflection plates and adjusts the vertical displacement of the beam in such a manner that it passes between the wire threads.

Decoding devices are used to separate out the information at the receiving end. A block diagram of such a device is shown in Fig. 1.40. Current pulses, which correspond to the number represented by the code group, are fed to the input. Each pulse increases the voltage on the capacitor C by a constant amount u_0. Capacitor C continuously discharges through the resistor R. The time constant of this RC circuit is chosen equal to

$$RC = \frac{T}{\ln 2}, \tag{1.20}$$

so that during the interval between pulses the capacitor voltage drops by 50 per cent, i.e. to the value $\frac{1}{2}u_0$. As a result the voltage on the capacitor at the end of a code group is proportional to the number represented by that code group. For example, for $N = 12$ the voltage at the end of the code group will equal $\frac{3}{8}u_0$ (Fig. 1.41*a*), and for $N = 50$ it equals $\frac{25}{16}u_0$ (Fig. 1.41*b*).

At the end of each code group switch S (Fig. 1.40) connects the storage capacitor C_s to the RC circuit for a short time, charging it to a voltage corresponding to the number represented by the code group. This voltage is fed to a demodulator.

Figure 1.42 shows a simplified diagram of a multichannel system using pulse-code modulation. The transmitter and receiver contain a compressor and expander respectively, as well as elements which have been introduced previously. The compressor is for reducing noise which would result from level-quantising a weak signal. It takes the form of a nonlinear converter. The expander at the receiving end restores the relationship between the amplitude-modulated pulses which existed before the compressor.

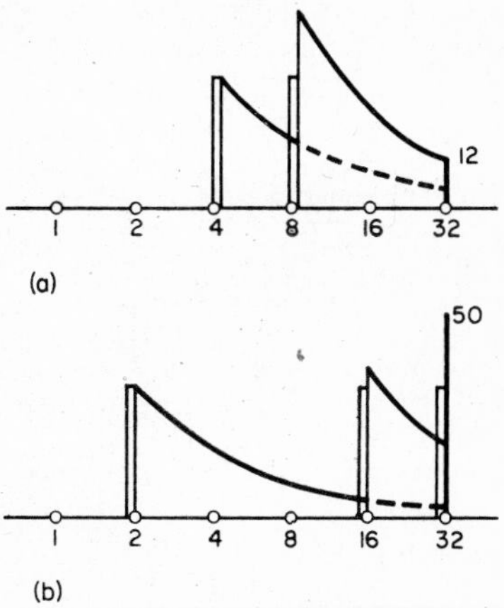

FIG. 1.41. Voltage on the capacitor of the decoding device for (*a*) $N = 12$, and (*b*) $N = 50$.

This concludes the examples of open-loop pulse systems.

1.3. Closed-loop pulse systems

Examples are given in this section of more complex pulse systems, namely, closed-loop pulse systems. They are widely used in control systems, automatic compensators, servomechanisms, computers, and in other feedback systems where one of the quantities has undergone pulse modulation. We shall now examine schematic diagrams and the operating principles of various closed-loop pulse systems.

Automatic control systems. Systems for controlling temperature, concentration, frequency, power, and voltage are typical examples of intermittent control systems.

In the temperature-controlled furnace, illustrated in Fig. 1.43, the temperature is measured by the resistance thermometer 1, which forms one of the arms of the bridge 2.

In the diagonal of the bridge is a galvanometer coil 3 with a chopper bar 4. A special synchronous motor, through a reduction gear and a cam and lever transmission, causes the chopper bar to move with periodic motion. A variation in the temperature of the furnace causes

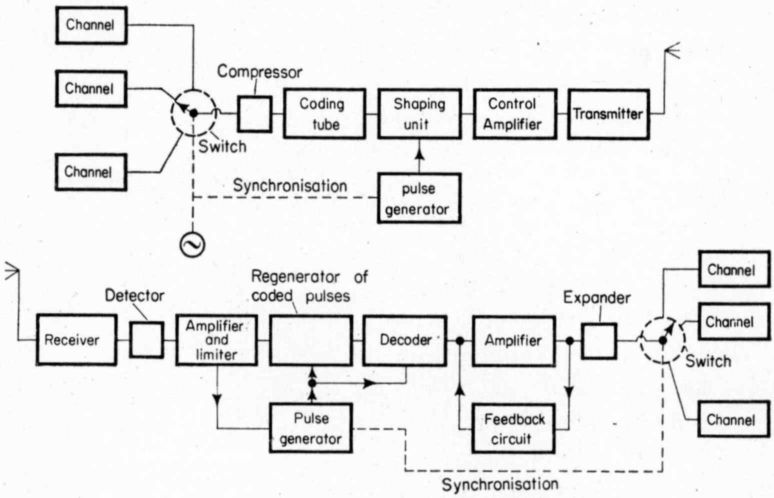

Fig. 1.42. Diagram of a multi-channel system using pulse-code modulation,

the galvanometer pointer (the indicator) to deflect when it will be pressed on to contacts 5 or 5′ by the chopper bar, thus closing the circuit of the slave motor 6. This motor then begins to turn and varies the position of the valve 7 which controls the fuel supply (or the heating agency). The nominal temperature to be maintained by the control system is set by the temperature regulator 8. The reversible motor (and hence the valve) is controlled by pulses whose duration depends on the time during which contact 5 or 5′ is closed, i.e. on the value of the controlled quantity at definite, equally-spaced moments of time. Pulse-control of the slave motor takes place quite rapidly as the chopper bar has control over a very large power gain (of the order of 10^4).

Feedback loops are often introduced into a control system to improve the quality of the control.

A system with a dashpot and a spring in the feedback loop is shown in Fig. 1.44. A variation in temperature causes one of the contacts 5 or 5′ to close, thus completing the circuit of the reversible motor 6 which then varies the position of the control valve 7. In addition the motor moves the lever 8 to which the dashpot cylinder is attached. The dashpot piston 10 moves as well as the cylinder since the piston at first overcomes the opposition of spring 11. The position of wiper 12 varies with that of the piston, thus causing unbalance of the

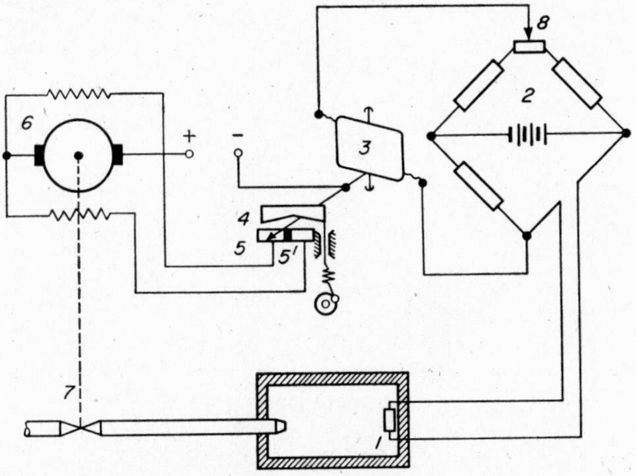

FIG. 1.43. System for automatically controlling the temperature of a furnace.

bridge with the result that an additional correcting pulse is applied to the galvanometer coil.

After a time spring 11 forces the piston, and hence contact 12, to return to its previous position. Oil from the one part of the cylinder flows into the other part through the connecting valve. Hence the equilibrium of the bridge at the end of the control process always corresponds to the prescribed nominal value of the controlled quantity. Spring feedback is characterised by two quantities: the time constant T_s, which depends on the dashpot parameters, and the feedback factor ϱ which depends on the ratio of the arms of lever 8.

If we put $T_s = \infty$, which corresponds to spring 11 being removed and the dashpot connecting valve being closed, we obtain a system with "stiff" feedback.

Spring feedback loops are not usually used in intermittent control systems, the so-called delayed feedback loops — which in practice are simpler and more logical — being preferred. In action, spring and delayed feedback loops are equivalent.

An example of a system using delayed thermal feedback is shown in Fig. 1.45. When one of the contacts 5 or 5′ closes, not only does the reversible motor 6 turn but, in addition, one of the resistances 8 is heated up. As a result the gas in the corresponding arm of the

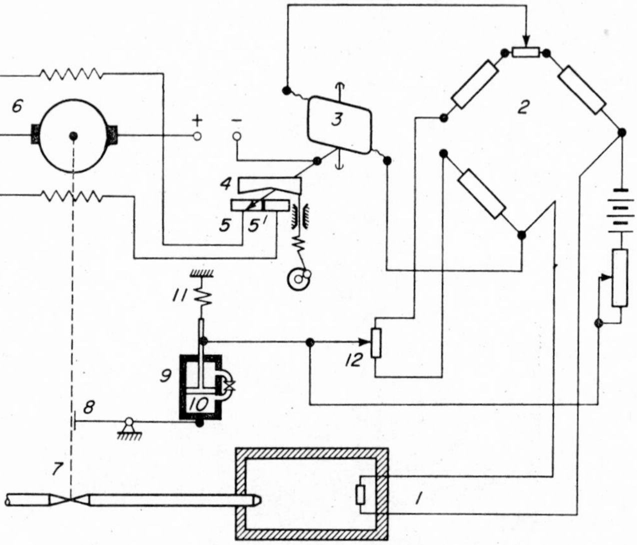

FIG. 1.44. System for automatically controlling the temperature of a furnace using mechanical spring-feedback.

U-tube expands, lowering the level of the mercury 9 in that arm and thus increasing the resistance of one of the arms of the bridge, of 10 say. The resulting unbalance of the bridge gives rise to an additional correcting pulse. At the end of the controlling process the equilibrium of the bridge will always correspond to the prescribed nominal value of the controlled quantity. Here, in contrast to the previous case, the input to the feedback element is not connected to the output of the slave unit but to its input, i.e. to the output of the pulse element.

Figure 1.46 shows a system using delayed thermo-electric feedback. When one of contacts 5 or 5′ closes, the reversible motor turns and at the same time one of the resistances 12 in the motor supply circuit is heated up. As a result an e.m.f. is generated by the corresponding group of the two groups of thermocouples 13. The current due to this e.m.f. causes the galvanometer pointer to return to the null position. The group of thermocouples 13 are wound in opposition. Obviously, resistance 12 is heated up for an interval equal to the time of closure of the contact and therefore to the time the reversible motor operates. Different values of the delayed feedback parameters (the feedback factor ϱ and the time constant $T_{f.b.}$) can be obtained

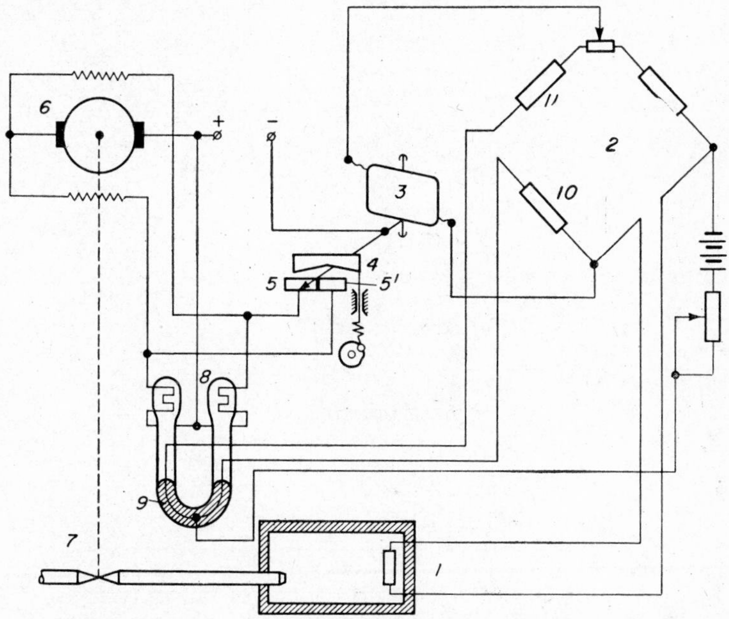

FIG. 1.45. System for automatically controlling the temperature of a furnace using delayed thermal feedback.

by varying respectively the position of the potentiometer wiper 14 and the distance between the thermocouples 13 by means of the adjusting screw 15.

Derivative action can also be introduced into the control law in order to improve the quality of the control.

In practice, preference is usually given to feedback loops, as effecting derivative action is often associated with difficulties of a constructional nature.

If the position of the setting wiper is varied according to a definite aw, we have a system with program control, i.e. a system in which the controlled quantity varies according to a given law.

Chopper-bar regulators are also used for controlling other quantities, e.g. the concentration or temperature of a mixture of two gases or liquids.

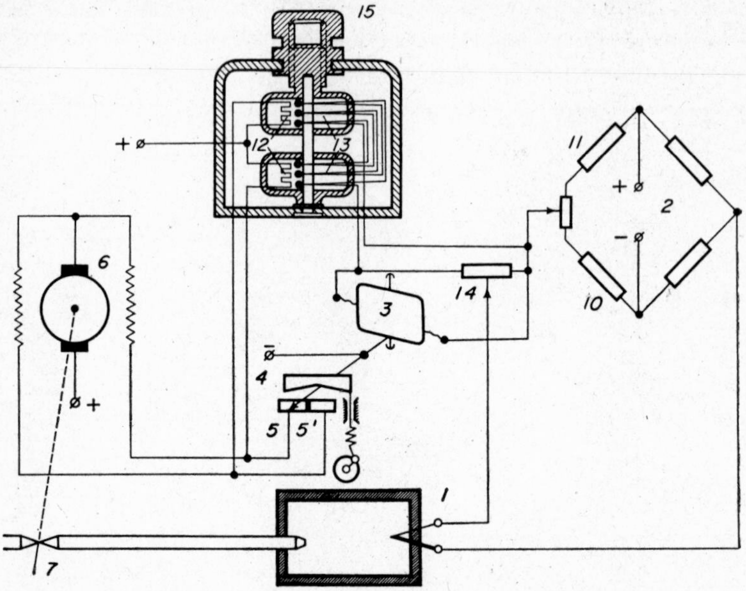

FIG. 1.46. Automatic-control system using delayed thermo-electric feedback.

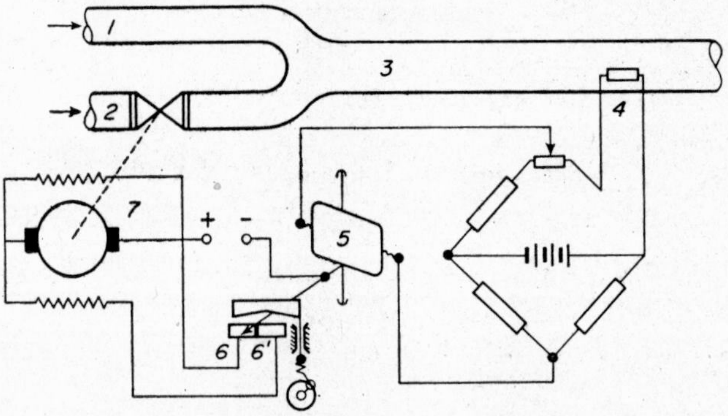

FIG. 1.47. System for automatically controlling the concentration of a mixture of two gases.

Figure 1.47 shows such system for one controlling the concentration of a mixture of two gases. Two different gases are fed along the different flow-tubes 1 and 2 and are mixed in the common flow-tube 3. The state of this mixture — temperature, concentration, quantity —

is measured by the measuring device 4, the measuring point being at a distance from the junction depending on technical considerations. A voltage proportional to the departure of this quantity from the prescribed value acts on the contact galvanometer 5 which, as before, controls the duration of closure of contacts 6 or 6′ which switch on the slave motor 7.

We now go on to examine systems which automatically control frequency and power.

An example of such a system+ is shown in Fig. 1.48.

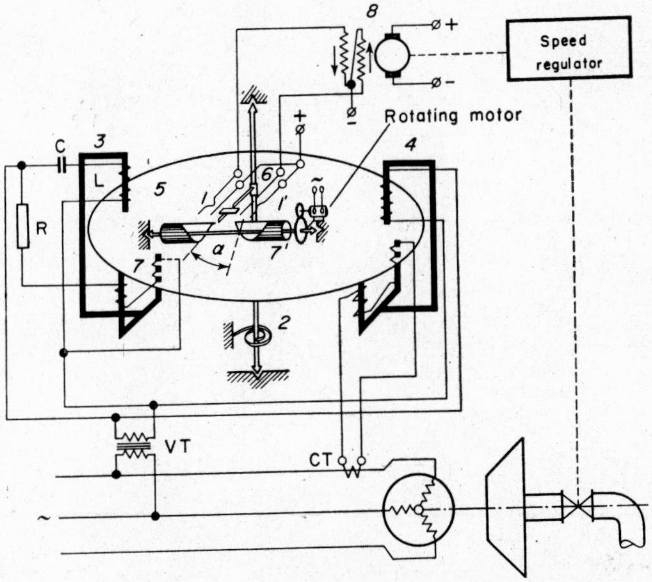

FIG. 1.48. System for automatically controlling frequency and power.

The LC circuit is tuned to a frequency close to 50 c/s. The tuning frequency of 50 c/s is chosen to be at the point where the resonance curve has maximum slope. The measuring device consists of a three-phase wattmeter in which the indicator mechanism has been removed and contact system 1—1′ and and a spring 2 added. The torque due to the spring is balanced by torques from the left 3 and right 4 parts of the meter, proportional respectively to the frequency and power deviations of the generator. Depending on the sign of the control voltage, which is proportional to the sum of the power and frequency

+ See P. P. Ostryi (1; 1956).

deviations, disc 5 along with pointer 6 rotates in one direction or the other until the pointer touches contact 7 or 7′ both of which are rotating with constant speed. This closes the circuit of the slave motor 8 which then begins to act on the speed regulator of the prime-mover driving the generator.

The contact surface of 7,7′ takes the form of a rolled-up triangle, and hence the duration of the pulses controlling the motor is proportional to the deflection of the pointer. Resistor R is for tuning the regulator.

Figure 1.49 shows a more up-to-date system for automatic control of power.+

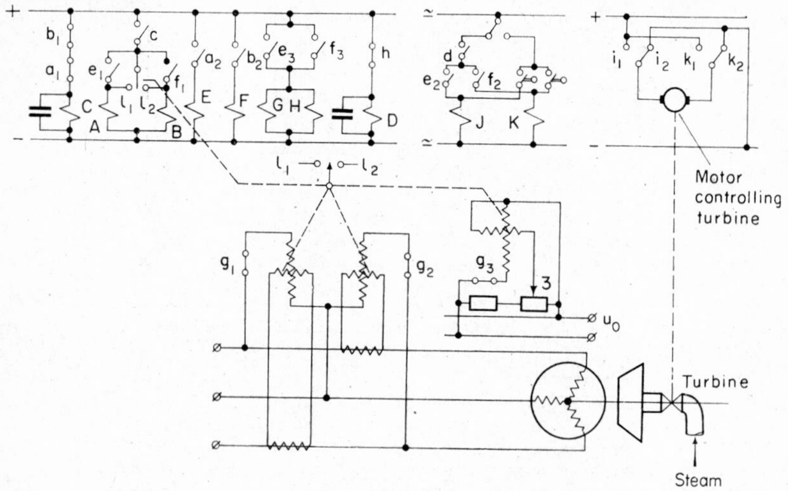

FIG. 1.49. System for automatically controlling power.

The measuring device consists of a three-phase wattmeter to whose coils are fed the voltage and current from the generator terminals. In the zero-current state the movable part of the wattmeter is adjusted using a spring so that contacts l_1 and l_2 are open.

The nominal power is set using 3. The wattmeter contacts l_1 and l_2 control a relay-contact system which turns on a motor. The motor acts on the controlling mechanism of the prime-mover driving the generator. Contact a_1 and a_2 of relays A and B open the circuit of the pulse-interval relay C and close the circuit of the pulse relay E which then, by contacts e_2 and e_3 (contact e_1 de-energises relay A), causes relays J, G and H to be energised. This turns on the driving

+ See Blase, Dietze (1; 1955).

motor (by means of contact i_1) which acts on the controlling mechanism of the prime-mover, and also opens the circuit of relay D which, however, releases after a short time (due to the shunting capacitor). At the same time the contacts of the null-relay G open the circuit of the voltage coil of the wattmeter and its movable part returns to the neutral position. There are two delay circuits in the system, namely relays C and D. When D releases, the driving motor is switched off; when C releases, by means of relays A, E and G, it switches the wattmeter to the mains for a new measuring cycle.

The sensitivity of the system is governed by the setting of contacts l_1 and l^2. If the sign of the departure from nominal changes, then relays B, F and K operate and the motor turns in the opposite direction.

The above system uses pulses of constant duration T_1 and variable repetition frequency

$$f = \frac{1}{T_1 + T_2}, \tag{1.21}$$

where $T_2 = k/P$, the interval between pulses, is inversesly proportional to the deviation of the power from nominal. The quantity k depends on the wattmeter inertia.

The use of such a principle removes, on the one hand, the effect of the line parameters on power transmission and, on the other, prevents short-term power fluctuations from acting on the control system.

We now examine another system for automatic voltage control.

Figure 1.50 shows a simplified form of the SN-91 automatic voltage control system.

The departure of the voltage from nominal is measured by the torque motor 1, powered through a transformer 2 from the terminals of the a.c. generator. A lever with a contact strip 3 and a balancing spring 4 is attached to the shaft of the torque motor. When the generator voltage is at its nominal value the contact strip takes up a horizontal position, when its contacts do not touch the star-wheel 5 which is driven at constant speed by the motor 6.

A variation in generator voltage varies the motor torque, thus causing the contact strip to turn (clockwise for a drop in voltage, anticlockwise for an increase) and one of the contacts to commence touching the star-wheel. This closes the circuit of the slave motor 7, which then varies the resistance in the field winding of the excitor 8.

The field voltage of generator 9 is thus changed, causing the generator voltage to vary.

The angle through which the contact strip turns increases as departure of the voltage from nominal increases. In this case the duration of contact of the star-wheel and the contact strip increases, i.e. the duration of the pulses controlling the slave motor increases. A dashpot 10 is used to stabilise the system.

A slave motor is not used in the automatic voltage control system shown in Fig. 1.51.

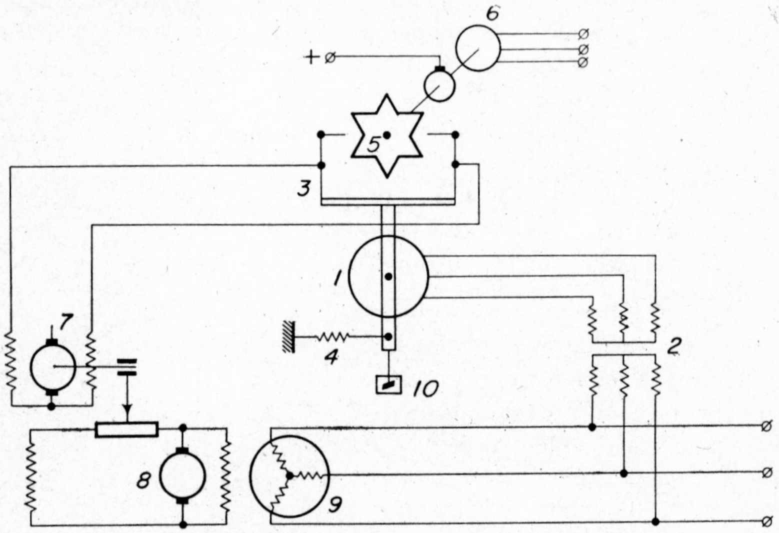

FIG. 1.50. Automatic voltage-control system Type SN—91.

The reed of an electro-magnet 1, whose coils are driven by current and voltage transformers, is attached to a lever 2 carrying one of the contacts. The second contact is attached to lever 3 which oscillates up and down under the action of cam 4 and an auxiliary motor as shown. As a result the contacts periodically close and open the circuit of the auxiliary relay 5, periodically shunting the resistance in the field circuit of the excitor 6. This contact system constitutes a pulse element.

A variation in voltage varies the distance between the contacts, i.e. varies the time they remain closed. This gives rise to a change in generator voltage in the opposite direction. The time interval for which the contacts remain closed depends on the position of lever 2, i.e. it is proportional to the deviation of the controlled quantity. In contrast to the previous system of Fig. 1.50, the automatic voltage control system of Fig. 1.51 has an oscillatory mode of operation. This is due to the fact that there is no slave device in the form of a motor in the latter system.

Pulse-width modulation is mainly used in industrial systems for controlling relatively slow processes (temperature, concentration, frequency). This enables full use to be made of slave motors, which operate at constant, maximum speed.

We remark that in all the systems described above, both the disturbing and controlling actions have been continuous in nature.

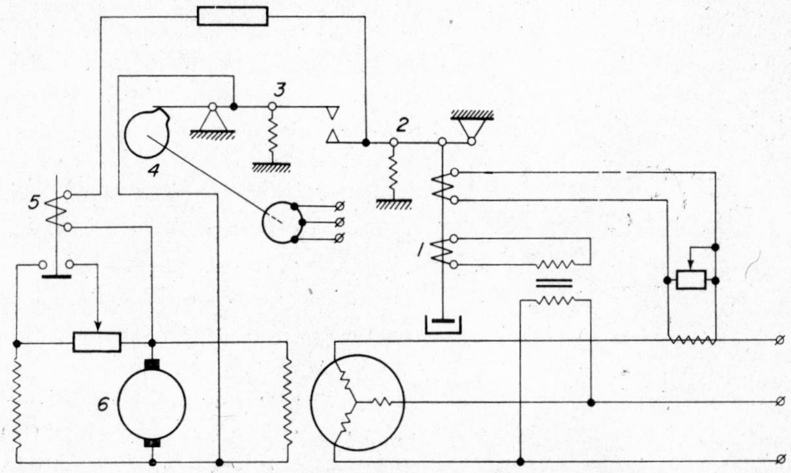

Fig. 1.51. An automatic voltage-control system.

Control-system pulse elements can be very diverse in character depending on the purpose and field of application of the control system. A few examples illustrating the construction of pulse elements are given in Table 1.2.

Automatic potentiometers (potentiometer recorders). An automatic potentiometer of the compensating type, such as is used for measuring temperatures, usually consists of a measuring device, a balancing system and a recording mechanism.+

The measuring device consists of a light movable coil attached, along with a pointer, to an axial supporting wire and placed in the field of permanent magnets. The recording mechanism consists of

+ See F. E. Temnikov (1; 1948).

a paper-carrying device and a carriage with a pen. The balancing system, which is essentially an amplifier, connects the measuring instrument with the recording mechanism. It drives the potentiometer into a position of equilibrium.

Figure 1.52 illustrates a typical electrical type of automatic potentiometer.

We shall now examine three examples of automatic potentiometer with intermittent amplification; they differ for the the most part in the construction of the balancing system.

Figure 1.53 shows the kinematics of an automatic potentiometer with a mechanical balancing system.

The balancing system converts a deflection of the sensitive galvanometer pointer 1 into a shift of the potentiometer wiper 2 and the pen carriage 3. It operates cyclically from the powered shaft carrying cams 4 and 5.

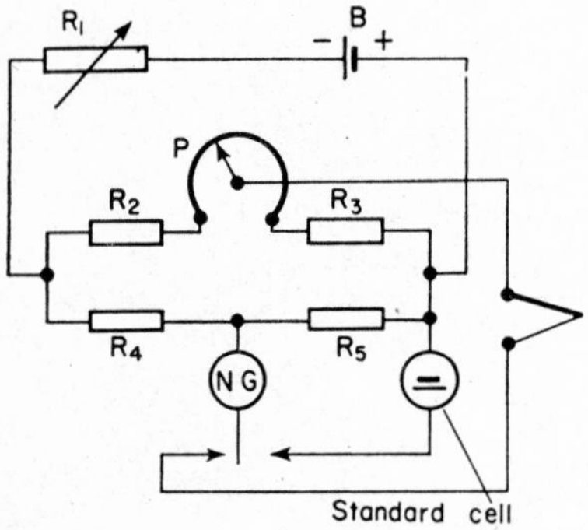

FIG. 1.52. Typical electrical diagram of an automatic potentiometer.

Cam 4 causes lever 7 to oscillate to and fro. When this lever moves under the action of the spring, the secondary pointer 8 on the end of rod 9 pushes bar 10 downwards along with the attached framework carrying the notched plate 11. At the lowest position lug 12 of plate 11 catches the rocking frame 13, pulling it downwards and thus releasing the pointer of the null-galvanometer.

The galvanometer pointer then takes up a new position in accordance with the electrical state of the system. After this cam 4 commences to drive lever 7, and so the secondary pointer 8 and rod 9 are released.

Rod 9 now commences to move in the opposite direction but in addition it moves along the direction of bar 10, due to the action of spring 14. Lug 12 now releases the rocking frame 13 which then clamps the end of pointer 1 to the reference bar 15. The notched plate 11 continues to rise until one of its notches catches the clamped end of the null-galvanometer pointer. This stops the rise of plate 11 and the rotation of the secondary pointer 8. Thus the angle of rotation of the secondary pointer is proportional to the deviation of the null-galvanometer pointer 1. In addition, pointer 8 turns the frame 17 which controls the motion of the power elements.

Cam 5 and the powerful spring 19 force the large lever 20 to oscillate with the same frequency as lever 7 but with a phase shift; counterclockwise motion corresponds to the idling stroke and clockwise motion (under the action of spring 19) to the working stroke. The

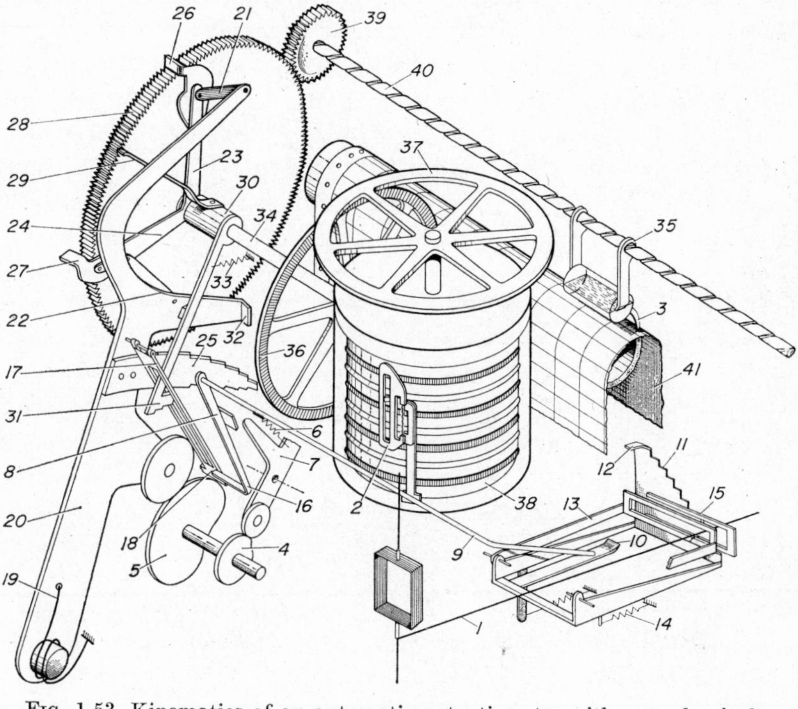

FIG. 1.53. Kinematics of an automatic potentiometer with a mechanical balancing system.

upper end of lever 20 branches into two parts, each having a drag-rod (21 and 22); by means of these drag-rods lever 20 makes the radial levers 23 and 24 approach and separate. The working stroke of the large lever 20 and the radial levers 23 and 24 is limited by a lug 18 on the rocking frame 17, which takes up an angle opposite the notched beak-shaped plate 25 on the large lever which depends on the magnitude and sign of the null-galvanometer deflection. If pointer 1 is at zero then lug 18 is located against the point of plate 25, stopping the working stroke of lever 20. If pointer 1 is deflected, then lug 18 is deflected up or down from the point of plate 25; the further it is deflected, the greater the working stroke of lever 20.

On the working stroke the radial levers, by means of ratchets 26 and 27, rotate the toothed wheel 28 which turns the working elements of the potentiometer. The direction of rotation depends on the sign of the galvanometer deflection and is governed by the flat spring 29, which engages one of the ratchets with the toothed wheel 28. Spring 29 is attached to a freely moving bush 30, which can be turned by a lever 31 with three lugs. On each idling stroke of the large lever, lug 32 catches lever 31, pulling it back through a certain angle and then releasing it on the working stroke when it moves till it comes in contact with the lower edge of the slit of frame 17. Depending on the position of frame 17 lever 31 is stopped by one of the three lugs, which correspond to the signs plus, zero and minus. These signs are reproduced by three positions of spring 29. The middle lug corresponds to the mean position of the spring and in this case none of the ratchets engages with wheel 28. If the lever is stopped by one of the other lugs then the spring presses on the ratchet of one of the radial levers, engaging it with toothed wheel 28; the wheel then turns and, as a result, the difference between the measured and balancing voltages is removed. The rotation of the toothed wheel 28 is transmitted to the wiper 2 of potentiometer 38 and also to the worm shaft 40, which shifts the pen carriage along the recording paper 41.

Figure 1.54 shows the kinematics of the 'micromax' automatic potentiometer, which has a different mechanical balancing system.

Cams 4,4′ 5, 14, 14′ are attached to a shaft 3 which is driven through a worm reduction gear by a motor 1. Cam 5 periodically raises and lowers the rocking table 6 which clamps the pointer 8 of a null-galvanometer to the stationary bar 7. When the galvanometer pointer is unclamped it takes up a position corresponding to the electrical state of the system; it is then clamped in this position by the rocking table. The arms 10 and 11 of the scissors mechanism, which are driven by cams 4 and 4′, then begin to approach. If the pointer is deflected then one of these arms will meet the clamped pointer earlier and stop, the second arriving at the pointer a little later. The lower pair of scissor arms 12 and 12′ will then have turned lever 13 through an angle proportional to the deflection of the galvanometer pointer. This concludes the measuring stage. The next stage deals with transforming the rotation of lever 13 into a movement of the balancing and recording mechanisms. It commences with the lever 13 being clamped to the disc 15. At this point cams 4, 4′ open the scissors mechanism and cam 5 lifts the table, so freeing the pointer. Cams 14, 14′ then come up to the ends of lever 13 and rotate it (along with the disc 15) into a horizontal position. Disc 15 is connected to the same shaft as the potentiometer 16 and the drum 17, the latter driving a wire for shifting the carriage. Hence a rotation of disc 15 turns the potentiometer, driving the system into equilibrium, and the drum 17 shifts the pen carriage.

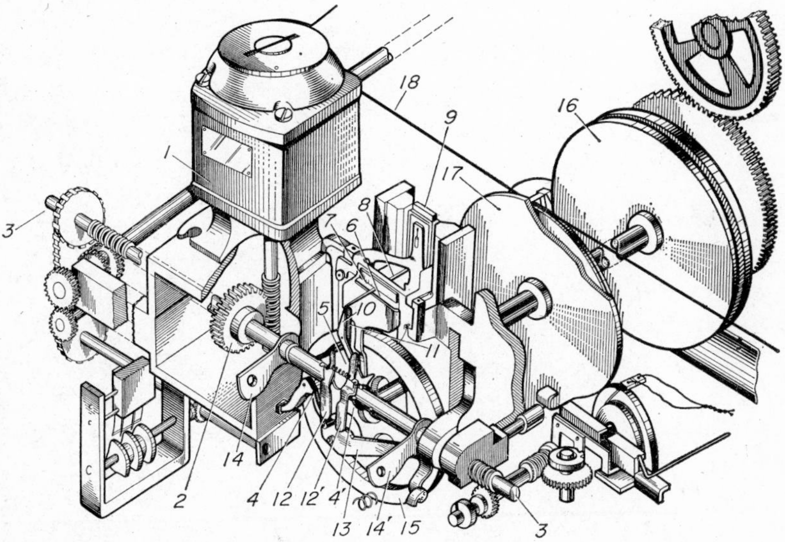

FIG. 1.54. Kinematics of the "micromax" automatic potentiometer.

Figure 1.55 shows the kinematics of an automatic potentiometer with an electrical amplifier and a contact galvanometer.

The long (about 130 mm) flexible pointer 2 of a null-galvanometer 1 passes under bar 3, to which it may be clamped by the stepped plates of levers 4. These levers are connected by a spring and their contacts 5, attached to the vertical arms, may close with contacts attached to table 6. Under the action of cam 8, table 6, along with levers 4, is periodically raised and lowered, pivoting about the axis 7. If pointer 2 is in the mean position then both the pairs of contacts 5 remain open and motor 9 stays at rest. If the pointer is deflected, then during the motion of levers 4 one of the stepped plates will be stopped by the clamped pointer and thus one of the contact pairs will close for a certain time. Due to the stepped shape of the plate this time interval will be greater the greater the deflection of the galvanometer pointer.

Hence the closure time of one or the other pair of contacts (depending on the sign of the unbalance) depends on the magnitude of the galvo-pointer deflection. The closing of a pair of contacts causes motor 9 to turn in a direction to remove the unbalance. By means of the gear transmission 10 the motor turns the driving screw **11**,

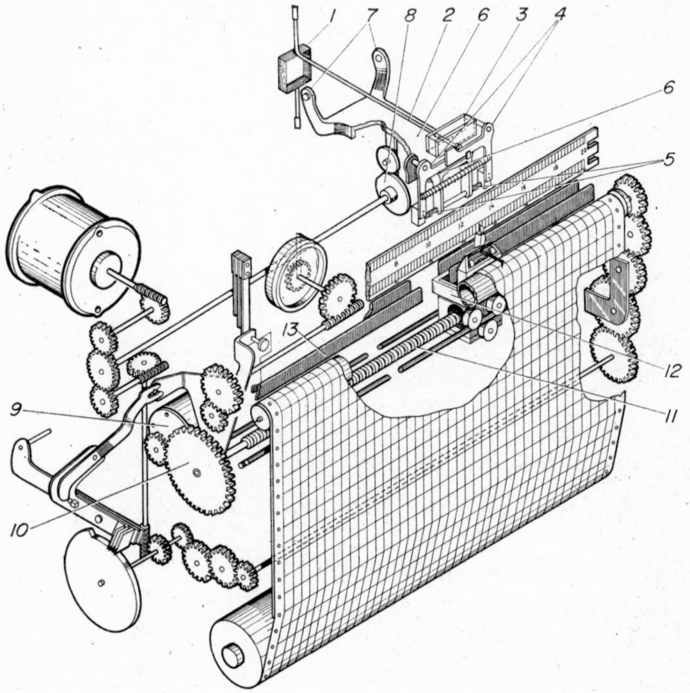

FIG. 1.55. Kinematics of an automatic potentiometer with an electrical amplifier.

which shifts the carriage 12 carrying the pen, indicator, and contact wiper, of the balancing potentiometer 13.

The instrument is of the slow acting type. There are several variations, including a multi-input type which can record several curves.

Servo-systems. The main aim of a servo-system is to reproduce an input action as accurately as possible, where the input action may be continuous or defined only at discrete moments of time.

We now consider a pulse servo-system which is used in multi-colour printing machines. It is necessary for good quality printing of a coloured picture, carried out by the successive superposition of imprints in the primary colours, that these imprints should not be displaced by more than a few hundredths of a millimeter. Superposition of the imprints to this accuracy gives rise to considerable difficulties as a result of the high speed of the paper (up to 5 m/sec), the large distance between rollers (up to 10 m) to allow the imprints to dry, the non-uniform thickness of the paper and so on.+

Figure 1.56 shows a multi-unit rotational printing machine with five sections, pulse servo-systems being used to achieve coincidence.

The printing rollers of all sections are driven at approximately synchronous speed by electric motors. The aim of the pulse system is to make the picture on each roller coincide with the picture on the paper. This is achieved by adjusting the speeds of the printing rollers individually. Neither the first section, which puts on a single-colour background, nor the second, which prints the first colour, require adjusting. The roller for the first colour (yellow) prints, as well as the picture, marks of width 0.5 mm and length 10 mm (directed along the axis of the roller) along the edge of the paper. The printing

+ See Fleisser (1; 1953); Blaum and Hölter (1; 1955).

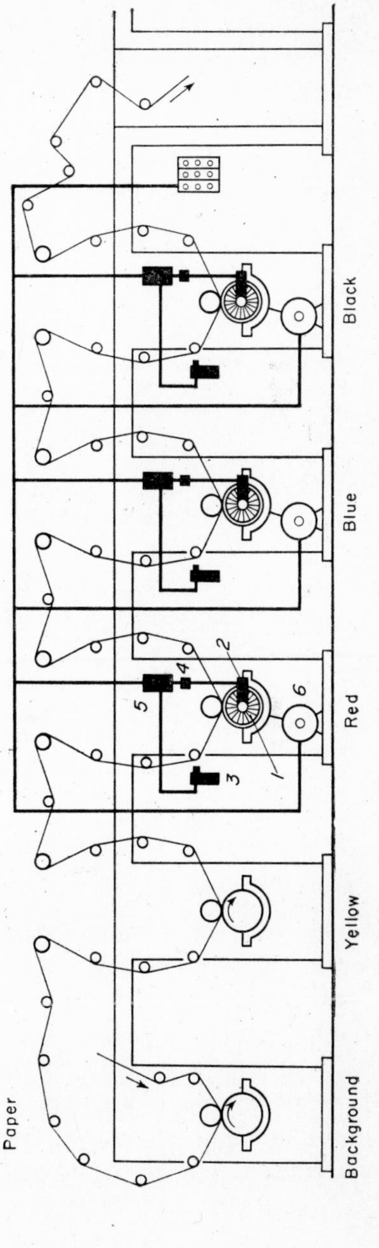

Fig. 1.56. A multi-unit rotary printing machine with pulse servo-systems.

rollers of the following sections are corrected relative to these marks.

Each section has a photo-electric pulse servo-system (Fig. 1.56) consisting of a screened drum 1, which is attached to the axis of the printing roller, photo-sensitive servo heads 2 and 3 with associated light sources for illuminating the paper and the roller, a selector switch 4, a comparator 5 and an electrical drive for adjusting the roller speed.

The principle of operation of the pulse servo-system (Fig. 1.57) is as follows. The photo-element of servo-head Φ_1 picks up light reflected from the paper and generates a rectangular pulse of duration

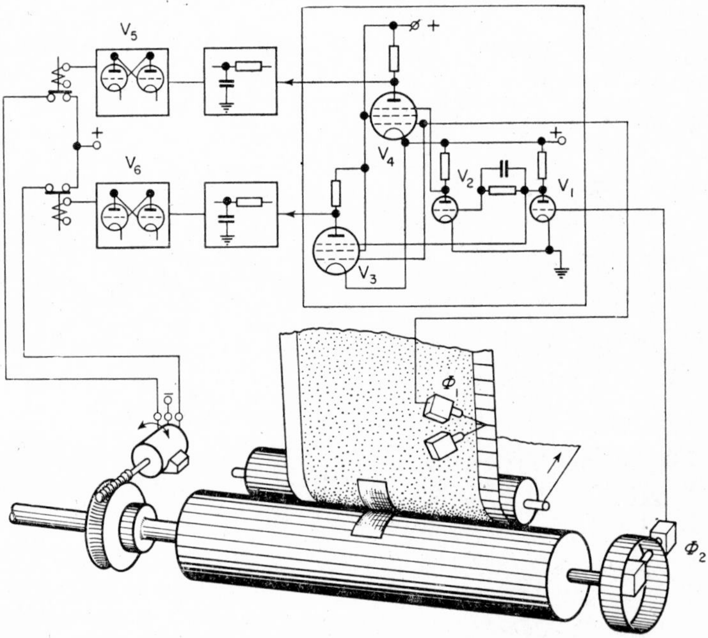

FIG. 1.57. Diagram of the pulse servo-system.

100 μsec whenever a yellow mark appears in its field of view. The photo-element is provided with a pale blue filter to accentuate the contrast of the yellow mark on the background. A photomultiplier then amplifies the signal from the photo-element. The screened drum has as many axial slits around its circumference as the first printing roller (yellow) makes marks (usually 16).

The working edges of the slits (the rear ones relative to the direction of rotation) are placed with great precision since it is with respect to them that adjustment is carried out. A light is placed inside the drum and a photo-sensitive servo-head Φ_2 outside it. When the roller is rotating the photo-element is periodically illuminated through the slits by the light inside the drum, and it consequently generates rectangular pulses of voltage. These pulses are amplified. The pulses from the servo-heads are fed to a comparator which gives out a signal proportional to the difference in position between the marks on the paper relative to the slits on the drum of the corresponding printing roller. The comparator consists of a double triode V_1 and V_2 and two pentodes V_3 and V_4. The signal from the roller servo-head is first fed to the grid of triode V_1 and, after amplification, to the suppressor grid of V_3. Triode V_1 feeds triode V_2. The latter thus supplies pulses to the suppressor of the second pentode V_4 which are similar to the pulses V_3 but shifted in phase such that the beginning of a pulse on the suppressor of V_4 coincides with the end of that pulse on the suppressor of V_3, thus determining the instant the working edge of the slit on the drum passes. The suppressor grids of the two pentodes are normally biased negatively. The potential on the control grids of the pentodes is raised by the signal from the servo-head for the paper Φ_1 but the pentodes remain cut off provided there are no pulses on their suppressor grids from triodes V_1 and V_2. If a signal from the roller servo-head Φ_2 is present then triode V_1 switches on pentode V_3 by means of the signal to its suppressor, and when the signal from V_1 ceases triode V_2 switches on pentode V_4.

If the passage of the working edge of the slit strictly coincides in time with the passage of the middle of the mark on the paper (Fig. 1.57), i.e. the tail of the pulse from the roller servo-head coincides with the middle of the pulse from the servo-head for the paper, then the output pulses from the anode circuits of the pentodes — the beginning of one coinciding with the end of the other — will be of equal duration and the system is thus in equilibrium. If the working edge of a slit is in front relative to the mark on the paper, then the duration of the output pulse from pentode V_3 (Fig. 1.57) is reduced and that from pentode V_4 increased, this being used to drive a correcting motor in the appropriate direction.

The comparator also has an amplifier and a magic eye indicator valve for visual observation of the deviation in position between roller and paper.

The signals from the output of each pentode pass through special circuits containing diodes and a broadening capacitor and are then fed to the control panel of the correcting electrical drive.

The electrical drive usually consists of a motor with an independently excited field, the armature being driven by amplifiers V_5 and V_6. The motor remains at rest in the absence of an error. Purely alternating current passes through the armature, removing the effects of static friction and dead-zone. The presence of an error causes a direct component to appear in the armature circuit, the sign of which depends on the sign of the error, and the armature of the motor commences

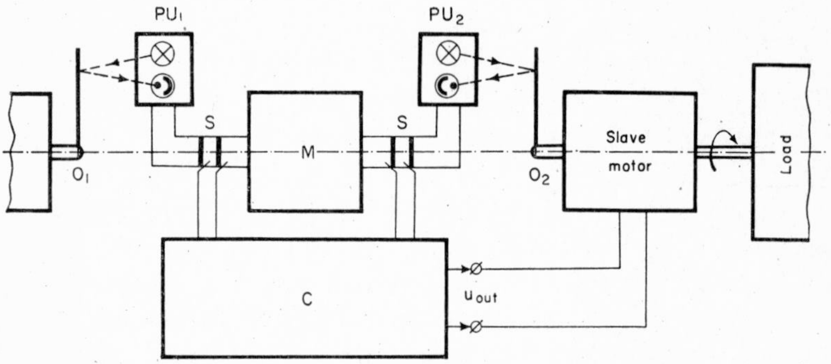

FIG. 1.58. Principle of operation of a zero-torque measuring system.

to turn, correcting — by means of a worm transmission and planetary differential — the position of the roller relative to the paper.

A measuring instrument introduces distortion into the measured quantity; one of the requirements of a servo measuring instrument is the reduction of such distortion. If the input quantity is an angular shift, distortion is introduced by additional torque loading of the the input shaft. This loading torque is equal to the resistive torque of the comparator or, as it is usually known, the error indicator.

The removal or reduction of loading torque is particularly important when the input shaft is driven by a low-power device. The error indicators currently used do not, as a rule, have zero loading torque and those that do (for example optical and ion instruments) require a change in shaft construction which is not always permissible.

We shall now examine the operating principles of photo-electric error indicators,+ which are used in 'zero-torque' servo systems.

+ See K. B. Karandeyev, Yu. N. Bobkov (1; 1956).

In this type of indicator a rotating beam of light is used which produces a photo-pulse when it intersects the pointer (or indicator) of the input shaft. The position of the slave shaft is similarly determined. The principle of operation consists of replacing the measurement of angular errors between the input and slave shafts by the measurement of the time intervals between the corresponding pulses, the polarity of the output voltage of the indicator giving the sequence of these pulses, i.e. the polarity depends on the sign of the error, and the mean value of the output voltage depends on the magnitudes of the error. A system illustrating this principle is shown in Fig. 1.58.

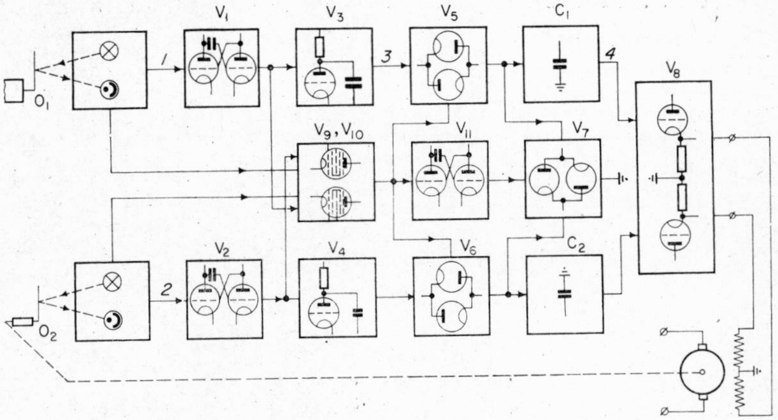

FIG. 1.59. A zero-torque servo-system with PAM.

Here O_1 and O_2 are the input and slave shafts respectively of the servo system; PU_1 and PU_2 are pulse units which produce photo-pulses corresponding to the positions of the respective shafts; M is a motor which rotates the pulse units with an angular velocity $\omega = 2\,\pi/T$; S are slip-rings for removing the photo-pulses; C is a converter, which produces the error signal.

We describe two converters.

Figure 1.59 shows a zero-torque servo-system in which the error signal is an amplitude-modulated rectangular pulse of duration γT The first of the two photo-pulses arriving during the repetition period T (suppose for example it is from O_1) switches on, via the Kipp relay V_1, its generator of linearly-increasing voltage V_3. The second pulse, during its time of action, closes the charging switch V_5 of capacitor C_1 and simultaneously opens the discharging switch V_7

for a time γT, which depends on the adjustable parameters of the Kipp relay V_{11}. During the time γT a voltage remains on capacitor C_1 which is proportional to the time shift between the two pulses (Fig. 1.60). If the sign of the error changes, the order of arrival of the pulses is reversed, which gives rise to a voltage of opposite polarity on capacitor C_2 since this capacitor is charged from a different generator of linearly-increasing voltage, V_4. The selector V_9, V_{10} chooses the appropriate pulses for operating the switches V_5, V_6, V_7. The output voltage of the indicator, which is taken from the storage capacitors C_1 or C_2, is passed through the differential cathode follower V_8 and used to control the motion of the slave shaft.

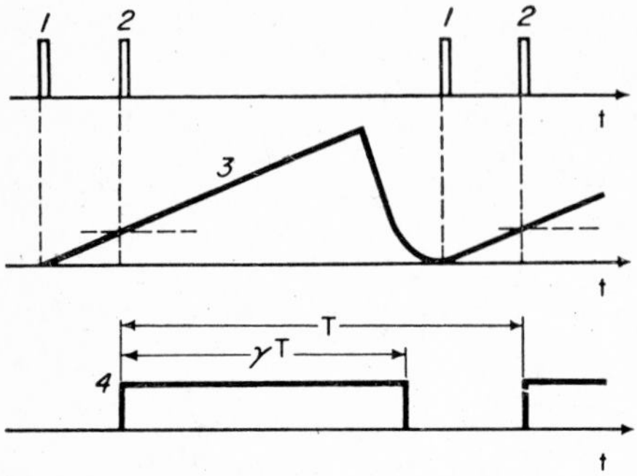

FIG. 1.60. Explanation of the zero-torque servo-system.

In the zero-torque servo-system shown in Fig. 1.61 the error signal takes the form of a train of width-modulated pulses of alternating

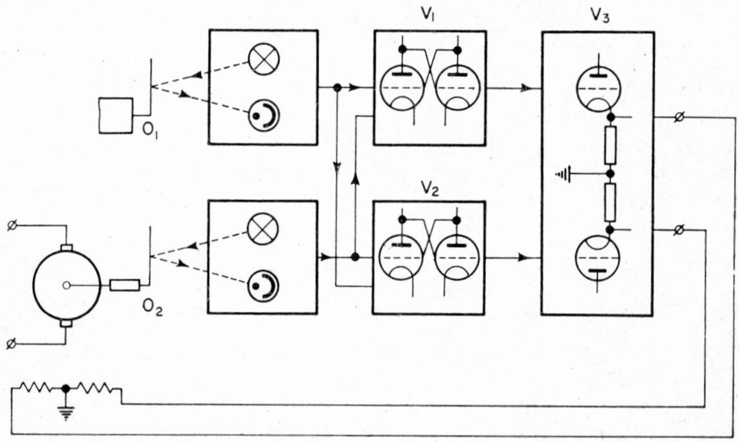

FIG. 1.61. Diagram of a zero-torque servo-system with PWM.

sign. In this system a photo-pulse is used to change the states of flip-flops V_1, V_2. The zero-stability of this system is determined by the stability of the output pulse amplitude. A modification (Fig. 1.62) of this system has a better zero-stability. In this case, when there is no error between the input and slave shafts, the duration of the output pulses equals zero. The difference from the preceding system lies in the fact that when one of the flip-flops, for example V_3, is switched out, the second flip-flop, V_4, is not switched in. Hence for maximum error the duration of the pulse is only $T/2$, i. e. the system is only half as sensitive as the previous one.

Relay servo-systems in which additional oscillations are induced

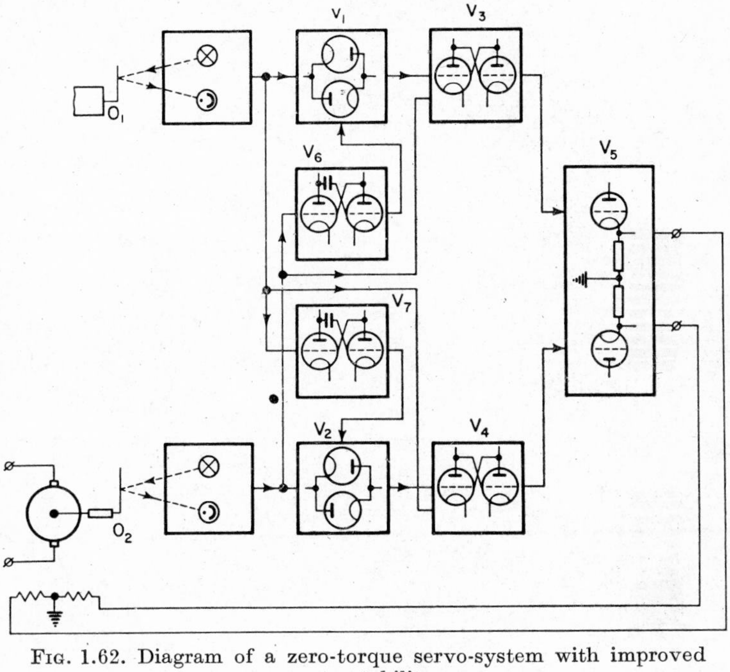

FIG. 1.62. Diagram of a zero-torque servo-system with improved zero-stability.

in the relay wipers or contacts may also be classed as pulse servo-systems.

Figure 1.63 shows a simple example of this type of system. A voltage proportional to the error between the input 2 and slave 3 shafts is fed to the coil of a sensitive polarised relay 1, and an additional alternating voltage of frequency 10 to 15 times greater than the highest frequency of the error voltage is supplied by transformer 4. If there is no error voltage, the relay wiper moves solely under the influence of the alternating voltage and the contacts 5,5′ close for equal intervals of time. Voltage pulses of equal duration and alternating polarity will thus appear at the motor armature. The motor will remain at rest due to the high repetition rate of the pulses. For an error voltage other than zero the relay wiper will close with one of the contacts for a longer time than with the other. In this case the difference between the times of contact is proportional to the error voltage. Now pulses of alternating polarity but different durations appear at the motor armature. A voltage with a direct component thus acts on the armature and the motor turns, driving — through a reduction gear — its load and therefore the slave shaft so as to reduce the error voltage to zero.

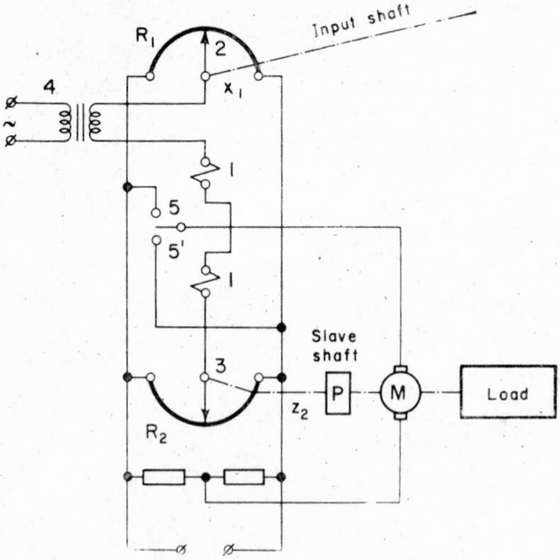

FIG. 1.63. Diagram of the simplest pulse servo-system.

The use of the additional alternating voltage, which gives rise to the forced oscillations of the relay wiper, converts the relay servo-system into a pulse servo-system with PWM and therefore confers the property of proportionality on the relay system.

A large number of similar systems have been described in the literature.+

Diagrams 6 and 11 in Table 1.2 illustrate relay elements with the properties of a type two pulse element.

In the servo-systems described above the input and output quantities take the form of positions; in fact they were the angular positions

+ See for example the author's book (4; 1955 c), where a detailed bibliography s given.

of input and slave shafts. We shall now examine another servo-system in which the phases of electrical voltages constitute the input and output quantities. This is the case with the automatic phase-tuning circuits used in the line-sweep generators of television receivers. Such

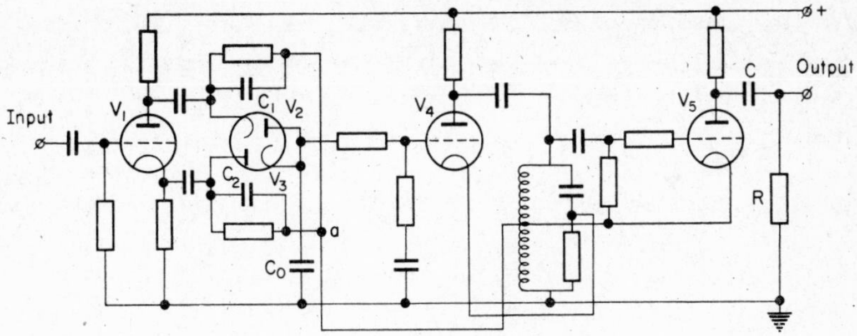

FIG. 1.64. Circuit diagram of an automatic phase-tuning system.

circuits synchronise a sinusoidal waveform with the input synchronising pulses (Fig. 1.64). The sync pulses are passed through the inverter V_1 and fed to the cathode and the anode of diodes V_2 and V_3 respectively; the sinusoidal voltage is fed to the point *a*. When a sync pulse is present diodes V_2 and V_3, which were cut off by the voltages on capacitors C_1 and C_2, are rendered conducting and the storage capacitor C_0 charges up to a voltage approximately equal to the sinusoidal voltage at that instant. Hence an error voltage appears on C_0 which is proportional to the phase shift of the sinusoidal voltage relative to the sync pulses (Fig. 1.65). This error voltage remains constant during the interval between sync pulses. It is fed to the input of a reactance valve V_4 which, depending on the magnitude and sign of the error, varies the effective inductance of the oscillator circuit and therefore the period of the oscillator waveform.

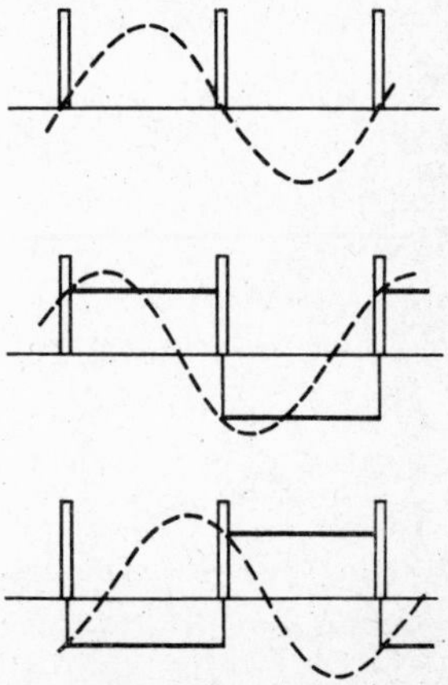

FIG. 1.65. Explanation of the automatic phase-tuning system.

The sinusoidal oscillator V_5 is a Hartley oscillator with inductive feedback. By means of the *RC* differentiating network, pulses of line-sweep frequency are formed in the anode circuit of the oscillator.

They are strictly locked in phase to the sinusoidal voltage, which controls the operation of the stages forming the current or voltage sweep.

In this pulse servo-system the pulse element takes the form of a pulse-phase detector; it carries out pulse-amplitude modulation and is therefore a type one pulse element.

Systems for converting discrete data into continuous and conversely. Several feedback systems for converting discrete data into continuous can be considered as pulse systems. In systems for converting discrete data into continuous, the discrete data are usually produced by a pulse generator controlled by a punched tape, magnetic recording, etc.

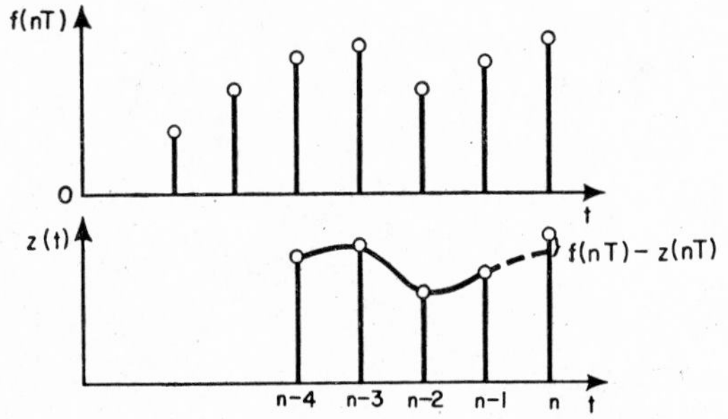

FIG. 1.66. Conversion of discrete data into continuous data.

To obtain a high accuracy of conversion it is necessary to compare at discrete moments the continuous function $z(t)$, generated in some manner or other, with the discrete values $f(nT)$ (Fig. 1.66) and to introduce corrections, depending on the difference between these functions at the discrete moments, such that this difference tends to zero. As the values of $f(nT)$ are defined only at discrete moments, it is necessary to assume some law which defines the behaviour of the continuous function inside each interval, i. e. we must assume some prediction law. This law is usually taken as the polynomial

$$z(t) = a_0 + a_1 t^2 + a_2 t^2 + a_3 t^3 . \tag{1.22}$$

The coefficients a_k are varied in such a manner that the difference $f(nT) - z(t)$ is made zero or minimum. Integrators are used for generating the function $z(t)$. The voltages fed to the integrators depend on the coefficients a_k.⁺

⁺ See Porter (1; 1954).

Figure 1.67 shows a simplified system for converting discrete data into continuous. The error at discrete moments is fed to a clamping circuit V_1 and through summing circuits or amplifiers with different gains to the integrators V_2, V_3. These are electronic Miller integrators. The final integrator takes the form of a velodyne servo-system, which transforms its output voltage into rate of rotation of the output shaft. A pneumatic or hydraulic servo-system is often used instead of an electro-mechanical one.

Feedback, obtained from the potentiometer P and the pulse element V_5, is fed to the comparator. The potentiometers P_1, P_2, P_3 at the inputs to the integrators are used for setting up the system

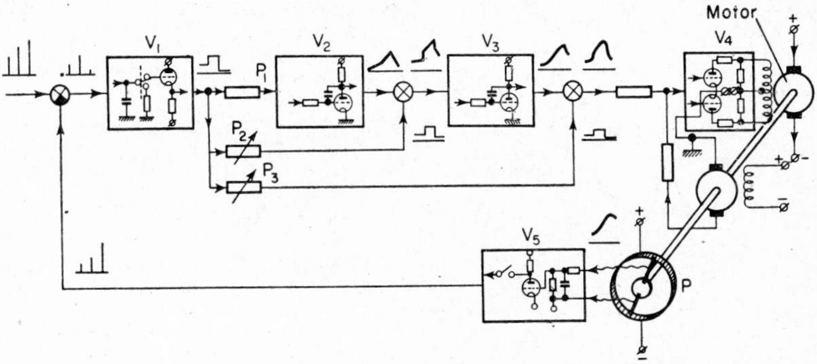

FIG. 1.67. Simplified diagram of a system for converting discrete data into continuous data.

A communication system using the so-called δ-modulation[+] provides an example of a system which converts continuous data into discrete. Figure 1.68 shows a block diagram of this system, the simplest of all the known systems using pulse-code modulation. The system operates as follows: A train of pulses from the pulse generator is fed to the pulse modulator. The latter passes pulses of the same polarity when the voltage u is positive and of the opposite polarity when u is negative. The voltage u is formed in the error measuring unit and is the difference between the modulating signal u_1 (which is to be transmitted) and the output u_2 of the integrating circuit. By a suitable choice of integrating circuit it is possible to make the integrator output voltage u_2 approximate to the signal u_1 being transmitted. If the received signal is fed from the pulse modulator to an integrating circuit, similar to that used in the transmitter, and then to a filter, the output will closely resemble

[+] See Schouten, de Jager, Greeftes (1; 1952).

the transmitted signal. This is the fact on which the system is based. Since the pulses become distorted during transmission they are first reshaped at the receiving end by means of a pulse generator (synchronised with the transmitter pulse generator) and a pulse modulator,

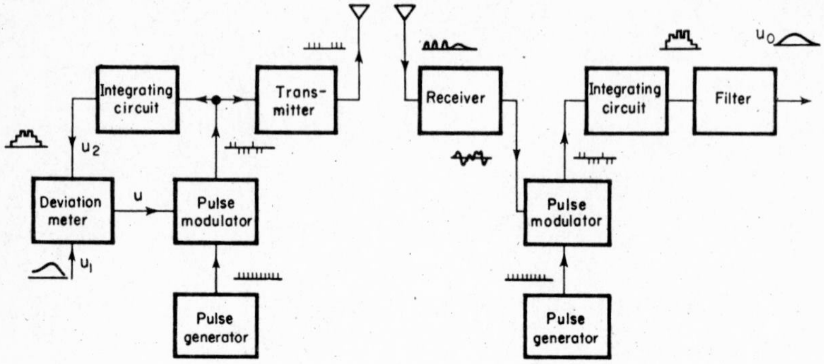

FIG. 1.68. Communication system using δ-modulation.

and fed to the integrating circuit whose output is taken to a smoothing filter.

A feedback system with a modulator (Fig. 1.69) can be considered as a system for converting continuous data into discrete. It takes the

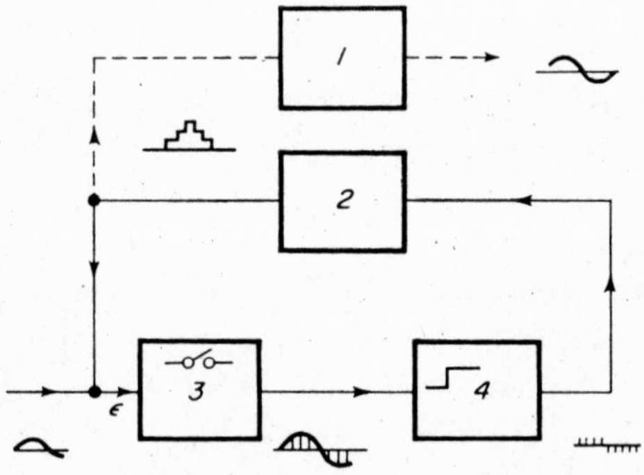

FIG. 1.69. A modulator as a pulse system.

form of a pulse servo-system with a relay element 4 which changes the polarity of the pulses whenever the polarity of the error ε changes. The conversion of the discrete data, which take the form of binary numbers, is carried out by the simple filter 1.

A large number of systems exist for converting discrete data into continuous. We refer the reader to the literature for further information.†

Control systems used in radar equipment. As examples of control systems used in radar equipment we consider automatic ranging, automatic gain control (AGC), and automatic frequency control (AFC), of radar receivers.‡

In the automatic ranging system the time taken for a radio-frequency pulse to travel from the radar transmitter to the moving object and back to the radar receiver is measured. This time is proportional to the distance of the object from the radar station. Thus in essence the automatic ranging system is a method for automatically measuring time. The system must be able to recognise only the signal from the chosen object alone. It is therefore necessary that the receiver should be active when a pulse from the chosen target arrives, and conduct only for the duration of the pulse. This requirement is met by using a special strobe pulse from a generator whose p.r.f. is the same as that of the radar transmitter.

The method for automatically measuring the time interval consists essentially of superposing the the reflected pulse from the chosen target and the strobe pulse, at the moment of appearance of the latter depending on an automatically controlled time-delay. If these pulses do not appear at the same time an error signal is produced which acts on the controlled time delay.

We now examine the simplified automatic ranging system shown in Fig. 1.70.

A pulse, corresponding to a selected range, appears at the output of the trigger stage (V_2) in synchronism with the radiated pulse but with a time delay determined by the controlled phantastron stage (V_1). This pulse is used to form both the strobe pulse for opening the receiver, and also two selector pulses which are used in the detection of the range-error signal.

First, the trigger pulse from V_2 triggers the blocking oscillator V_3 to produce the first selector pulse, the instant of appearance of which coincides with the instant the trigger pulse is applied. The first selector

† See, for example, Lippel (1; 1953), Berk (1; 1953), V. M. Kuntsevich (1; 1957).
‡ See, for example, A. F. Bogomolov (1; 1954).

pulse triggers blocking oscillator V_4 to produce the second selector pulse, the beginning of which coincides with the end of the first. In this way two half-pulses are formed which control the coincidence stage by means of the suppressor grids of the pentodes. The video signal (the echo pulse from the chosen target) from the receiver output is fed to the control grids of pentodes V_5, V_6. The bias voltage of the grids is such that the valves conduct only when the video signal and selector pulses are present simultaneously. Hence the output of the coincidence stage consists of those parts of the video pulse which coincide in time with the first and second selector pulses.

Figure 1.71 illustrates the case of accurate range measurement (accurate ranging). By means of the differential detector V_7 (Fig. 1.70)

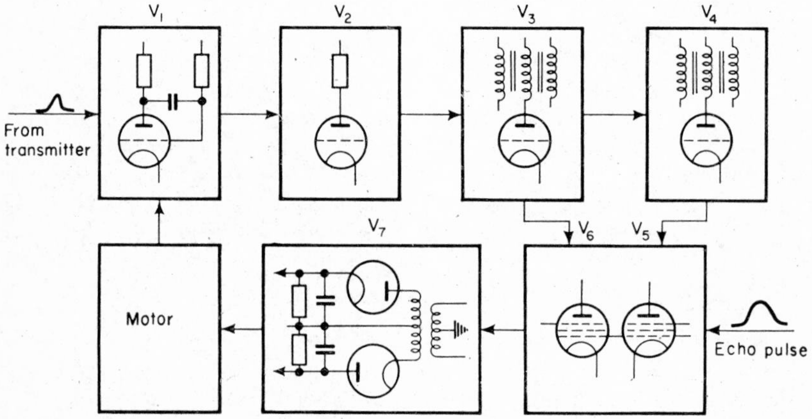

FIG. 1.70. Simplified diagram of an automatic range tracking system.

one part of the video pulse is subtracted from the other and the resultant pulse broadened to a mark-space ratio of unity. If both the selector pulses are symmetrically placed with respect to the reflected signal, the output voltage of the detector will equal zero. If there is asymmetry, then a voltage pulse appears at the detector output which is proportional in magnitude to the error in range. The sign of the error is determined by the direction in which the selector pulses are displaced relative to the reflected pulse.

The error signal is then fed through an amplifier to a motor. The latter drives the so-called range potentiometer in the controlled-delay stage until the error signal vanishes and the motor comes to rest. Thus, after first picking up the target, the radar station can follow it automatically in range.

Due to motor inertia and a number of other causes it is possible that the error may be over-corrected, giving rise to hunting. To eliminate this without losing the rapid response a second (electronic) continuous or discrete integrating unit is used in the control circuit of the ranging system. The purpose of this unit is to extrapolate or predict the range data using the previous measurement. This is possible since the second integrator stores the rate of change of range. A modulator and a detector play the roles of pulse element and clamping device in the system.

The range-tracking of only one target has been considered above. It is sometimes necessary to observe, and track simultaneously, several

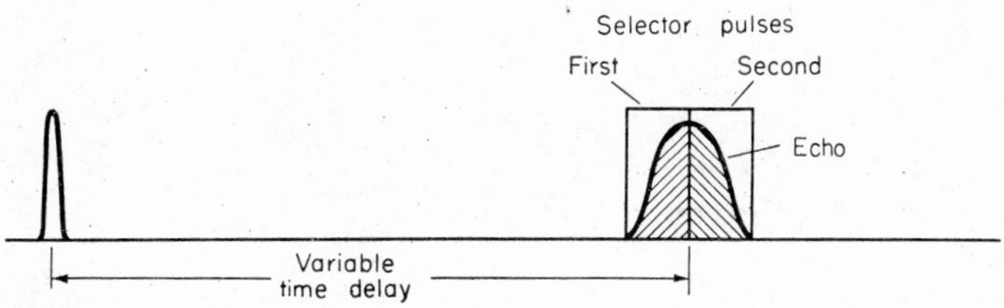

FIG. 1.71. Explaining the operating principles. The case of accurate range tracking.

targets. In this case the radar antenna is rotated azimuthally with constant angular velocity. Here the data for each target occupy only a small portion of the time of a scan cycle, when the antenna beam intersects the target, and the receiver will therefore receive from each target a relatively short pulse train. Extrapolation now becomes more significant. As a target movement during a single pulse train is less than the dynamic error of the system, extrapolation is not carried out at the transmitter pulse repetition frequency but at the much smaller frequency corresponding to the angular velocity of the antenna. Much stricter demands must now be imposed on the velocity-storage unit.

Let us now examine the method of automatic gain control (AGC) used in radar receivers.

AGC is a direct result of the large range of amplitude variation possible in pulses arriving at the receiver. AGC reduces the overload of the intermediate-frequency (IF) amplifier for large pulses and improves the operation of the detector at small pulse levels.

As side reflections and noise appear at the receiver input as well as useful pulses, a time-selection circuit, which generates strobe pulses of frequency equal to the transmitter p.r.f., is usually employed for picking out the useful pulses.

The dynamic variation in gain is of the order of 60db. Hence the application of gain control to a single stage, as is usually done in radio-communication sets, is insufficient in radar receivers. In most radar receivers AGC is applied to between three and seven I. F. stages. The criterion determining the actual number is the absence of overload on subsequent stages.

To reduce overload on the control stage itself it is best to control the gain by means of the control grid, although in some cases control is by means of the screen or suppressor grid.

There are two methods of controlling the gain of a radar receiver. In the first, control is effected only during the time when a pulse is present; in the second, control takes place over the entire pulse repetition period, the control depending on the peak value of the pulse. The controlling signal is extrapolated according to the peak value of the pulse by means of a clamping circuit. In both cases the receiver is cut off when there is no useful signal, and is gated on by a strobe pulse from the ranging system which corresponds in range to the chosen target.

A radar receiver AGC circuit using the second method of control is shown in Fig. 1.72.

For simplicity only one I.F. amplifying stage V_1 is shown, which has AGC applied to the control grid. The video pulses from the output of the receiver detector V_2 are fed to the comparison stage V_3. The video-pulse amplitude is compared here with an amplitude-setting voltage, i.e. with a voltage whose value determines the gain level of the receiver; this voltage is initially set by an operator using potentiometer R. The sign of the output voltage of the comparison stage depends on the sign of the difference between the video-pulse amplitude and the amplitude-setting voltage. The AGC detector follows the comparison stage; it is a clamping circuit controlled by pulses synchronised with the strobe pulses. The voltage at the output of the clamping circuit, i.e. on capacitor C, takes the form of a stepped waveform with a mark/space ratio of unity. This voltage is amplified by V_5, smoothed by the R_1C_1 filter and fed to the control grids of the I.F. stages to which AGC is to be applied, in particular to stage V_1.

In this manner the receiver gain is maintained at a relatively constant pre-set level. The speed of AGC action depends on the time constant of the filter. The circuit and parameters of the AGC filter are therefore important factors. For example in receivers for automatic

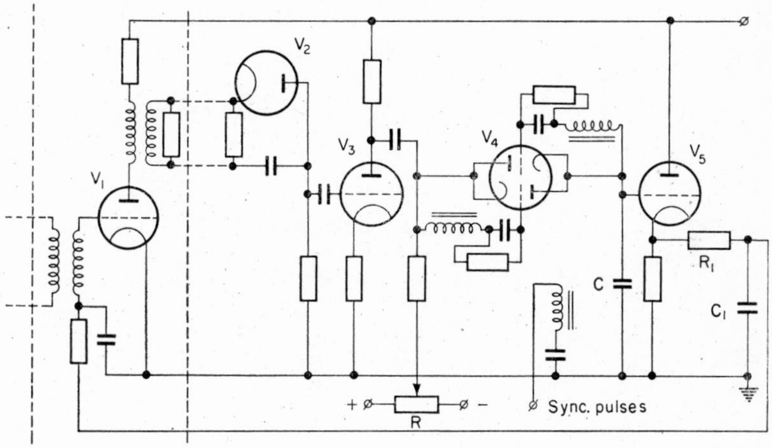

FIG. 1.72. Circuit diagram of an automatic gain control system.

tracking, the filter parameters must be chosen so that the AGC system does not reduce the amplitude modulation of conical scanning and yet suppresses unwanted modulations at frequencies close to spin frequency, e. g. due to fading, imperfect rotating joints of waveguides, etc. Moreover the filter parameters determine the stability of the AGC system.

We shall now examine the automatic frequency control (AFC) system used in radar receivers.+ It differs considerably from the corresponding system used in radio communication.

It is usually the case in radio communication that one transmitter serves a large number of receivers; it is thus advantageous economically to use a special device for stabilising the transmitter frequency.

In radar stations there is a transmitter for each receiver and hence it is not necessary to keep constant the absolute value of the station

+ See, for example, S. Ratcliff (1; 1954).

carrier-frequency. To maintain the required intermediate frequency it is sufficient to control the receiver local oscillator frequency, although in this case the range of possible variation of heterodyne frequency will be much greater than in radio-communication receivers since the transmitter frequency is not stabilised. In a radar receiver the heterodyne usually consists of a klystron oscillator, the frequency of which is controlled by varying the voltage on the reflector. In this case the region of frequency control is limited by the width of the electron-tuning region of the klystron. If we remember that the width of this region determines the only possible values of klystron

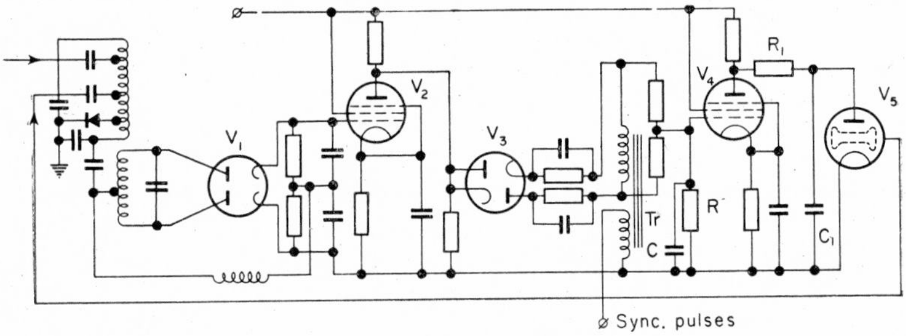

FIG. 1.73. Circuit diagram of an automatic frequency control system.

frequency, we see the necessity of having a mechanical tuning system. Consequently, the total AFC system contains an automatic electro-mechanical sweep system, and an electronic following system which is switched in as soon as the required value of heterodyne frequency enters, during the sweep, the catch-band of the electronic-tuning system of the klystron. In the following discussion we shall only be concerned with the second part of the AFC system.

Another distinctive feature of the radar receiver AFC system lies in the fact that a deviation of intermediate frequency from the set value can only be determined during the intervals when pulses are generated by the receiver. Hence the AFC system must extrapolate the value of transmitter frequency for the intervals when pulses are absent. This is done by various types of clamping or, in general, extrapolating devices.

Figure 1.73 shows a circuit diagram of a radar receiver AFC system which illustrates the above remarks. Radio-pulses at I.F. are fed to the input of the system from the mixer (first detector) output.

Stage V_1 is a discriminator. A signal proportional to the difference between the nominal I.F. and the actual value is fed, after amplification by V_2, to a clamping circuit consisting of a switch V_3 and a storage capacitor C.

The clamping circuit operates when a synchronising pulse from the receiver appears at the transformer Tr. The current which flows through the diodes forms an automatic-bias voltage on the RC circuits of the switch so that the diodes remain cut off during the interval between synchronising pulses. Capacitor C thus remains charged even when the pulse has finished. The time constant RC is much greater than the pulse repetition frequency.

After subsequent amplification by V_4 the control voltage from C is passed through the filter R_1C_1 to the reflector of the klystron V_5, varying its frequency so that the I.F. remains at the nominal value.

Computing devices. Digital computers and certain types of multipliers and correlators can be classed as pulse computing devices.

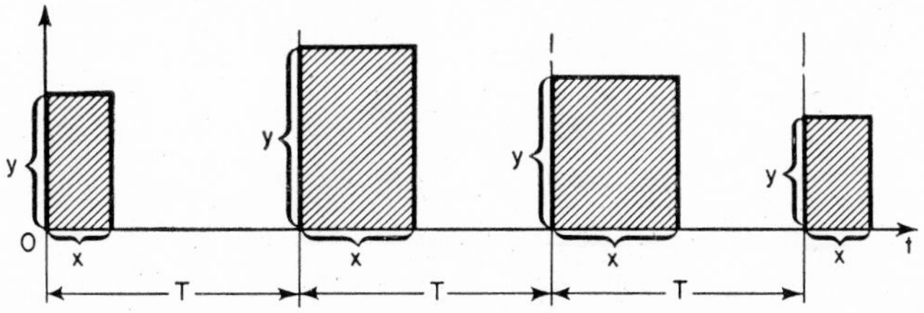

FIG. 1.74. Principle of multiplication of two quantities.

In the pulse multiplier the aim is to obtain a train of rectangular pulses whose height is proportional to one factor and whose width, or duration, is proportional to the other (Fig. 1.74). The mean value of this pulse train is proportional to the area of the pulses, and consequently to the product of the factors. In this manner, multiplication of two quantities in the multiplier corresponds to the double modulation of the pulses in amplitude and duration. This can be achieved with the circuit shown in Fig. 1.75.+

Switch S_1 periodically (with period T) feeds the voltage u_1 to the amplifier A_1 for a time interval γT. Capacitors C_1, C_2 and resistors R_1, R_2 form a filter which removes the alternating component, and

+ See A. A. Feld'baum and A. I. Manukhin (1; 1957).

thus only a direct component, proportional to γ, appears at the amplifier input

$$u_{A1} = k_1 \gamma u_1 . \tag{1.23}$$

The remainder of the circuit is for varying the relative duration γ in proportion to the voltage u_2. The output voltage of the flip-flop u_{FF} controls the electronic switches S_1 and S_2. A direct voltage u_0 is fed to switch S_2. The voltage on the other side of this switch takes the form of an unmodulated pulse train, which is then smoothed by the filter $R_d C_d$ and the resulting direct component

$$u_{=} = k_2 \gamma u_0 \tag{1.24}$$

fed through resistor R_3 to amplifier A_2 so that it subtracts from the input voltage u_2. The output voltage of the amplifier controls the

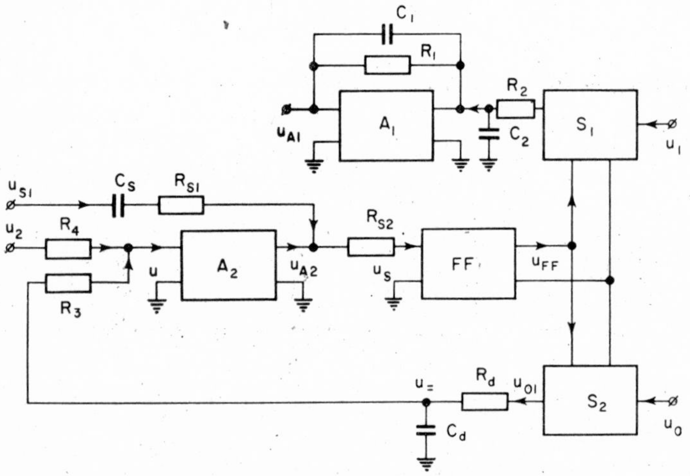

FIG. 1.75. Diagram of a pulse multiplier.

change-over moment of the flip-flop FF. Thus we see that the flip-flop, switch S_2, and the filter form a feedback loop for amplifier A_2.

A saw-tooth voltage u_{s1} of relatively high frequency (up to 2000 c/s), produced by a generator not shown in Fig. 1.75, is fed through C_s, R_{s1} and R_{s2} to the flip-flop input along with the output voltage of A_2. Consequently, the total voltage at the flip-flop input is $u_{A2} + u_{s1} = u_s$ (Fig. 1.76*a*). The dotted horizontal lines in Fig. 1.76 denote the threshold values at which the flip-flop goes over from the first state to the second (u_{th1}) and from the second state to the first (u_{th2}). The dots show the actual instants when the flip-flop changes over. The voltage u_{01}

on the other side of S_2 can have only two values, $+u_0$ or $-u_0$, and consequently has the form shown in Fig. 1.76*b*. The relative duration of the values $+u_0$ and $-u_0$ in this waveform depends on the output voltage of the amplifier u_{A2}.

The voltage at the input of A_2 equals

$$u = \frac{R_3}{R_4 + R_3} u_2 - \frac{R_4}{R_4 + R_3} u_= . \quad (1.25)$$

If the gain of A_2 is sufficiently large we can assume

$$u \approx 0 \quad (1.26)$$

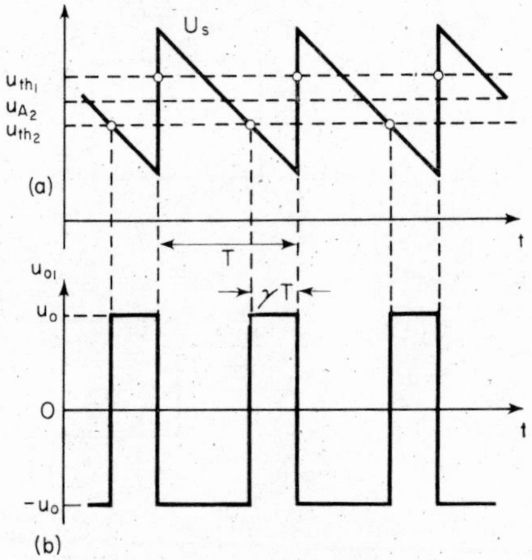

FIG. 1.76. Voltage at the input (*a*) and output (*b*) of the flip-flop.

and thus from (1.25) we obtain

$$u_= \approx \frac{R_3}{R_4} u_2 . \quad (1.27)$$

Using (1.24) we see that

$$\gamma \approx \frac{R_3}{R_4} \frac{1}{k_2 u_0} u_2 . \quad (1.28)$$

Thus, under the assumptions made above, the relative time the switch is closed γ is proportional to the input u_2.

Part of the multiplier is a servo-system in its own right in which the value of γ is automatically varied in proportion to the input voltage u_2. The accuracy of such a system is very great and is due to the high gain of amplifier A_2. As with all balancing systems, a slight nonlinearity in the saw-tooth waveform has no appreciable effect on the accuracy of the device.

In the above system γ can only assume positive values, which implies that the sign of the factor u_2 must remain constant. This restriction can be removed by reckoning γ from the middle of the period and using a sign reversing amplifier (Fig. 1.77). Resistors R_1, R_2, R_3 must satisfy the requirement

$$R_3 = 2(R_1 + R_2), \tag{1.29}$$

in order that the output voltages of A_1 during the open and closed

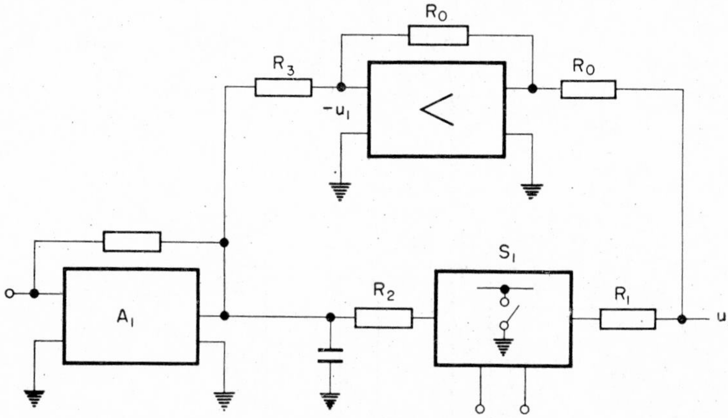

FIG. 1.77. Diagram of a pulse multiplier for multiplying two quantities which may take negative values.

positions of the switch should be equal in magnitude and opposite in sign.

If u_0 is considered as a variable, we see from (1.28) that the system can be used for dividing two quantities.

It is essential, both with multiplication and division, that the variables change only slightly during the pulse interval.

A similar principle of multiplication is used in electronic correlators, which are used to analyse random functions in the form of voltages for hidden periodicities and, more recently, to determine the dynamic characteristics of a system from its response to a random excitation.

It is well known that the cross-correlation function of two random voltages $u_1(t)$ and $u_2(t)$ (Fig. 1.78) is given approximately by

$$R(\tau) \approx \frac{1}{N} \sum_{n=1}^{N} u_1(nT)\, u_2(nT - \tau)\,. \tag{1.30}$$

We see from this formula that the computation of the correlation function reduces to multiplying the values of the functions at times separated by τ, adding these products, and dividing by N.

Consequently, on adding a delay element of variable delay τ and an electronic integrator I, the correlation function can be computed using the previous multiplying circuit without the smoothing filter (Fig. 1.79). For a sufficiently large number of pulses the integrator gives the value of the correlation function for a given τ. Moreover, the calculating process repeats itself for different τ. Other types of pulse and digital correlators are described in the literature.+

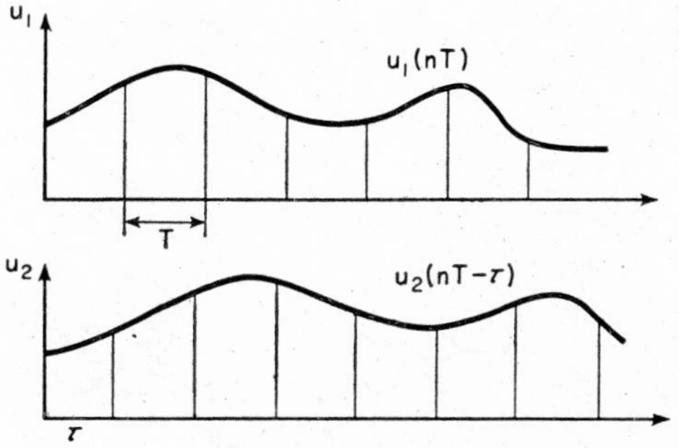

FIG. 1.78. Concerning the definition of the cross-correlation function.

We now go on to describe the operating principles of digital computers.‡

When the process of solving a problem can be reduced to repeated applications of elementary arithmetical or logical operations, a digital computer can be used to obtain the actual numerical solution. Irrespective of the method used to carry out the calculations it is always necessary to store the initial data and, when necessary, to use them in the subsequent computations. Whatever the individual peculiarities, all computers have a storage unit as well as the proper arithmetic or computing unit. Logical, as well as arithmetical operations take place in the arithmetic unit.

The sequence of carrying out the operations is determined by the program, in accordance with which the computer control unit directs the operation of all the functional units of the computer. Digital computers can be divided into universal computers and fixed-program

+ See, for example, Shire and Runcorn (1; 1951); Lee and Wiessner (1; 1955).
‡ See also A. I. Kitov (1; 1956).

computers, depending on the nature of the program. In the former, the program is held in the storage unit. In the latter, the program is built into the construction of the computer itself.

As well as the storage, arithmetic and control units, a digital computer also has a unit for inserting and extracting numerical data. The form and purpose of this depend on the specific use for which the computer is designed.

The numbers in digital computers are usually represented in binary code. For operation with a real time scale those numbers representing initial data are fed into the computer from outside, whereas other numbers — for example constant coefficients, tables of functions,

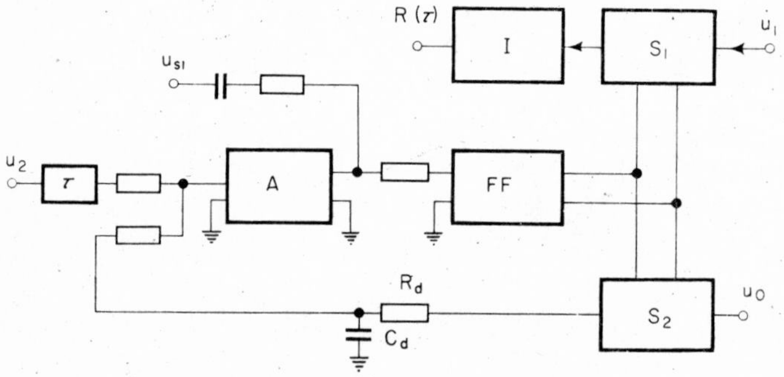

FIG. 1.79. Diagram of an electronic correlator.

etc. — are invariably kept in the storage unit, from which they are extracted when required.

The storage unit of a computer consists of a definite number of registers. Each register can contain a number, the amount of digits in which is limited to the design value for the particular computer; this number of digits governs the accuracy of the computer. As directed by the program, the control unit extracts numbers from specified registers, sends them to the arithmetic unit and inserts the result of the calculation into a suitable register. When one operation has been completed another commences automatically.

We shall now briefly consider the organisation of a computation on a universal digital computer.

The elementary actions which a digital computer can perform are determined by its set of operations. Each operation and each storage register is identified by means of an assigned number. The number denoting a particular operation is called a function number; the number denoting a particular register is known as its address.

The problem of programming a computation can be formulated as follows: construct the required sequence of instructions by relating the number of each specific operation with the addresses of specific registers. A multi-digit number, called an instruction code, is obtained by writing in turn, each in binary code, the function number and the addresses of the registers associated with it.

The address part of an instruction code indicates the storage registers from which numbers have to be extracted for use in the specified operation. The part of an instruction code denoting the operation (the function code) causes the arithmetic unit to carry out this operation.

A digital computer is said to have a one-, two-, three- or four-address instruction system depending on the number of addresses associated with each instruction. So, for example, in the widely used computers with the three-address instruction system, the instruction code for addition consists of the function code and the address codes of the registers containing the first and second terms of the addition and the register to which the result of the operation has to be sent.

In appearance instruction codes differ in no way from the codes of actual numbers used in calculations, and so both instruction codes and number codes can be held in the same storage unit. The only difference is that when the computer is operating the instruction codes are fed to the control register of the control unit, and the number codes are fed to the arithmetic unit.

In programming, the registers of the storage unit are conventionally divided into two groups; the first is for storing the instruction codes of the program, and the second for storing the initial data and the intermediate and final results of the computation.

The fact that instructions are represented in the same code as is used for numbers is of considerable significance. By operating with instructions in the same way as with ordinary numbers it is possible to make a considerable reduction in the number of instructions when programming a calculation which repeats in cycles, different initial data being used for each cycle. This type of computation often arises when solving problems on automatic control.

An important feature of a digital computer is the possibility of changing the path of subsequent calculations not only by a direct instruction from the control unit, but as a result of examining the outcome of the previous calculations. The corresponding operation is called a conditional jump.

On the basis of the above, a digital computer can be represented schematically as in Fig. 1.80. The continuous lines in the diagram denote channels along which instructions and numbers are sent. The dotted lines depict electrical signals from the control unit, by means of which it carries out its controlling functions. The control counter and control register shown in the diagram are elements of the control unit. Before commencing a calculation all the digits in the control register and control counter are set to zero.

When the starting button is pressed the control unit, as a result of the number in the control counter, i.e. zero, proceeds to extract

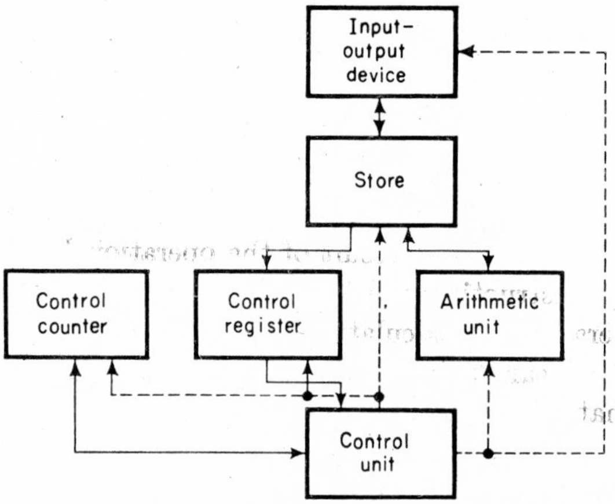

FIG. 1.80. Block diagram of a general-purpose digital computer.

the first instruction of the program from the zeroth register of the store. The instruction is sent to the control register. The function code of the received instruction, by means of the control unit, prepares the arithmetic unit to carry out the instruction and the address codes prepare the channels between the arithmetic unit and the specified registers of the store. The first step towards completing the instruction in the zeroth register of the store has now been completed.

In the second stage the specified numbers are sent from the store to the arithmetic unit, which carries out the required computations with them. With a three-address instruction the second stage is concluded by sending the result of the computation from the arithmetic unit to the store. When the instruction has been completed a pulse is sent to the control counter, indicating the completion of the first part of the program.

With the so-called normal sequence of instructions, all the remaining stages of the program are carried out in the above manner. When the instructions are out of sequence, each instruction is concluded by sending to the control counter the address from which the next instruction must be taken.

With the conditional jump instruction the arithmetic unit examines the result of the preceding calculation, and transmits the address portion of a certain instruction to the control counter if the condition is satisfied, and does not transmit it if the condition is not satisfied. In the latter case a pulse is sent in the usual sequence to the control counter, denoting the completion of that particular instruction.

In the former case, the instruction is carried out which was planted in the control counter as a result of the conditional jump operation.

When a digital computer is used in a control system it is necessary at some time to introduce into it new values of initial data, and to extract the results of the preceeding computations. These requirements call for special instructions. There is also a special instruction for stopping the computer.

In a universal computer a program can be planted in the store and removed at will and a large set of operations is possible. Consequently, universal digital computers are very flexible computing devices which enable a wide range of mathematical problems to be solved.

With automatic control systems, however, we are usually required to solve relatively simple problems, described for example by linear difference equations of the form

$$z(nT) = \sum_{\nu=0}^{l} b_{l-\nu} f\big((n-\nu)\,T\big) + \sum_{\nu=1}^{l} a_{l-\nu} z\big((n-\nu)T\big), \qquad (1.31)$$

where $f(nT), z(nt)$ are the input and output quantities respectively at discrete moments of time; a_ν, b_ν are coefficients, some of which may equal zero. The most important requirement here, however, is that the computations must be carried out on a real time scale. Universal computers cannot always be used to solve control problems, if for no other reason than their large size and high power consumption. The complex and laborious programming involved is another obstacle.

Special-purpose digital computers are becoming more and more widely used as elements of control systems.

In a number of cases special-purpose computers are constructed on the same principles as universal computers and differ only by having a smaller computing accuracy, a smaller selection of arithmetical operations and a smaller capacity store. Efforts to reduce the size of a computer may reduce the operating speed.

Fixed-program computers are special-purpose computers. They have several advantages over universal computers, although inferior in arithmetical and logical possibilities. In a fixed-program computer the sequence of carrying out the operations is built into the construction of the computer; consequently programming is greatly simplified and the control unit need only carry out very simple functions.

In order to solve the above equation (1.31) on a real time scale we require a device for storing the appropriate number of coefficients (assumed for simplicity to be constant) and the continuously changing initial data. Here and below we understand, by initial data, the numerical values of the input and output quantities used in the calculations. The set of operations of the computer must include two arithmetical operations, addition and multiplication, and a control operation called conventionally the initial-data displacement operation. This operation causes the shift within the store of the intial data, which is steadily being supplemented, relative to the constant coefficients. A fixed-program computer of this type can be made using the so-called serial store.+

Let us consider as an example the simple digital computer shown in Fig. 1.81. In this case the serial store takes the form of a single-track magnetic drum. The entire length of the track is divided into regions — the registers of the store — which in number equal the number of the initial data. These regions are conventionally split up into pairs, the one pair following the next. The number code of one of the initial data is written on the first region of a pair; the second region always contains the coefficient which multiplies the number written on the first region.

Two reading heads *RH* and one writing head *WH* are arranged around the length of the drum. The reading heads are separated by a distance equal to two of the basic regions and they read the numbers of the initial data and coefficients.

An initial-data value, written in binary code, is read by the first reading head and sent both to a so-called shifting register, which

+ See Conn (1; 1953).

plays the role of multiplier in the arithmetic unit, and also to the writing head for rewriting. Immediately after this the second reading head begins to read the value of the corresponding coefficient, which appears in the form of a pulse train. These pulses, which form the shift signals, are fed to the second input of the multiplier. This causes a number to be set up in the multiplier equal to the product of the initial-data value and its coefficient. The initial data are rewritten in registers located beside those of the coefficients they will multiply in the next computing cycle. The current numerical value of the input quantity is fed directly to the multiplier. It is simultaneously written in the corresponding register for use in subsequent calculations.

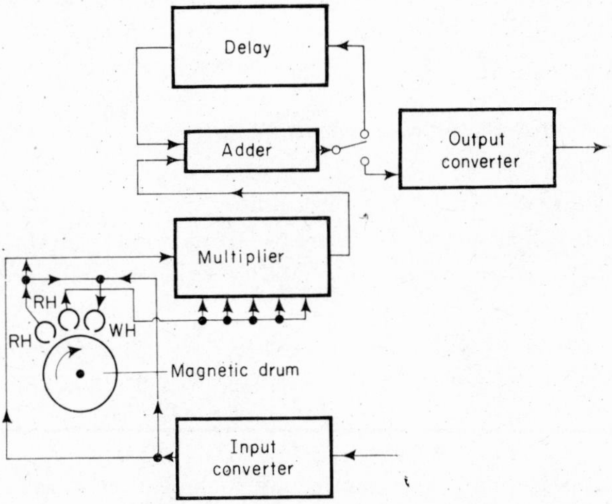

FIG. 1.81. Block diagram of a special-purpose digital computer.

A special signal causes the signal to be sent from the multiplier to the serial adder of the arithmetic unit. At the same time, by synchronisation, a local storage unit (for example a delay line) feeds to the second input of the adder the sum of the results of the previous multiplications of the particular computing cycle.

After the number of additions required by the given equation has been carried out, the adder output is switched from the local storage unit to output circuits which supply the solution of the equation in numerical form. At the same time the result is written in a particular register for use in subsequent calculations.

In this way we see that the calculating process in a digital computer reduces to operating on a given sequence of numbers according to a definite program. The results of the computations are extracted from the computer in the form of another sequence of numbers, each of which is the result of handling a specific quantity of input data. In a digital computer with one input and one output a single numerical result corresponds to a given numerical set of input data.

The accuracy of computation depends on the number of digits in the standard-length number of the computer. Increasing the accuracy of computation is associated, first of all, with increasing the number of digit elements available in the registers of the store, arithmetic unit, etc. If the number of digits is large enough discreteness in level can be neglected, when the computer can be considered as a pulse system. In general this is a closed-loop pulse system since, as is evident from equation (1.31), the result of the calculation depends not only on the input data but also on the output data at previous moments of time.

In the case of interest, programming reduces to constructing a sequence of elementary operations for solving the difference equation (1.31). However, in future we shall not concern ourselves with the technical details of programming. This is described fully enough in the specialist literature.† We only note that the construction of an actual program for one specific calculation will depend solely on the features of the particular type of computer to be used.

An automatic control system using a digital computer. In recent years there has been a rapid advance in the use of digital computers as elements of control systems. Digital computers are widely used as the input and control mechanisms of automatic metal-cutting lathes for producing master tools and precision prototypes of complex surface form, such as, for example, turbine blades, various three-dimensional cams, etc.

The operating principles of such systems will be illustrated by a description of a numerically-controlled milling lathe for producing three-dimensional cams.‡ We first give a brief description of the method of forming the program for the lathe.

† See, for example, A. I. Kitov (1; 1956).
See Johnson (1; 1956).

The cam is prepared by moving the cross slide according to a given law, the spindle and the horizontal carriage velocities being kept constant.

The required movement of the cutter with respect to the workpiece can be specified by the co-ordinates of a series of reference points on its trajectory. For engineering reasons the cutting tool in this machine is a ball-end milling cutter. The cutting surface is the hemispherical end of a driven rod and moves perpendicular and parallel to the cylindrical co-ordinates of the reference points for the centre of the hemispherical cutter (Fig. 1.82).

Figure 1.83 shows a section of the cam and the corresponding

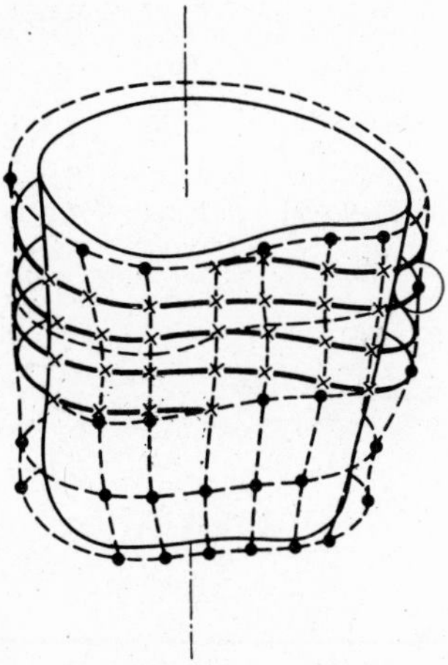

FIG. 1.82. Diagram of a three-dimentional cam.

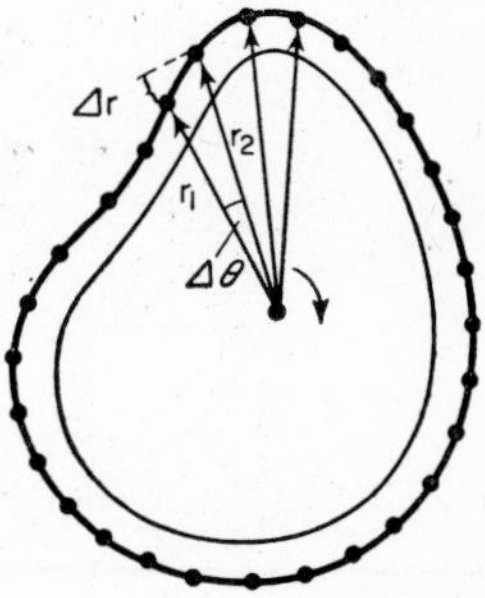

FIG. 1.83. Cross-section of the cam.

reference points for the centre of the ball-end milling cutter. The co-ordinates of the reference points of the trajectory are determined by the radii r_1, r_2, etc. for given increments of polar angle $\Delta\theta$. Each subsequent radius equals the preceeding radius plus first difference Δr. Consequently, to prescribe all the radii of the reference points, it is sufficient to give the radius of the starting point and the sequence of first differences for the remaining reference points.

The binary-coded first differences of the reference points are punched on a tape to form the initial information of the control program. Figure 1.84 shows a portion of the tape corresponding to the interval between two neighbouring reference points. Two rows of the tape correspond to each such interval. Holes are punched in the tape for 'ones' and not punched for 'zeros'. In addition to the coded magnitude of the first difference of the radius, holes are punched in these two rows for specifying both the angular increment $\Delta\theta$ corresponding to the radius difference, and the sign of this difference. The presence of a hole corresponds to the sign plus. Two code positions are used for the angular increment $\Delta\theta$, permitting four different code combinations. In the present machine these code combinations correspond to values of $\Delta\theta$ equal to 5°, 10°, 20° and 80°.

A radius is given as the required factor which multiplies the basic increment in which the machine works, which in the present case is 0.0002 in. This factor is punched in binary code on the tape. Consequently, the portion of tape shown in Fig. 1.84 specifies that

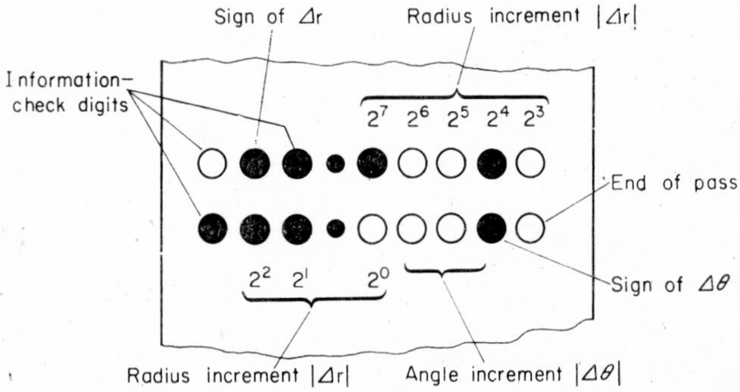

FIG. 1.84. Portion of punched tape containing information for one cutting interval.

in passing from the one reference point to the next the workpiece must be rotated through an angle of 5° (assuming that the absence of holes corresponds to this value of $\Delta\theta$) and that the radius must change by 0.03 in. in the conventionally positive direction.

As well as the above information there is a code position on the tape for specifying the direction of rotation of the spindle, and a position for a hole indicating the end of a single pass of the workpiece. The remaining code positions are used to check the correctness of the coded data on the tape. This is achieved by introducing special code elements which ensure error detection.

We now go on to examine the simplified control circuit of the lathe shown in Fig. 1.85. Information from the tape is fed to the registers of a temporary store, not shown on the figure, and thereafter to the control circuit.

When the cutting information for a (preceding) interval $\Delta\theta$ has been carried out by the machine, a signal is sent which sets in to the control circuit the new information for the following interval. At this instant the information for the next succeeding begins to be read into the temporary store.

The code specifying the interval $\Delta\theta$ is converted by the decoder into a control voltage which opens, to the timing pulses, a path to the digital interpolator circuit. This is done as follows. By means of the reading contact a hole in the tape causes a positive voltage u_1 to be fed to one of the inputs of the control flip-flops of the decoder. The potentials on the flip-flop anodes control the decoder diode matrix; a high anode voltage cuts off the corresponding diodes and a low anode voltage renders them conducting. A certain combination of control voltages will appear at the flip-flops depending on the combination of holes on the tape. As a result no current will flow through one of the vertical control lines of the decoder. The positive control voltage u_2 is fed along this single selected line into the next part of the circuit. In each of the other three lines only one of the two associated diodes need conduct in order to drop u_2 across the resistors R, preventing it from being fed along these lines to the next part of the circuit. The control voltage u_2 opens a coincidence circuit, composed for example of a multigrid valve, at the digital interpolator input. As a result the timing pulses begin to be fed into one of the flip-flops of the digital interpolator.

Linear digital interpolation is used in the present instance. This enables the interpolator to be of relatively simple construction.

The digital interpolator consists of a system of flip-flops connected to form a pulse counter, four input coincidence circuits, and output coincidence circuits — one for each flip-flop. The aim of the interpolator is to "convert", depending on the value of the given interval $\Delta\theta$, the coded first difference Δr punched on the tape into a train of uniformly spaced pulses the number of which in the given interval $\Delta\theta$ equals the value of $|\Delta r|$.

For a given interpolation interval the interpolator must be provided with information stating the particular value of $\Delta\theta$ — the increment of the independent variable, and the particular value of $|\Delta r|$ — the modulus of the first difference.

By means of the timing pulses the independent variable is fed into the interpolator in the form of a sequence of discrete points. The timing pulses are supplied by a rotary pulse generator whose axis rotates in fixed relation to the lathe spindle. The generator produces 256 pulses for each 5° rotation of the spindle.

Depending on the value of $|\Delta r|$ a portion of the timing pulses will be passed on to the interpolator output through the frequency dividing flip-flops. The timing pulses appearing at the output are, 'on the average', uniformly selected from the timing pulse train.

Frequency division in the interpolator is explained by reference to Fig. 1.85. Each subsequent flip-flop is triggered whenever a fall in potential occurs on the 'triggering' anode of the preceding flip-flop. A drop in potential of the second anode of a flip-flop occurs at the same instant as the triggering anode rises in potential. The output pulse train of the interpolator is obtained by differentiating the negative going potentials on the second anodes and collecting the resulting pulses on the common line; each pulse of the output train coincides with one of the timing pulses. The number of pulses in the train depends on the number of flip-flops switched to the common line.

The switching of the flip-flops to the common output line is effected by means of coincidence circuits controlled by the code of $|\Delta r|$, which is read directly from the tape. The first such code position on the tape (corresponding to the highest digit) controls the first flip-flop, and the last code position controls the last flip-flop.

The working 'length' of the interpolator counter chain depends on the flip-flop to which the timing pulse train is fed. The size of an interval $\Delta\theta$ is determined by the number of timing pulses necessary to fill the working length of the counter from zero to overflowing. In this time the number of pulses which have appeared at the interpolator output will be exactly equal to the value of the binary-coded first difference $|\Delta r|$. The overflow pulse is used to initiate the transition to the next working interval.

Command pulses are fed from the interpolator output to the positive or negative input of the digital comparator, depending on the sign code of Δr on the tape.

The digital comparator takes the form of a reversible flip-flop counter with controlled interstage couplings.

The operating condition of the counter is governed by the control flip-flop. In either state of this flip-flop a gating voltage is fed to only one of the control lines of the interstage couplings. Accordingly, the counter can count in either the one or the other direction.

If the first command pulse from the digital interpolator output arrives at the positive input of the comparator, and the control flip-flop happens to be in the state corresponding to subtraction, then this pulse triggers the control flip-flop and simultaneously the Kipp relay. The time-constant of the Kipp relay is chosen so as to be slightly longer than the duration of the transient process on the control line of the interstage coincidence circuits. At the instant the Kipp relay returns to its original state a pulse is sent to the first flip-flop of the counter which, due to the conducting path through the additional couplings, is added to the content of the counter. The following pulses are stored in the counter in the same manner, the control flip-flop in this case remaining unchanged.

As pulses become stored up by the counter its flip-flops actuate the coincidence circuits of the decoder, the purpose of which is to convert code into voltage. This decoder takes the form of a resistor matrix, to the different points of which direct current generators (as distinct from voltage generators) may be switched. The direct current generators are switched in by means of the coincidence circuits. The coincidence circuits act as controlled current generators. Depending on the actual points at which they are attached to the matrix, the different current generators induce different voltage drops across the output resistor of the decoder matrix. The matrix resistors are chosen so that the output voltage varies strictly according to the binary-coded number set up in the reversible counter.

The voltage from the decoder output is fed to an amplifier, from the amplifier to the control circuit and then to the servo-motor. The servo-motor drives, in accordance with the given law, the cross slide with the attached cutter.

As the shaft of the servo-motor rotates, a pulse generator, similar to that which produces the timing pulses, produces feedback pulses which are sent to the comparator. These pulses are sent either into the addition or subtraction channels depending on the direction of rotation of the servo-motor shaft. Each such pulse is sent when the cross slide moves through 0.0002 in.

Non-coincidence of the command and feedback pulses is an essential condition for normal operation of the servo-system. Special steps must be taken to ensure this.

With steady motion the command and feedback pulses must be fed into the reversible counter at different inputs and be displaced relative to each other in time by a definite amount.

Movement of the cross slide will obviously continue until all the command pulses, which have been fed into the reversible counter, are 'used up' by the servo-motor.

The simplest fixed-program digital computer can be used in the above control system. The computer processes the input numerical data, i.e. carries out digital interpolation, which reduces to the conversion of a number into a uniformly distributed (with respect to time) sequence of units which add up to the number. There is still another digital computing element in the system, namely the comparator. Digital interpolation may be carried out by computers which are much more complex than the one described; they enable not only linear but much more complex interpolation laws to be followed.

This concludes the examples of pulse systems; we have far from covered them all. However, even this brief review indicates the very wide range of applications of pulse systems in the various branches of technology

STANDARD PULSE ELEMENTS TABLE 1.2

No	Circuit Diagrams of Pulse Elements	Explanation
1	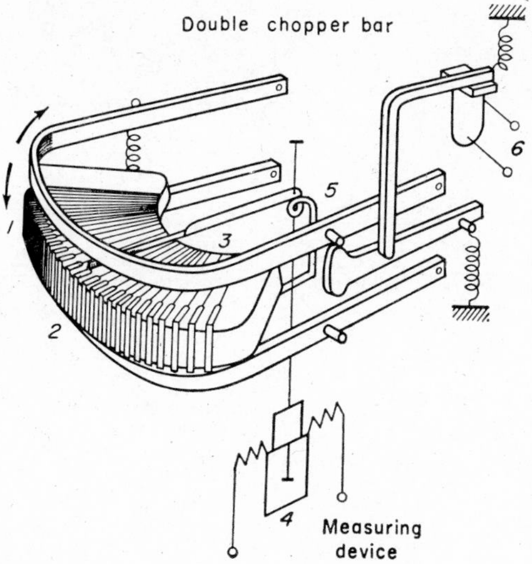	The measuring device 4 turns the contacts 2 and 3, connected by a spring 5. Due to the periodic action of the electromagnet 6, the falling chopper bars alternately press the contacts to the resistance 1, thus changing the amplitude of the voltage pulses in the circuit. In this pulse element $\gamma = 1$.
2	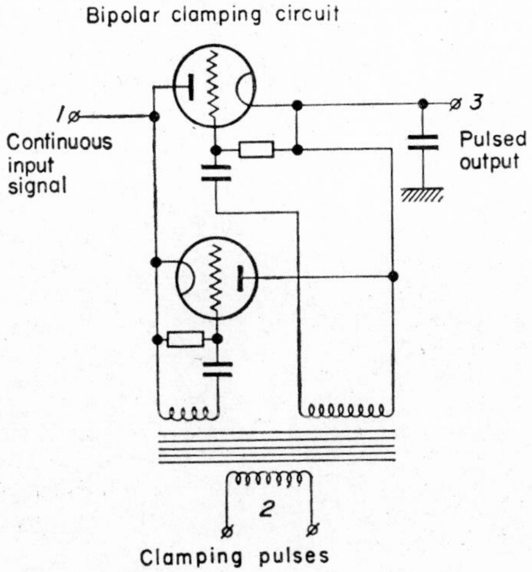	The circuit is used in pulse engineering for transforming the continuous signal at 1 into pulses of varying amplitude at 3. The clamping pulses at 2 determine the recurrence period.

CONTINUED 1.2

Nº	Circuit Diagrams of Pulse Elements	Explanation
3	Notched chopper bar with mercury contacts 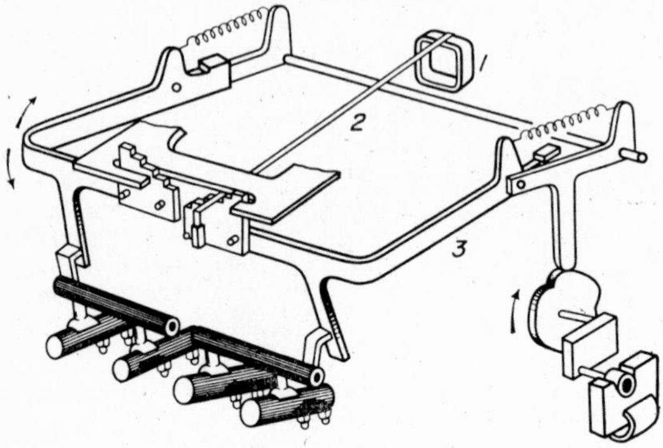	The measuring device 1 (galvanometer) turns the (arm) 2. The periodically moving chopper bar 3, moving up until stopped by the arm, tips over the mercury contacts. The duration of their contact is proportional to the angle of the (arm) 2 from the central position.
4	Chopper bar with contact sectors 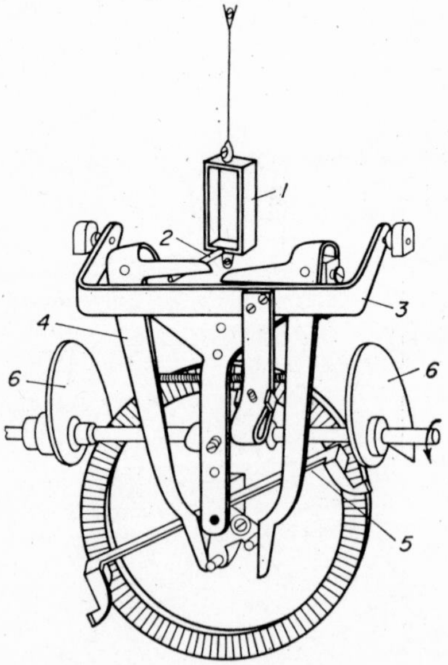	The measuring device 1 turns the (arm) 2. The periodically moving chopper bar 3, pressing the (arm) to the lever 4, turns it, together with the contact lever 5. The rotating contact segments 6, make contact with the lever 5, turning it into a horizontal position. The duration of closing contact is proportional to the angle of the arm 2 from the central position.

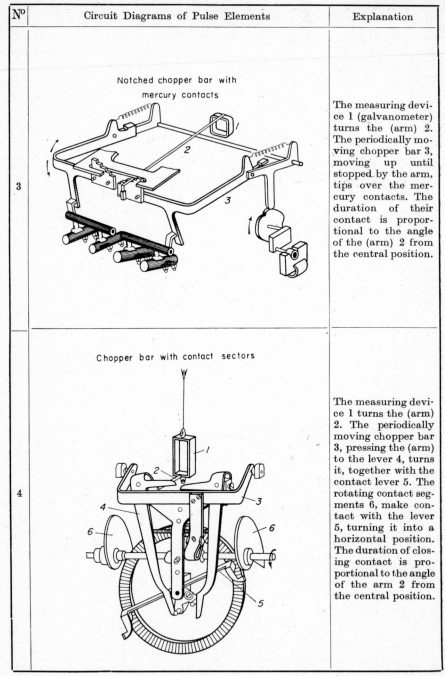

CONTINUED 1.2

Nº	Circuit Diagrams of Pulse Elements	Explanation
5	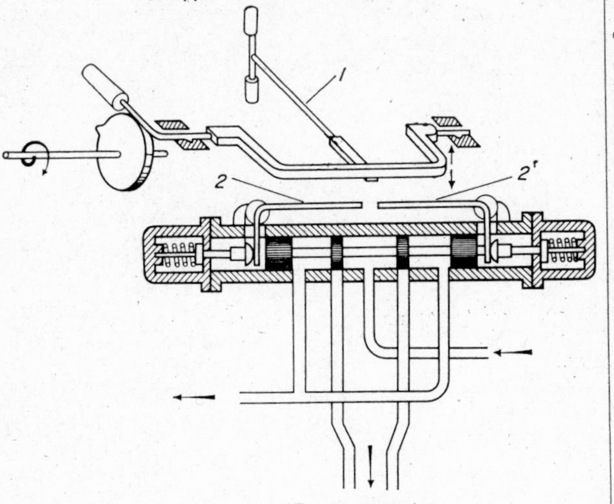	The measuring device turns the (arm) 1, which is periodically pressed to the lever 2 or 2′ by a chopper bar. Due to the rotation of the lever, the throttle piston is moved, opening an aperture for the passage of oil into the servo motor. The length of time the apertures are open is proportional to the angle of the (arm) 1 from the central position.
6	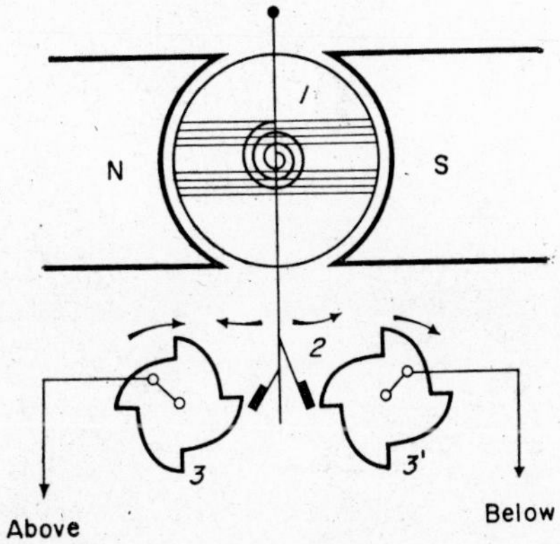	The measuring device 1 turns the (arm) with contacts 2, which are closed with the rotating cogged discs, 3 and 3′. The length of time they are closed is proportional to the angle of the (arm) from the central position.

CONTINUED 1.2

N°	Circuit Diagrams of Pulse Elements	Explanation
7	Pulse element of voltage regulator SN-91 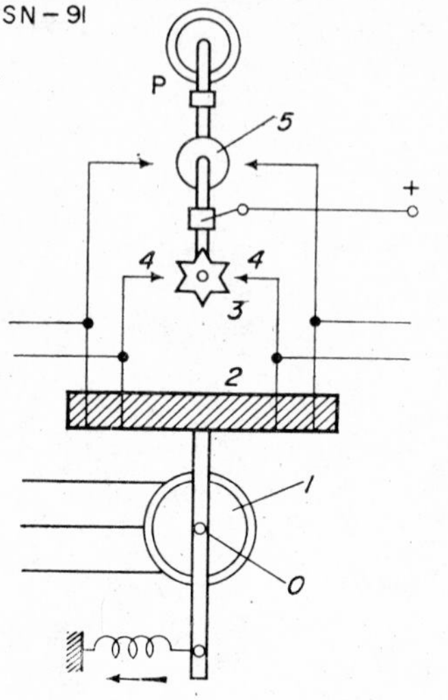	The measuring device 1, a torque balance, turns the contact system, 2, in the vertical plane, and the rotating teeth of the star, 3, begin to make contact with the contacts, 4, at an interval of time proportional to the angle of incline of the contact system to the vertical axis. At large angles of rotation of the contact system the contact disc, 5, comes into contact, forming a continuous contact.
8	Chugunov's photo-electric pulse element 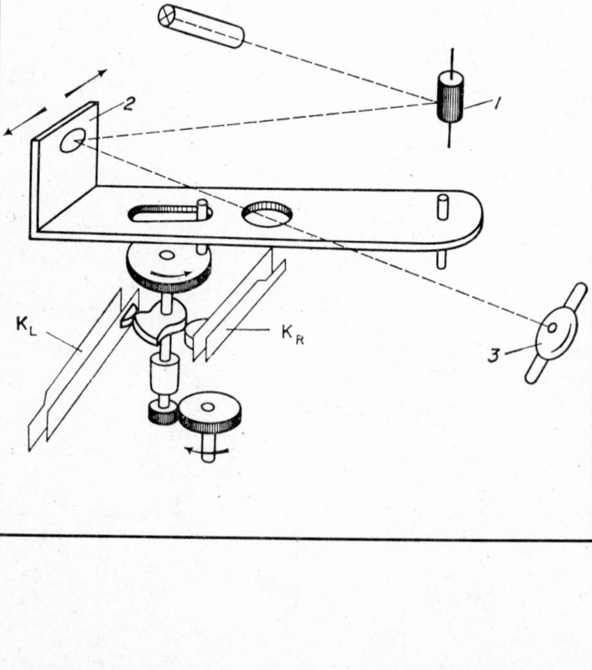	The measuring device turns the mirror 1, deflecting a light ray. This ray, reflecting from the periodically oscillating mirror, 2, falls on the photo element, 3, controlling, together with the contacts, K_L and K_R the ignition angle of two thyratrons (not shown). In the anode circuits of the latter there are the split field windings of a motor. The time the motor is switched on is proportional to the angle of the mirror, 1, from the central position.

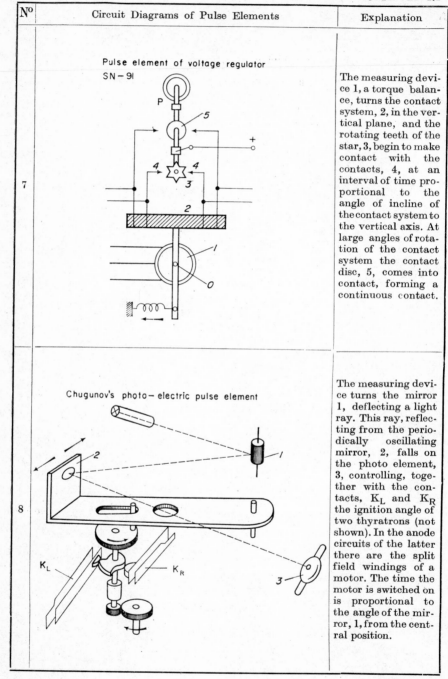

CONTINUED 1.2

Nº	Circuit Diagrams of Pulse Elements	Explanation
9	Pulse element of the electronic mixture-air ratio – regulator type ERS-60 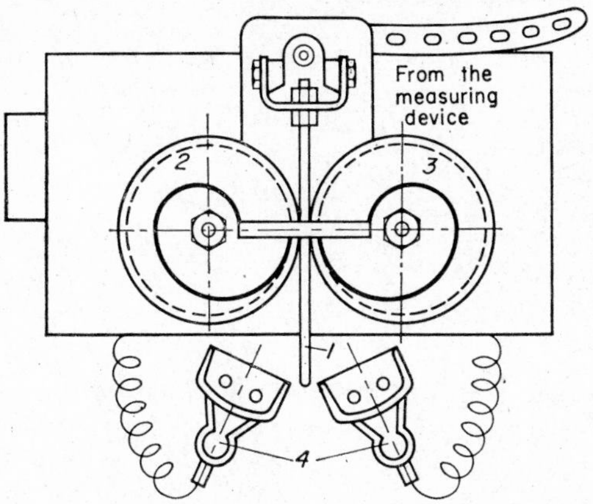	The measuring device turns the lever, 1. The end of this lever, being slightly raised up by the radial cut of the gauges 2 or 3, tips over the mercury contact, 4. The duration of contact is proportional to the lever, 1, from the central position.
10	Pulse element with oscillating disc 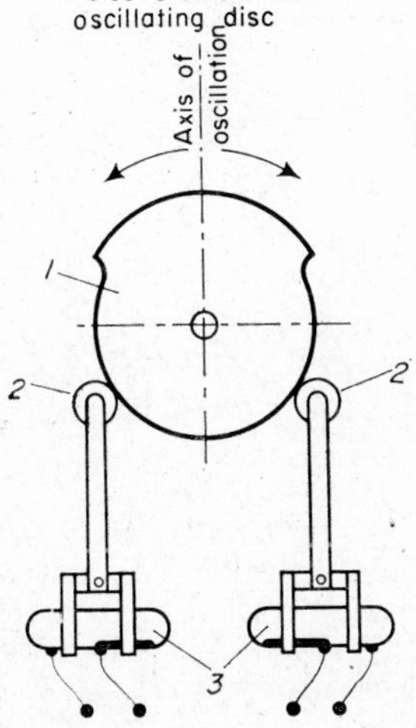	The measuring device (membrane) with the help of a differential turns the periodically oscillating disc, 1. The flanges of the disc, touching the rollers, 2, tip over the mercury contact, 3. The duration of closed contact is proportional to the angle of rotation of the axis of the discs oscillations.

CONTINUED 1.2

Nº	Circuit Diagrams of Pulse Elements	Explanation
11	Pulse element in the form of a two-relay system 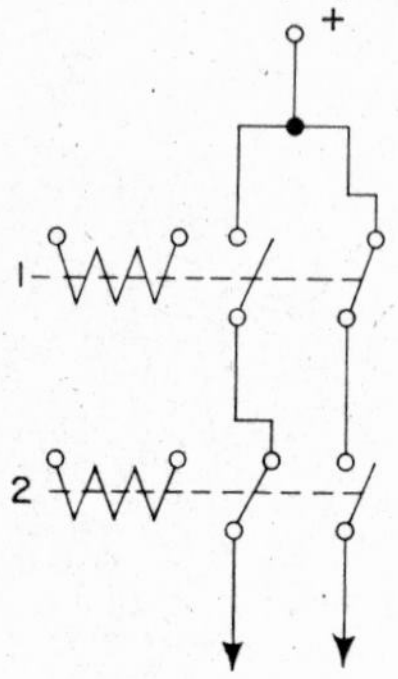	The relay system 1 is switched on and off from the telemetry pulses, the duration of which is proportional to the measured volume, while relay 2 is switched by constant duration pulses. The circuit of the slave device is closed for a time period proportional to the difference in duration of the pulses in the two trains.
12	Direct chopper bar with mercury contact 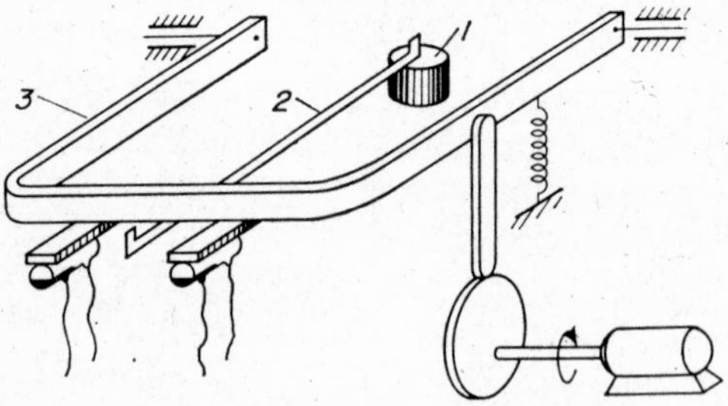	The measuring device 1 (galvanometer) turns the (arm) 2. The periodically moving chopper bar 3 presses the (arm) to the mercury contacts and tips them over. The duration of their contact is constant.

CHAPTER II

FUNDAMENTALS OF THE DISCRETE LAPLACE TRANSFORMATION AND DIFFERENCE EQUATIONS

2.1. Lattice functions and difference equations

A pulse system responds to the external input excitation only at discrete equally-spaced moments of time. Thus the external excitation can always be replaced by the so-called *lattice function*, i.e. by a function which varies only at discrete equally-spaced moments of

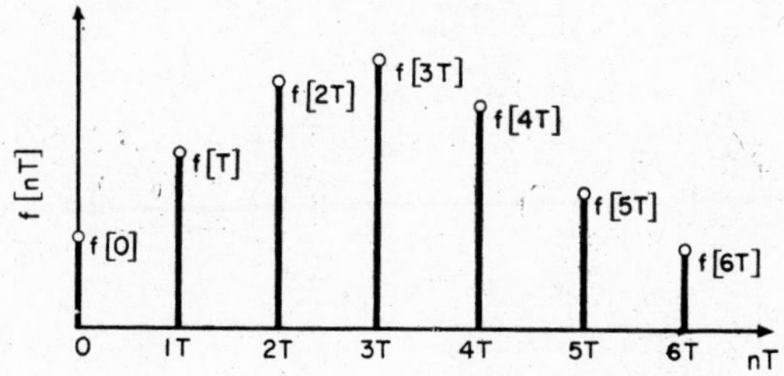

FIG. 2.1. The lattice function $f\,[n\,T]$.

time; between these moments the value of the function equals zero (Fig. 2.1). The lattice function is denoted by the symbol $f[nT]$, where T is the positive quantity defining the interval between neighbouring discrete values of the independent variable, and n is any positive number.

Suppose we are given some continuous function $f_T(t)$ (Fig. 2.2*a*). The ordinates of this function, corresponding to discrete equally-spaced values of the independent variable $t = nT$, form a lattice function (Fig. 2.2*b*). To obtain a lattice function from any given continuous function $f_T(t)$ it is only necessary to replace t by nT in the latter.

So, for example, the lattice function corresponding to the continuous function $e^{a_1 t}$ is given by

$$f[nT] = f_T(t)\big|_{t=nT} = e^{a_1 nT} .$$

If in the continous function $f_T(t)$, shown by the dotted line in Fig. 2.3, we put $t = nT + \Delta t$ where Δt is a fixed quantity in the interval $-T \leqslant \Delta T \leqslant T$, then $f_T(nT + \Delta t)$ defines a lattice function; we shall denote it by $f[nT, \Delta t]$. Δt can be considered here as a parameter.

For $\Delta t > 0$ the values of the independent variable are displaced

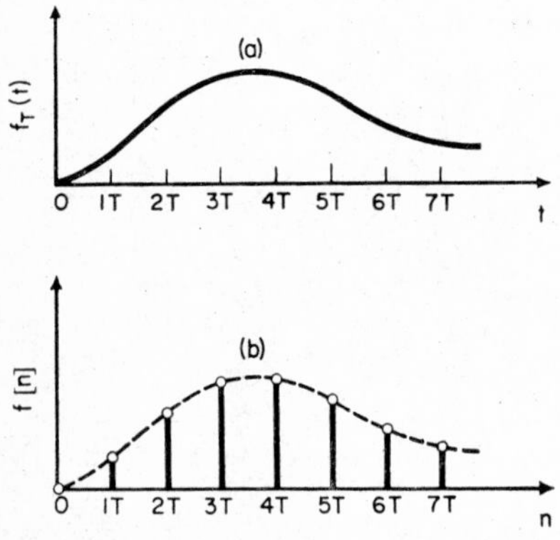

FIG. 2.2. The continuous function $f_T(t)$ and the corresponding lattice function $f\,[n\,T]$.

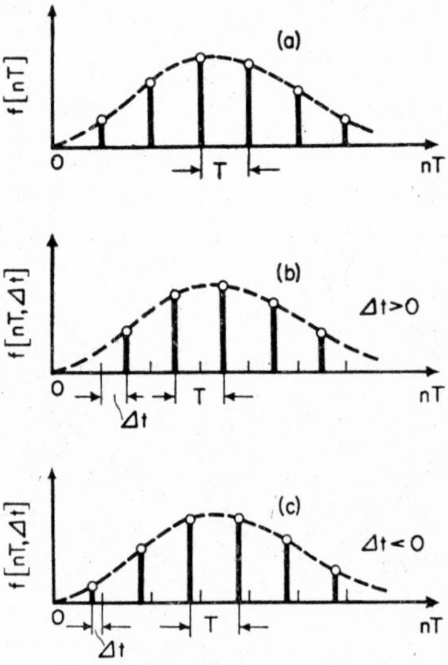

FIG. 2.3. Displaced lattice functions: (*a*) $\Delta t = 0$, (*b*) $\Delta t > 0$, (*c*) $\Delta t < 0$.

to the right (Fig. 2.3*b*) and for $\Delta t < 0$ they are displaced to the left with respect to the values for $\Delta t = 0$ (Fig. 2.3*a*), i.e. with respect to $f[nT, 0] = f[nT]$.

Obviously, as Δt varies, not only does the displacement of the lattice function vary but the ordinates themselves vary (Fig. 2.3). This type of lattice function will be called a displaced lattice function.

One lattice function will correspond to a variety of continuous or discontinuous functions, since it is only required that the ordinates of the latter equal those of the lattice function (called the discreta) at the discrete moments $t = nT$. These functions may be called the envelopes of the lattice function. The stepped function obtained by drawing lines through the ordinates of the lattice function parallel to the abscissa axis (curve 3 in Fig. 2.4) can be considered as the simplest envelope of the lattice function.

Consequently, the lattice function $f[nT]$ does not completely reflect the properties of the continuous function $f_T(t)$. This also applies to the displaced lattice function $f[nT, \Delta t]$ for a fixed value of the parameter Δt.

If the parameter Δt varies continuously from 0 to T, $f[nT, \Delta t]$ becomes identical to $f_T(t)$.

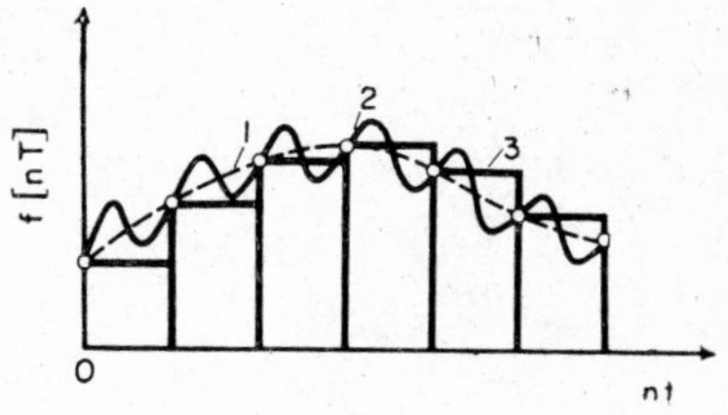

FIG. 2.4. A lattice function and its envelope.

It should be noted that a lattice function does not have to be formed from a corresponding continuous function. Any table of numbers, in which the argument changes by equal steps, or any sequence of numbers can be represented geometrically as a lattice function.

It is often convenient to have the distance between adjacent values of the independent variable equal to unity. This can be done by first introducing a new, dependent variable $\bar{t} = t/T$, so that $f_T(t) = f_T(T\bar{t})$. For simplicity we write $f_T(T\bar{t})$ as $f(\bar{t})$. The lattice function corresponding to $f(\bar{t})$ equals $f[n]$, i.e. it coincides with $f(\bar{t})$ at the values of the new independent variable $\bar{t} = n$.

Hence, for example, after replacing the independent variable in the function $f_T(t) = e^{\alpha_1 t}$, we obtain

$$f(\bar{t}) = e^{\alpha_1 T\bar{t}} = e^{a\bar{t}},$$

where $a = a_1 T$; the corresponding lattice function equals

$$f[n] = e^{an}.$$

It is shown in Fig. 2.5 for (a) $a > 0$, and (b) $a < 0$. The dotted line shows the continuous function $f(\bar{t}) = e^{a\bar{t}}$.

A lattice function $f[n]$ changes its value at integral values of the independent variable. In future we shall be mainly concerned with this type of lattice function, and not with $f[nT]$.

We shall now write the displaced lattice function in the form $f[n, \varepsilon]$, where $\varepsilon = \Delta t/T$ is the relative change of Δt. We conventionally assume that the values of the argument of $f[n, \varepsilon]$ are positive. Should it be necessary, however, to consider negative values of ε, we must write $f[n, \varepsilon]$, where $\varepsilon < 0$, in the form $f[n-1, 1+\varepsilon]$, so that the values of the argument of the function are positive. In the displaced lattice function ε is a parameter. For simplicity we shall only consider $f[n]$ in future, since all the results obtained will also hold for $f[n, \varepsilon]$.

The rate of change of a lattice function is characterised by its first difference, which is the analogue of the derivative of a continuous function.

The *first-order difference,* or *first difference,* of a lattice function is written as $\Delta f[n]$ and equals

$$\Delta f[n] = f[n+1] - f[n]. \tag{2.1}$$

Geometrically, the first difference $\Delta f[n]$ is the difference between

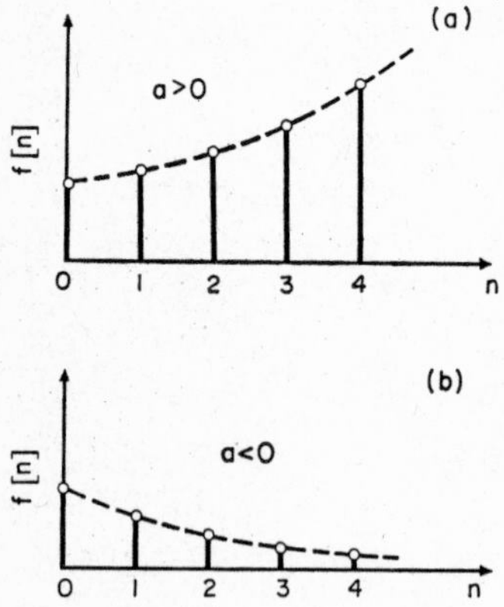

FIG. 2.5. Exponential functions e^{at} and the corresponding lattice functions (*a*) $f[n] = e^{an}$, for $a > 0$ and (*b*) $a < 0$.

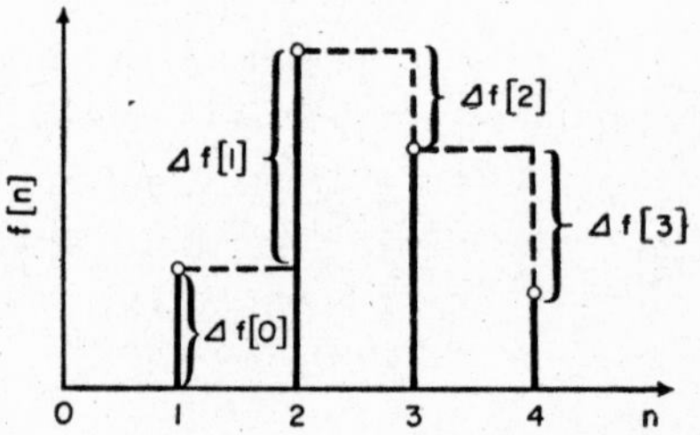

FIG. 2.6. The first difference, or first-order difference, $\Delta f[n]$ of a lattice function $f[n]$.

the heights of the $(n+1)$th and nth ordinates of the lattice function (Fig. 2.6).

The *second-order difference,* or *second difference,* $\Delta^2 f[n]$ equals

$$\Delta^2 f[n] = \Delta f[n+1] - \Delta f[n], \tag{2.2}$$

or, on substituting for $\Delta f[n+1]$ and $\Delta f[n]$,

$$\Delta^2 f[n] = f[n+2] - 2f[n+1] + f[n].$$

The *k-th order difference,* or *k-th difference,* is defined by the recurrence relation

$$\Delta^k f[n] = \Delta^{k-1} f[n+1] - \Delta^{k-1} f[n]. \tag{2.3}$$

By putting $k = 3, 4, 5, \ldots$ etc. we can easily write this expression in the form of linear function of $f[n], f[n+1], \ldots f(n+k]$. Thus

$$\Delta^3 f[n] = f[n+3] - 3f[n+2] + 3f[n+1] - f[n],$$

$$\Delta^4 f[n] = f[n+4] - 4f[n+3] + 6f[n+2] - 4f[n+1] + f[n]$$

and in general

$$\Delta^k f[n] = \sum_{\nu=0}^{k} (-1)^\nu \binom{k}{\nu} f[n+k-\nu], \tag{2.4}$$

where $\binom{k}{\nu} = \frac{k!}{\nu!\,(k-\nu)!}$ are the binomial coefficents.

Example 1. For the lattice function

$$f[n] = an$$

the first difference equals the constant a:

$$\Delta f[n] = a(n+1) - an = a.$$

The second and higher differences equal zero.

Example 2. For the lattice function

$$f[n] = e^{an}$$

the first difference equals

$$\Delta f[n] = e^{a(n+1)} - e^{an} = (e^a - 1)\, e^{an},$$

i.e. the first difference is proportional to the lattice function itself. The second difference is easily found and is

$$\Delta^2 f[n] = (e^a - 1)^2\, e^{an}$$

and in general for the kth difference

$$\Delta^k f[n] = (e^a - 1)^k\, e^{an}.$$

There is an obvious similarity to the derivative of the exponential function.

Replacing n by $n-1$ in (2.1) gives

$$\Delta f[n-1] = f[n] - f[n-1]. \tag{2.5}$$

Sometimes the difference defined in this way is called the *forward difference,* and is written $\nabla f[n]$.

If $f[n]$ is zero for negative values of n we have

$$\Delta f[n-1] = \begin{cases} f[0] & \text{when } n = 0, \\ f[n] - f[n-1] & \text{when } n \geqslant 1. \end{cases} \tag{2.6}$$

This observation will be of use in future work.

If $f_T(t)$ corresponds to some varying physical quantity, for example a voltage, then the forward difference $\nabla f[nT] = \Delta f[(n-1)T]$ can be found using a delay element, or a magnetic tape or other storage device. The delay element must have property of reproducing its input without distortion but with a constant time delay $\tau = T$(Fig. 2.7). In order to form the forward difference the delay element and an amplifier are connected as shown in Fig. 2.8*a*. The output of the device is the difference between $f_T(t)$ and $f_T(t - T)$, which equals (2.6) for $t = nT$. Higher differences can be obtained by a similar method; Fig. 2.8*b* shows a system of delay elements and amplifiers which produces the k-th order forward difference $\nabla^k f[n] = \Delta^k f[n-k]$ in accordance with formula (2.4).

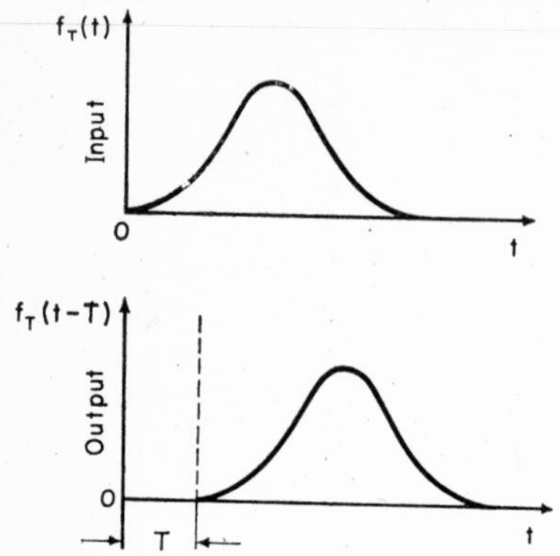

FIG. 2.7. Illustrating the properties of a delay element.

The sum of a lattice function

$$\sum_{m=0}^{n-1} f[m] = \sum_{m=1}^{n} f[n-m] \tag{2.7}$$

plays the same role in connection with the lattice function as the integral plays in continuous analysis.

The sum

$$\sum_{m=1}^{n} f_T(t - mT) \tag{2.8}$$

can also be obtained using a system with delay elements (Fig. 2.9). For $t = nT$ it corresponds to (2.7).

Lattice functions, their differences and sums, form tools, which in many respects recall those of continuous analysis, for studying the theory of finite differences.+

A relationship between a lattice function $y[n]$ and its differences of various orders $\Delta^\mu y[n]$ ($\mu = 1, 2, \ldots l$) is called an *equation in finite differences*, or a *difference equation*. If this relationship is linear, the difference equation is said to be *linear*.

+ See, for example, Ya. S. Bezikovich (2; 1939); A. O. Gel'fond (2; 1952); Sh. E. Mikeladze (2; 1953).

A linear difference equation with constant coefficients can be written as

$$b_l \Delta^l y[n] + b_{l-1} \Delta^{l-1} y[n] + \dots + b_0 y[n] = f[n]. \qquad (2.9)$$

Here the right side of the equation $f[n]$ is a known, given function and $y[n]$ an unknown function — the solution of the difference equation.

The difference equation can be written in another form by replacing

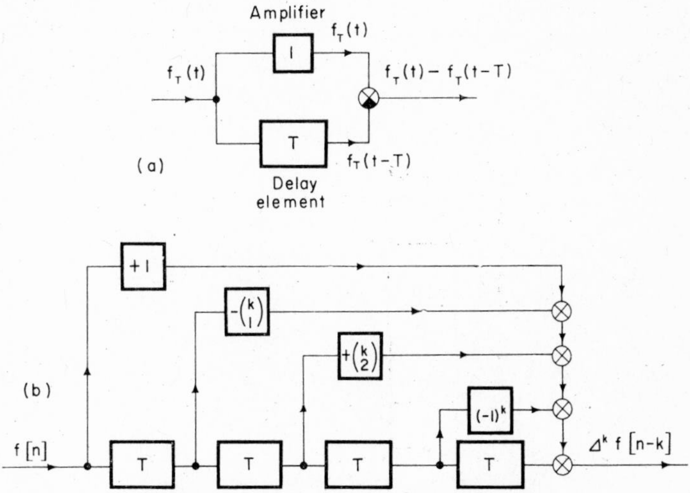

FIG. 2.8. A method of forming the forward difference, (a) the first-order difference, (b) for kth-order difference.

the differences of the lattice function $y[n]$ in (2.9) by their values from (2.4):

$$a_l y[n+l] + a_{l-1} y[n+l-1] + \dots + a_0 y[n] = f[n], \qquad (2.10)$$

this form is often more convenient.

The coefficients in these difference equations are related by

$$a_{l-k} = \sum_{\nu=0}^{k} b_{l-\nu} (-1)^{k-\nu} \binom{l-\nu}{k-\nu},$$

$$b_{l-k} = \sum_{\nu=0}^{k} a_{l-\nu} \binom{l-\nu}{k-\nu}.$$

We note that when written in the form (2.10) the difference equation can be considered as a recurrence relationship which, if $y[0]$, $y[1]$, ... $y[l-1]$ are given, enables $y[n+l]$ to be calculated for $n = 0, 1, 2, \dots$

successively. Hence (2.10) is sometimes called a *recurrence equation*.† This property distinguishes difference equations from differential equations and will be used repeatedly in future.

Difference equations (2.9), (2.10), which have a right side, are said to be *non-homogeneous*. If $f[n] \equiv 0$ the difference equation is said to be *homogeneous*.

A difference equation containing $y[n]$ and $y[n+l]$ is called an lth order difference equation. Thus equation (2.10) for $a_0 \neq 0$ and $a_l \neq 0$ is an lth order non-homogeneous difference equation.

If the difference equation is written in the form of (2.9) its order may not be the same as the order of the highest difference appearing

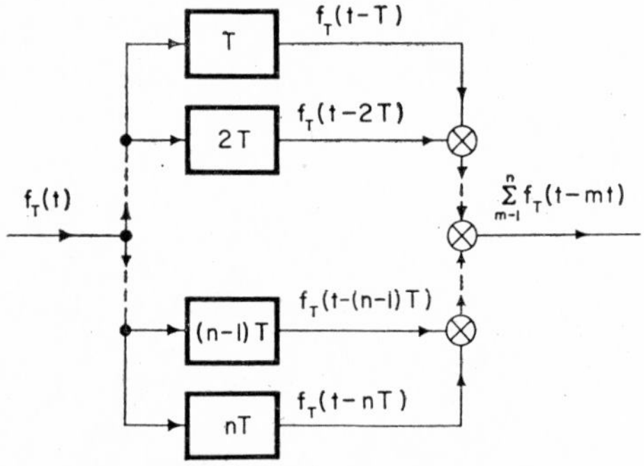

FIG. 2.9. A method of obtaining the sum of a lattice function.

in the equation. For example, the difference equation

$$\Delta^3 y[n] + 4\Delta^2 y[n] + 5\Delta y[n] + 2y[n] = 0$$

on replacing the differences by their values from (2.4), takes the form

$$y[n+3] + y[n+2] = 0$$

or, replacing $n+2$ by n, it can be written

$$y[n+1] + y[n] = 0,$$

i.e. it is a first-order homogeneous difference equation.

The classical method of solving difference equations which is usually given in text-books on the calculus of finite differences,‡ is in many respects similar to the classical method of solving differential equations.

† See, for example, G. Doetsch [2. 3].

‡ See footnote on p. 98

If an lth order difference equation has the form (2.9) its initial, or, in general, boundary conditions are given as the values of the lattice function $y[n]$ and its differences from the first to the $(l-1)$-th at $n = 0$; if it takes the form (2.10), the boundary conditions are given as the values of the lattice function at $n = 0, 1, \ldots (l-1)$.

Difference equations arise in the analysis of physical systems in which some of the variables vary discretely, or step-wise. For example the numbers of the section sin chain-type systems (filters which are equivalent to long lines, insulator chains, voltage dividers, etc.) form such a variable. Such a variable is time, in circuits with stepwise changing parameters.

Difference equations also arise in investigations of a quite different nature, for example in economics.[+]

We now give a few examples of physical problems which give rise to difference equations.

Chain-type system. Consider the chain-type system consisting of four-terminal two-part T-section networks. One of the sections is shown in Fig. 2.10. Let a generator of sinusoidal e.m.f. be switched to the input of the system. We shall only concern ourselves with steady-state conditions. Let u_n and i_n denote the complex voltage and current at the output of the nth section. These quantities can be considered as lattice functions

$$u_n = u[n], \quad i_n = i[n].$$

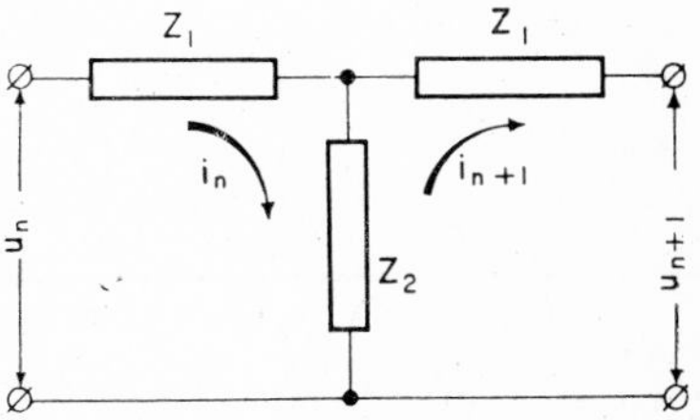

FIG. 2.10. A T-section four-pole network. A section of a chain or ladder network.

Let $z_1(j\omega) = \mathbf{z}_1$ be the total series impedance of the section and $z_2(j\omega) = \mathbf{z}_2$ the total parallel impedance. From Kirchhoff's laws we then have

$$\left.\begin{aligned} (\mathbf{z}_1 + \mathbf{z}_2)\, i[n] - \mathbf{z}_2\, i[n+1) - u[n] &= 0\,, \\ \mathbf{z}_2\, i[n] - (\mathbf{z}_1 + \mathbf{z}_2)\, i[n+1] - u[n+1] &= 0\,. \end{aligned}\right\} \qquad (2.11)$$

Equations (2.11) are two first-order homogeneous difference equations. If one of the unknowns is eliminated from this system, a single second-order difference equation results which is equivalent

+ See Geyer and Oppelt (2; 1957).

to the above system. Thus, for example, putting $n+1$ for n in the first equation and subtracting from the second gives

$$\mathbf{z}_2\, i[n+2] - 2(\mathbf{z}_1 + \mathbf{z}_2)\, i[n+1] + \mathbf{z}_2\, i[n] = 0\,,$$

or

$$i[n+2] - 2\left(1 + \frac{\mathbf{z}_1}{\mathbf{z}_2}\right) i[n+1] + i[n] = 0\,. \tag{2.12}$$

We can similarly obtain the difference equation for the other variable $u[n]$:

$$u[n+2] - 2\left(1 + \frac{\mathbf{z}_1}{\mathbf{z}_2}\right) u[n+1] + u[n] = 0\,, \tag{2.13}$$

which has the same form as (2.12).

Equations (2.12) and (2.13) are second-order homogeneous difference equations. The boundary conditions for these equations will depend both on the generator voltage and on the load of the ladder network. These conditions are given in explicit form later, when we shall be concerned with solving various problems on ladder networks.

Electrical circuit with periodically switched parameters. In the circuit of Fig. 2.11*a* the switch S periodically connects the capacitor C to resistor R_1 in series with the constant voltage u_0 during the intervals $nT \leqslant t \leqslant (n+\gamma)T$, and during the subsequent intervals $(n+\gamma)T \leqslant t \leqslant (n+1)T$ the switch discharges the capacitor through the resistor R_2.

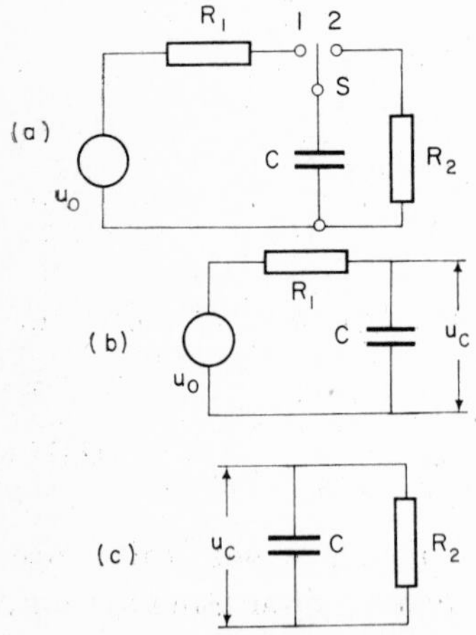

FIG. 2.11. (*a*) Circuit with switched parameters. (*b*) Circuit corresponding to the switch in position 1 and (*c*) in position 2.

This is the basic circuit of, for example, the saw-tooth voltage generator used in the line-sweep stage of television equipment (see p. 24).

The circuit equation for the intervals $nT \leqslant t \leqslant (n+\gamma)T$ (Fig. 2.11*b*) takes the form

$$R_1 C \frac{\mathrm{d}u_C}{\mathrm{d}t} + u_C = u_0,$$

where u_C is the voltage on the capacitor.

The circuit equation for the intervals $(n+\gamma)T \leqslant t \leqslant (n+1)T$ (Fig. 2.11*c*) takes the form

$$R_2 C \frac{\mathrm{d}u_C}{\mathrm{d}t} + u_C = 0.$$

Introducing a new variable — the relative time:

$$\bar{t} = \frac{t}{T},$$

where T is the switching period, and writing

$$\beta' = \frac{R_1 C}{T} = \frac{T_1}{T}, \qquad \beta'' = \frac{R_2 C}{T} = \frac{T_2}{T},$$

the circuit equations can be rewritten in the form

$$\beta' \frac{\mathrm{d}u_C}{\mathrm{d}\bar{t}} + u_C = u_0, \qquad n \leqslant \bar{t} \leqslant n + \gamma \tag{2.14}$$

and

$$\beta'' \frac{\mathrm{d}u_C}{\mathrm{d}\bar{t}} + u_C = 0, \qquad n + \gamma \leqslant \bar{t} \leqslant n + 1. \tag{2.15}$$

The solution of equation (2.14) has the form

$$u_C(\bar{t}) = u_0 + A_1 \mathrm{e}^{-\beta'(\bar{t}-n)}, \qquad n \leqslant \bar{t} \leqslant n + \gamma.$$

At $\bar{t} = n + \gamma$

$$u_C(\bar{t}) = u_C(n + \gamma).$$

At $\bar{t} = n$, i.e. $\gamma = 0$, we have

$$u_C(\bar{t}) = u_C(n).$$

A_1 is found by substituting this value in the solution of (2.14):

$$A_1 = u_C(n) - u_0$$

and so

$$u_C(\bar{t}) = u_0 + [u_C(n) - u_0]\,\mathrm{e}^{\beta'(\bar{t}-n)}, \qquad n \leqslant \bar{t} \leqslant n + \gamma. \tag{2.16}$$

The solution of equation (2.15) takes the form

$$u_C(\bar{t}) = A_2 \mathrm{e}^{-\beta''(\bar{t}-n-\gamma)}, \quad n + \gamma \leqslant \bar{t} \leqslant n + 1.$$

We obtain from (2.16) for $\bar{t} = n + \gamma$

$$u_C(\bar{t}) = u_C(n + \gamma) = u_0 + [u_C(n) - u_0]\,\mathrm{e}^{-\beta'\gamma}$$

A_2 is found by substituting this value in the solution of equation (2.15) for $\bar{t} = n + \gamma$:

$$A_2 = u_C(n + \gamma) = u_0 + [u_C(n) - u_0]\,\mathrm{e}^{-\beta'\gamma}.$$

On substituting this value of A_2, the solution of (2.15) takes the form

$$u_C(\bar{t}) = \{u_0 + [u_C(n) - u_0]\,\mathrm{e}^{-\beta'\gamma}\}\,\mathrm{e}^{-\beta''(\bar{t}-n-\gamma)}, \quad n + \gamma \leqslant \bar{t} \leqslant n + 1. \tag{2.17}$$

Putting $\bar{t} = n + 1$ in (2.17) and introducing the lattice function notation

$$u_C[n] = u_C(n)\,,$$

we obtain, after simple manipulation, a non-homogeneous first-order difference equation with constant coefficients

$$u_C[n+1] - e^{-\beta'\gamma - \beta''(1-\gamma)}\, u_C[n] = u_0(1 - e^{-\beta'\gamma})\, e^{-\beta''(1-\gamma)}. \quad (2.18)$$

This equation determines the voltage on the capacitor at the discrete moments $\bar{t} = n$. If, by some means or other, we solve equation (2.18) and find $u_C[n]$, then by substituting this solution in (2.16) and (2.17) we obtain the voltage on the capacitor at any instant of time.

Many problems reduce to difference equations, problems in interpolation theory for example. Difference equations play an important role in digital computers. As was mentioned in § 1.3, a digital computer is described by the difference equation which represents the sequence of operations of the computer and which is usually called the program.

We now go on to study the discrete Laplace transformation which, on the one hand enables difference equations to be easily solved and which, on the other, is the basic mathematical apparatus of the theory of the pulse systems examined in subsequent chapters.

2.2. Definition of the discrete Laplace transformation

The *discrete Laplace transformation* is a functional transformation of the lattice function $f[n]$ and is defined by the relationship

$$F^*(q) = \sum_{n=0}^{\infty} e^{-qn} f[n] \quad (2.19)$$

or, for the displaced lattice function $f[n, \varepsilon]$,

$$F^*(q, \varepsilon) = \sum_{n=0}^{\infty} e^{-qn} f[n, \varepsilon]\,. \quad (2.20)$$

Here $q = \sigma + j\bar{\omega}$ is a complex number called the *transformation parameter*, and ε is a real parameter. If (2.19) or (2.20) is compared with the definition of the usual Laplace transformation of a function $f(\bar{t})$

$$F(q) = L\{f(\bar{t})\} = \int_0^{\infty} e^{-q\bar{t}} f(\bar{t})\, d\bar{t}\,, \quad (2.21)$$

we can readily see the similarity. The integral with the infinite limit corresponds to an infinite sum — the series in (2.19) and (2.10); the continuous variable $\bar{t}$ corresponds to the discrete variable n, and finally the arbitrary continuous function $f(\bar{t})$ corresponds to the lattice function $f[n]$ or the displaced lattice function $f[n, \varepsilon]$.

The relationship (2.20) sets up a correspondence between the lattice function $f[n, \varepsilon]$ and the function $F^*(q, \varepsilon)$ of the complex variable q. We call the former function the original and the latter the image, in analogy with the usual terminology of the Laplace transformation. The correspondence between an original and its image is written conventionally in the form

$$F^*(q) = D\{f[n]\} \xrightarrow{\cdot} f[n], \tag{2.22}$$

or, for the displaced lattice function,

$$F^*(q, \varepsilon) = D\{f[n, \varepsilon]\} \xrightarrow{\cdot} f[n, \varepsilon]. \tag{2.23}$$

Here the symbol $D\{\ \}$ indicates the operation of transforming the lattice function $f[n]$ or the displaced lattice function $f[n, \varepsilon]$, just as the symbol $L\{\ \}$ is used to indicate the operation of transforming the function $f(\bar{t})$ in (2.21).

Since the parameter ε does not affect the properties of the discrete Laplace transformation, we mainly consider in this chapter for simplicity the lattice function $f[n]$, and not the displaced lattice function $f[n\ \varepsilon]$. The latter will be extensively used, however, in subsequent chapters and also in § 2.8 of the present chapter.

For the image of a lattice function to be defined it is necessary that the series (2.19) should converge. We prove that if this series converges for⁺ Re $q = \sigma_0$ then it is convergent, moreover absolutely and uniformly convergent, for all q satisfying the condition Re $q > \sigma_0$.

Consider the series (2.19) for Re $q = \sigma_0$:

$$F^*(q) = \sum_{n=0}^{\infty} e^{-qn} f[n] = \sum_{n=0}^{\infty} e^{-(\sigma_0+j\bar{\omega})n} f[n]. \tag{2.24}$$

By stipulation this series converges, hence its general term $e^{-(\sigma_0+j\bar{\omega})n} f[n]$ tends to zero as $n \to \infty$ and is bounded for all $n > 0$, i.e.

$$\left| e^{-(\sigma_0+j\bar{\omega})n} f[n] \right| = e^{-\sigma_0 n} \left| f n] \right| < A. \tag{2.25}$$

⁺ Re q denotes the real part of q.

Consider now the series for $\operatorname{Re} q = \sigma > \sigma_0$. For it

$$\sum_{n=0}^{\infty} \left| e^{-(\sigma+j\bar{\omega})n} f[n] \right| = \sum_{n=0}^{\infty} e^{-\sigma n} \left| f[n] \right|. \tag{2.26}$$

This expression can be rewritten in the form

$$\sum_{n=0}^{\infty} e^{-\sigma_0 n} \left| f[n] \right| e^{-(\sigma-\sigma_0)n}. \tag{2.27}$$

As $\sigma > \sigma_0$ and thus $e^{-(\sigma-\sigma_0)n} < 1$ for $n > 0$, we see, using inequality (2.25), that the terms of the series (2.27) are less than the terms of the convergent geometrical-progression series $\sum_{n=0}^{\infty} A\, e^{-(\sigma-\sigma_0)n}$. Hence the series (2.27) converges. The terms of series (2.24) are greater in absolute value than the terms of (2.27) and (2.19) for $\operatorname{Re} q > \sigma_0$. Consequently, series (2.19) is absolutely convergent. We conclude, using a criterion for uniform convergence,+ that it also converges uniformly for $\operatorname{Re} q = \sigma > \sigma_0$. Obviously, if the series (2.19) diverges for $\operatorname{Re} q = \sigma_c$, it will also diverge for all $\operatorname{Re} q = \sigma < \sigma_c$. The value of σ_c such that series (2.19) converges for $\sigma > \sigma_c$ and diverges for $\sigma < \sigma_c$, is called the *abscissa of convergence.*

The abscissa of convergence is thus the greatest lower bound of the values σ_0 at which series (2.19) converges.

If, for a given lattice function $f[n]$, the abscissa of convergence $\sigma_c < \infty$, then series (2.19) converges at all points q satisfying the condition $\operatorname{Re} q = \sigma > \sigma_c$. In this case the lattice function is said to be *transformable.*

To any transformable lattice function $f[n]$ there corresponds an image $F^*(q)$.

If, for a given lattice function $f[n]$, the abscissa of convergence $\sigma_c = +\infty$, then series (2.19) diverges for all q. In this case no image of $f[n]$ exists.

Example 1. Let $f[n] = 1[n]$ (Fig. 2.12). Provided $\operatorname{Re} q > 0$, the image of this 'constant' lattice function equals

$$F^*(q) = \sum_{n=0}^{\infty} e^{-qn} \cdot 1 = \frac{1}{1 - e^{-q}} = \frac{e^q}{e^q - 1}.$$

Thus

$$F^*(q) = D\{1[n]\} = \frac{e^q}{e^q - 1}. \tag{2.28}$$

+ See A. I. Markushevich (2; 1950).

The formula for an infinite geometrical progression is used here to evaluate the summation. In this case the axis of convergence is $\sigma_c = 0$.

EXAMPLE 2. Let $f[n, \varepsilon] = e^{a(n+\varepsilon)}$, where a is a real number (Fig. 2.13). The image of this exponential displaced lattice function equals

$$F^*(q,\varepsilon) = \sum_{n=0}^{\infty} e^{-qn}\, e^{an}\, e^{a\varepsilon} = \frac{e^{a\varepsilon}}{1 - e^{-(q-a)}} = \frac{e^q\, e^{a\varepsilon}}{e^q - e^a};$$

if $\varepsilon = 0$ we obtain

$$F^*(q) = D\{e^{an}\} = \frac{e^q}{e^q - e^a}. \tag{2.29}$$

The summation is only possible if Re $q > a$. In this case the abscissa of convergence is $\sigma_c = a$.

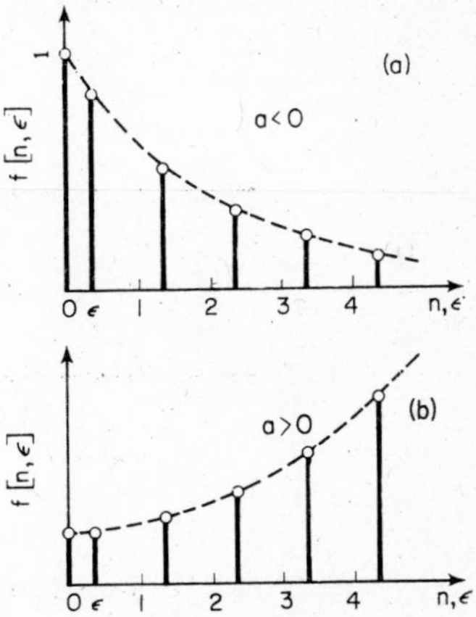

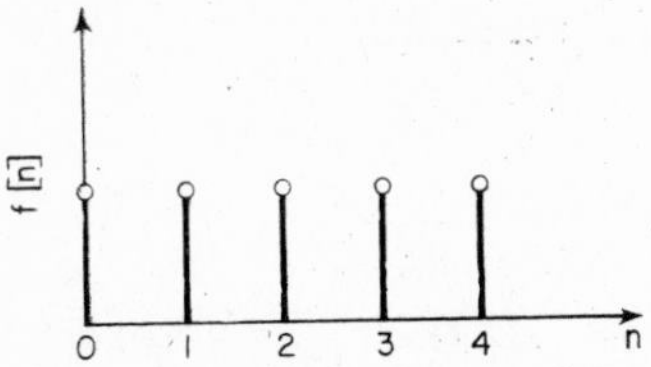

FIG. 2.12. The unit step or "constant" lattice function
$$1\,[n] = \begin{cases} 1, & n \geqslant 0, \\ 0, & n < 0. \end{cases}$$

FIG. 2.13. Displaced exponential lattice function $e^{a(n+\varepsilon)}$ for (a) $a = -0{\cdot}5$, and (b) $a = +0{\cdot}5$.

EXAMPLE 3. Let $f[n] = n!$ or $f[n] = e^{an^2}$.
The images of these lattice functions do not exist as in both cases the abscissa of convergence equals infinity.

The existence of an abscissa of convergence $\sigma_c < \infty$ ensures the existence of the image function. It follows from (2.25) that if the lattice function satisfies the condition

$$|f[n]| < A\, e^{\sigma_0 n},$$

i.e. if its order of growth is less than the order of growth of $e^{\sigma_0 n}$, then the abscissa of convergence $\sigma_c < \sigma_0$ and hence the image of such a lattice function will always exist.

The above examples show that the image of a lattice function is a continuous function of e^q. This is a typical property of the discrete Laplace transformation. To emphasise this, and to distinguish the image of a lattice function (2.19) from the image of the corresponding continuous function (2.21), an asterisk is used in the notation for the former.

We now consider $F^*(q)$ on the complex q-plane. As $F^*(q)$ is a function of e^q, and as e^q is a periodic function along the imaginary axis $j\bar{\omega}$ (since $e^{q+2k\pi j} = e^q$), it follows that $F^*(q)$ is also a periodic function along the imaginary axis. Hence if Re $q > \sigma_c$ the image of a lattice function is completely defined in any strip of width 2π parallel to the real axis. It proves convenient, as will appear later, to choose

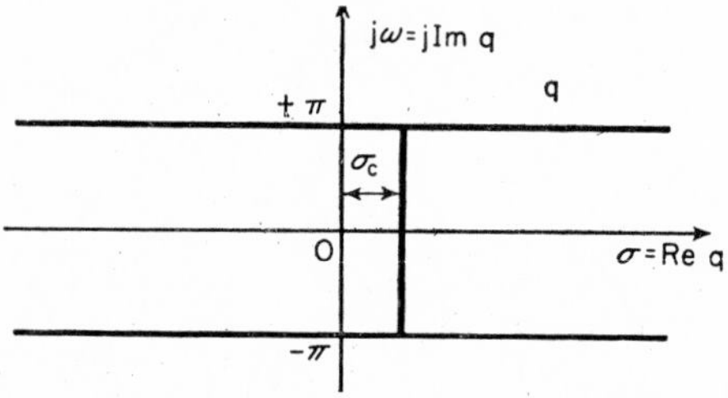

FIG. 2.14. Complex q-plane.
Strip $-\pi < \text{Im } q \leqslant \pi$.

a strip symmetrical about the real axis, i.e. so that $-\pi < \text{Im } q < \pi$⁺ (Fig. 2.14). The image $F^*(q)$ is an analytic function of e^q and q in the half-strip Re $q > \sigma_c$. In many cases $F^*(q)$ can be analytically continued into the left half-strip Re $q < \sigma_c$.

If the lattice function $f[n]$ is transformable, then for Re $q \geqslant \sigma_c$ $F^*(q)$ is the unique image of $f[n]$ and, conversely, under certain restrictions which do not affect practical applications, an image $F^*(q)$ corresponds for $n \geqslant 0$ to a unique lattice function $f[n]$. Hence under these conditions there is a one-to-one correspondence between the original $f[n]$ and the image $F^*(q)$.

In addition to the *single-sided* discrete Laplace transformation defined by (2.19), we may introduce a *double-sided* discrete Laplace transformation defined by

$$F^*(p) = \sum_{n=-\infty}^{\infty} e^{-qn} f[n] . \tag{2.30}$$

⁺ Im q denotes the imaginary part of q.

If, for $n < 0$, the lattice function is identically zero, the double-sided discrete Laplace transformation reduces to the single-sided form. In future, unless there is a remark to the contrary, we shall always have in mind the single-sided discrete Laplace transformation.

2.3. Fundamental rules and theorems

In this section we give the fundamental rules and theorems of the discrete Laplace transformation; these establish the correspondence between operations carried out in the domains of the original and the image.

These rules and theorems enable the images of many lattice functions to be obtained very simply, avoiding direct summation which often gives rise to difficulties. Also, they enable the discrete Laplace transformation to be used to solve difference equations, and in the steady-state and transient analysis of pulse systems.

THEOREM 1. LINEARITY OF ORIGINALS AND IMAGES (LINEARITY THEOREM).

Suppose we are given a lattice function

$$f[n] = \sum_{\nu=1}^{k} a_\nu f_\nu[n].$$

We denote

$$D\{f_\nu[n]\} = F_\nu^*(q),$$

and

$$D\{f[n]\} = D\left\{\sum_{\nu=1}^{k} a_\nu f_\nu[n]\right\} = F^*(q).$$

Since

$$D\left\{\sum_{\nu=1}^{k} a_\nu f_\nu[n]\right\} = \sum_{\nu=1}^{k} a_\nu D\{f_\nu[n]\},$$

we obtain

$$F^*(q) = \sum_{\nu=1}^{k} a_\nu F_\nu^*(q) \tag{2.31}$$

or

$$\sum_{\nu=1}^{k} a_\nu F_\nu^*(q) \;\dot{\rightarrow}\; \sum_{\nu=1}^{k} a_\nu f_\nu[n]. \tag{2.32}$$

The image of a linear combination of lattice functions equals the linear combination of their images.

The linearity theorem enables us to find the image of a lattice function which can be written as a linear combination of lattice functions, the images of which are known.

EXAMPLE 1. Let $f[n] = \sinh a\,n$.

As $\sinh a\,n = \frac{1}{2}(e^{an} - e^{-an})$, we have from Theorem 1

$$D\{\sinh a\,n\} = \frac{1}{2} D\{e^{an}\} - \frac{1}{2} D\{e^{-an}\}.$$

Substituting the image of e^{an} (2.29) gives

$$D\{\sinh a\,n\} = \frac{1}{2}\,\frac{e^q}{e^q - e^a} - \frac{1}{2}\,\frac{e^q}{e^q - e^{-a}} = \frac{e^q \sinh a}{e^{2q} - 2\,e^q \cosh a + 1}. \quad (2.33)$$

EXAMPLE 2. Let $f[n] = \cosh a\,n$.

As $\cosh a\,n = \frac{1}{2}(e^{an} + e^{-an})$, we find similarly that

$$D\{\cosh a\,n\} = \frac{1}{2}\,\frac{e^q}{e^q - e^a} + \frac{1}{2}\,\frac{e^q}{e^q - e^{-a}} = \frac{e^q\,(e^q - \cosh a)}{e^{2q} - 2\,e^q \cosh a + 1}. \quad (2.34)$$

If we put $a = j\,\bar{\omega}$ in (2.33) and (2.34) and use the well-known relationships

$$\sinh j\,\bar{\omega}\,n = j \sin \bar{\omega}\,n,$$

$$\cosh j\,\bar{\omega}\,n = \cos \bar{\omega}\,n,$$

we can easily find the images of the trigonometrical lattice functions

$$D\{\sin \bar{\omega}\,n\} = \frac{e^q \sin \bar{\omega}}{e^{2q} - 2\,e^q \cos \bar{\omega} + 1}, \quad (2.35)$$

$$D\{\cos \bar{\omega}\,n\} = \frac{e^q (e^q - \cos \bar{\omega})}{e^{2q} - 2\,e^q \cos \bar{\omega} + 1}. \quad (2.36)$$

In Fig. 2.15, a and b show $\sin \bar{\omega}\,n$ for $\bar{\omega} = \frac{\pi}{6}$, $\bar{\omega} = \frac{\pi}{2}$ and Fig. 2.15c shows $\cos \bar{\omega}\,n$ for $\bar{\omega} = \pi$.

THEOREM 2. TRANSLATION OF THE INDEPENDENT VARIABLE IN THE ORIGINAL DOMAIN (ORIGINAL-TRANSLATION THEOREM).

Let

$$D\{f[n]\} = F^*(q).$$

We wish to find the image of the lattice function $f[n + k]$, where k is a positive integer. By definition

$$D\{f[n + k]\} = \sum_{n=0}^{\infty} e^{-qn} f[n + k].$$

On the right side put $n + k = r$. We then obtain

$$D\{f[n+k]\} = \sum_{r=k}^{\infty} e^{-q(r-k)} f[r] = e^{qk}\left[\sum_{r=0}^{\infty} e^{-qr} f[r] - \sum_{r=0}^{k-1} e^{-qr} f[r]\right].$$

As the summation from 0 to ∞ does not depend on the notation used for the variable, we have

$$\sum_{r=0}^{\infty} e^{-qr} f[r] = F^*(q),$$

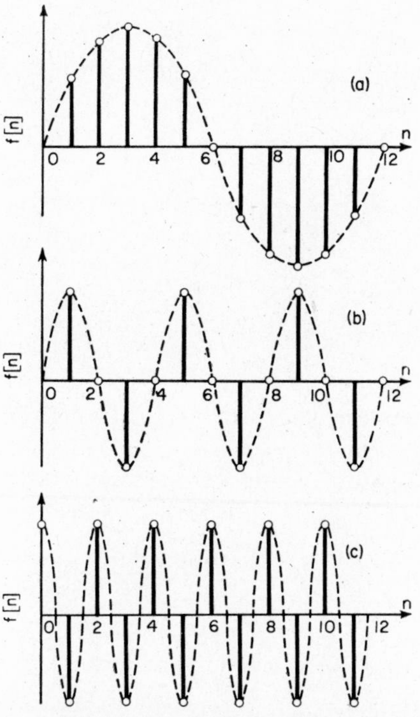

FIG. 2.15. Harmonic lattice functions: (a) $\sin\frac{\pi n}{6}$, (b) $\sin\frac{\pi n}{2}$ and (c) $\cos \pi n$.

and so

$$D\{f[n+k]\} = e^{qk}\left[F^*(q) - \sum_{r=0}^{k-1} e^{-qr} f[r]\right]. \tag{2.37}$$

For the particular case when

$$f[0] = f[1] = \ldots = f[k-1] = 0 \tag{2.38}$$

i.e. when the lattice function for $n < k$ is identically equal to zero, (2.37) gives

$$D\{f[n+k]\} = e^{qk} F^*(q) . \tag{2.39}$$

We now find the image corresponding to the lattice function $f[n-k]$. We have

$$D\{f[n-k]\} = \sum_{n=0}^{\infty} e^{-qn} f[n-k] .$$

Putting $n - k = r$ on the right side we obtain

$$D\{f[n-k]\} = \sum_{r=-k}^{\infty} e^{-q(r+k)} f[r]$$

$$= e^{-qk} \left[\sum_{r=0}^{\infty} e^{-qr} f[r] + \sum_{r=-k}^{-1} e^{-qr} f[r] \right] .$$

Since

$$\sum_{r=-k}^{-1} e^{-qr} f[r] = \sum_{r=1}^{k} e^{qr} f[-r],$$

we obtain finally

$$D\{f[n-k]\} = e^{-qk} \left[F^*(q) + \sum_{r=1}^{k} e^{qr} f[-r] \right] . \tag{2.40}$$

For the particular case when the lattice function $f[n]$ is identically equal to zero for negative values of the independent variable

$$f[-1] = f[-2] = \ldots = f[-k] = 0 \tag{2.41}$$

i.e. $f[n-k] \equiv 0$ for $n < k$, we obtain from (2.40)

$$D\{f[n-k]\} = e^{-qk} F^*(q) . \tag{2.42}$$

If conditions (2.38) *and* (2.41) *are satisfied, a shift of the independent variable of the original by* $\pm k$ *corresponds to multiplying the image by* $e^{\pm qk}$. The original-translation theorem is often called the advance and retard theorem.

EXAMPLE 1. Let $f[n] = 1[n-k]$.
We have from (2.28)

$$D\{1[n]\} = \frac{e^q}{e^q - 1} .$$

Using the original translation theorem (2.42) we obtain

$$D\{1[n-k]\} = e^{-pk} \frac{e^q}{e^q - 1} = \frac{1}{(e^q - 1)\, e^{q(k-1)}} . \tag{2.43}$$

For $k = 1$ (Fig. 2.16) we have

$$D\{1[n-1]\} = \frac{1}{e^q - 1} .\qquad(2.44)$$

EXAMPLE 2. Let $f[n] = e^{-a(n-1)}$; $f[n] \equiv 0$ for $n < 1$ (Fig. 2.17). From (2.29)

$$D\{e^{-an}\} = \frac{e^q}{e^q - e^{-a}} .$$

Using (2.42) we find

$$D\{e^{-a(n-1)}\} = e^{-q}\frac{e^q}{e^q - e^{-a}} = \frac{1}{e^q - e^{-a}} .\qquad(2.45)$$

A shift of the independent variable by an amount $\varepsilon > 0$ gives rise to the displaced lattice function. Such a shift does not change

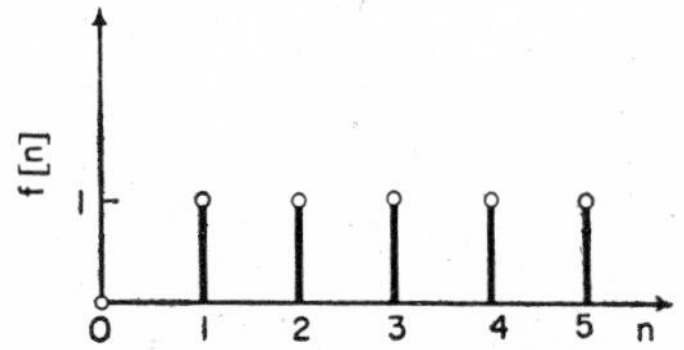

FIG. 2.16. The delayed "constant" lattice function $1(n-1)$.

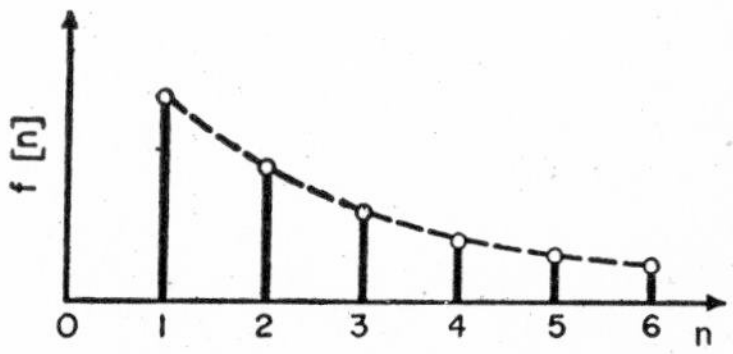

FIG. 2.17. The delayed exponential lattice function $e^{-0.5(n-1)}$.

the formulation of the theorems of the discrete Laplace transformation. In this case ε is considered as a parameter independent of n. We recall that the values of the argument of $f[n, \varepsilon]$ are displaced an amount $\varepsilon > 0$ to the right of those of $f[n]$.

THEOREM 3. DISPLACEMENT OF THE INDEPENDENT VARIABLE IN THE IMAGE DOMAIN (IMAGE-TRANSLATION THEOREM).

On replacing q by $q \pm \lambda$ in (2.19) we obtain

$$F^*(q \pm \lambda) = \sum_{n=0}^{\infty} e^{-(q\pm\lambda)n} f[n] = \sum_{n=0}^{\infty} e^{-qn} \left[e^{\mp\lambda n} f[n]\right],$$

from which it follows that

$$F^*(q \pm \lambda) = D\{e^{\mp\lambda n} f[n]\}\qquad(2.46)$$

or

$$F^*(q \pm \lambda) \overset{\cdot}{\underset{\cdot}{\longrightarrow}} e^{\mp\lambda n} f[n] .\qquad(2.47)$$

The displacement of the independent variable in the image domain by $\pm \lambda$ corresponds to multiplying the original by $e^{\mp\lambda n}$

The image-translation theorem is the dual of the original-translation theorem. In these theorems the operations in the original and image domains change places.

In subsequent work we shall often come across similar cases of duality.

EXAMPLE. Let $f[n] = e^{\lambda n} \sinh a\, n$.
Using the image of sinh an (2.33), the image-translation theorem gives that

$$D\{e^{\lambda n} \sinh a\, n\} = \frac{e^{(q-\lambda)} \sinh a}{e^{2(q-\lambda)} - 2e^{(q-\lambda)} \cosh a + 1} = \frac{e^q e^\lambda \sinh a}{e^{2q} - 2e^q e^\lambda \cosh a + e^{2\lambda}}. \quad (2.48)$$

Similarly, using (2.34):

$$D\{e^{\lambda n} \cosh a\, n\} = \frac{e^q(e^q - e^\lambda \cosh a)}{e^{2q} - 2e^q e^\lambda \cosh a + e^{2\lambda}}. \quad (2.49)$$

Putting $a = j\bar{\omega}$ in these relationships gives

$$D\{e^{\lambda n} \sin \bar{\omega}\, n\} = \frac{e^q e^\lambda \sin \bar{\omega}}{e^{2q} - 2e^q e^\lambda \cos \bar{\omega} + e^{2\lambda}}, \quad (2.50)$$

$$D\{e^{\lambda n} \cos \bar{\omega}\, n\} = \frac{e^q(e^q - e^\lambda \cos \bar{\omega})}{e^{2q} - 2e^q e^\lambda \cos \bar{\omega} + e^{2\lambda}}. \quad (2.51)$$

THEOREM 4. IMAGES OF DIFFERENCES.

The first difference of a lattice function equals

$$\Delta f[n] = f[n+1] - f[n].$$

Using the original-translation and linearity theorems we find

$$D\{\Delta f[n]\} = e^q\,[F^*(q) - f[0]] - F^*(q)$$

or

$$D\{\Delta f[n]\} = (e^q - 1)\, F^*(q) - e^q f[0]. \quad (2.52)$$

Consider the second difference of a lattice function

$$\Delta^2 f[n] = \Delta f[n+1] - \Delta f[n].$$

We obtain using the original-translation theorem and (2.52)

$$D\{\Delta f[n+1]\} = e^q\,[D\{\Delta f[n]\} - \Delta f[0]] =$$
$$= e^q\,[(e^q - 1)\, F^*(q) - e^q f[0]] - e^q \Delta f[0],$$

and so

$$D\{\Delta^2 f[n]\} = e^q\,[(e^q - 1)\, F^*(q) - e^q f[0] -$$
$$- e^q \Delta f[0] - (e^q - 1)\, F^*(q) + e^q f[0]$$

or

$$D\{\Delta^2[n]\} = (e^q - 1)^2 F^*(q) - e^q(e^q - 1) f[0] - e^q \Delta f[0]. \quad (2.53)$$

The image of the k-th difference of a lattice function is found by repeating the above process

$$D\{\Delta^k f[n]\} = (e^q - 1)^k F^*(q) - e^q \sum_{\nu=0}^{k-1} (e^q - 1)^{k-1-\nu} \Delta^\nu f[0]. \quad (2.54)$$

Here we must define $\Delta^0 f[0] = f[0]$. Solving (2.54) for $F^*(q)$ gives an expression which is useful for calculating the image of certain functions:

$$F^*(q) = \frac{e^q}{e^q - 1} \sum_{\nu=0}^{k-1} \frac{\Delta^\nu f[0]}{(e^q - 1)^\nu} + \frac{1}{(e^q - 1)^k} D\{\Delta^k f[n]\}. \quad (2.55)$$

EXAMPLE 1. Let $f[n] = n$; then

$$\Delta f[n] = (n+1) - n = 1,$$

$$\Delta^2 f[n] = 1 - 1 = 0.$$

All higher order differences equal zero. Putting $k = 2$ in (2.55), and remembering that $f[0] = 0$ and $\Delta f[0] = 1$, we obtain

$$D\{n\} = \frac{e^q}{(e^q - 1)^2}. \quad (2.56)$$

EXAMPLE 2. Let $f[n] = \binom{n}{2} = \frac{n(n-1)}{2!}$; then

$$\Delta f[n] = \binom{n+1}{2} - \binom{n}{2} = \frac{(n+1)n}{2!} - \frac{n(n-1)}{2!} = n,$$

$$\Delta^2 f[n] = (n+1) - n = 1.$$

All higher order differences equal zero. Remembering that

$$f[0] = 0, \quad \Delta f[0] = 0, \quad \Delta^2 f[0] = 1,$$

we find from (2.55) for $k = 3$

$$D\left\{\binom{n}{2}\right\} = \frac{e^q}{(e^q - 1)^3}. \quad (2.57)$$

Similarly, it is easy to show that

$$D\left\{\binom{n}{m}\right\} = \frac{e^q}{(e^q - 1)^{m+1}}. \quad (2.58)$$

The binomial coefficients can be written in the form

$$\binom{n}{m} = \frac{n^{(m)}}{m!}.$$

The function $n^{(m)} = n(n-1)\ldots[n-(n-1)]$ is called the *factorial function*. It is analogous to the power function of continuous analysis. The difference of the factorial function is easily seen to be

$$\Delta n^{(m)} = (n+1)^{(m)} - n^{(m)} = mn^{(m-1)} .$$

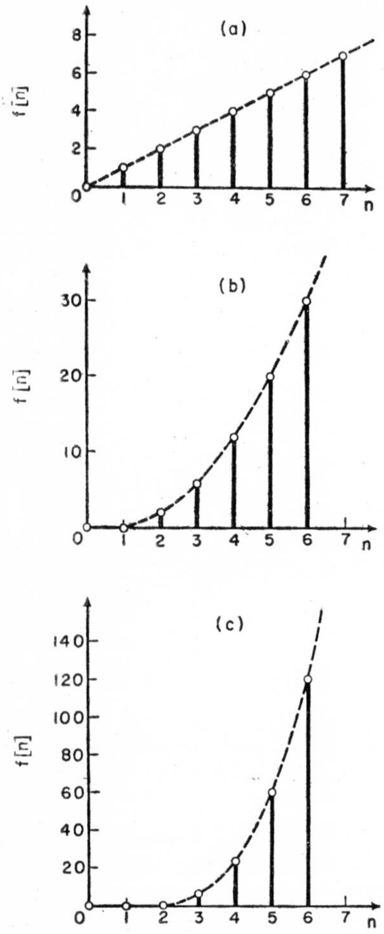

Fig. 2.18. Factorial function $n^{(m)}$ for (*a*) $m = 1$, (*b*) $m = 2$, and (*c*) $m = 3$.

The factorial functions for $m = 1, 2, 3,$ are shown in Fig. 2.18.

Example 3. Let $f[n] = n^2$; then

$$\Delta f[n] = (n+1)^2 - n^2 = 2n + 1,$$

$$\Delta^2 f[n] = [2(n+1)+1] - (2n+1) = 2.$$

All higher differences equal zero. As $f[0] = 0$, $\Delta f[0] = 1$, $\Delta^2 f[0] = 2$, we find from (2.55) for $k = 3$

$$D\{n^2\} = \frac{e^q}{(e^q-1)^2} + \frac{2\,e^q}{(e^q-1)^2} =$$

$$= \frac{e^q}{(e^q-1)^3}(e^q+1) . \qquad (2.59)$$

If $\Delta^\nu f[0] = 0$ for $\nu = 0, 1, \ldots, k-1$ or,

$$f[0] = f[1] = \ldots = f[k-1] = 0 ,$$

then (2.54) yields the particularly simple relationship

$$D\{\Delta^k f[n]\} = (e^q - 1)^k F^*(q) \qquad (2.60)$$

or

$$(e^q - 1)^k F^*(q) \to \Delta^k f[n] . \qquad (2.61)$$

Thus, in this case, the operation of taking the k-th difference in the original domain corresponds to multiplying by $(e^q - 1)^k$ in the image domain.

Theorem 5. The image of a sum.

The sum of a lattice function is defined by

$$\sum_{m=0}^{n-1} f[m] .$$

We form the first difference of this sum

$$\Delta \sum_{m=0}^{n-1} f[m] = \sum_{m=0}^{n} f[m] - \sum_{m=0}^{n-1} f[m] = f[n] .$$

From the preceding theorem [see (2.52)] the image of this difference equals

$$D\left\{\Delta \sum_{m=0}^{n-1} f[m]\right\} = D\{f[n]\} = (e^q - 1)\, D\left\{\sum_{m=0}^{n-1} f[m]\right\},$$

since the value of the sum for $n = 0$ equals zero. Hence

$$F^*(q) = (e^q - 1)\, D\left\{\sum_{m=0}^{n-1} f[m]\right\},$$

and so

$$D\left\{\sum_{m=0}^{n-1} f[m]\right\} = \frac{F^*(q)}{e^q - 1} . \tag{2.62}$$

Thus, *summation in the original domain corresponds to division by* $(e^q - 1)$ *in the image domain.*

By generalising the above process we can show that *a summation repeated k times in the original domain corresponds to division by* $(e^q - 1)^k$ *in the image domain.*

EXAMPLE 1. Find the original of the image

$$F^*(q) = \frac{e^q}{(e^q - 1)(e^q - e^a)} .$$

Noting that

$$F_1^*(q) = \frac{e^q}{e^q - e^a} \;\dot{\to}\; e^{an},$$

we obtain using theorem (5)

$$\frac{F_1^*(q)}{e^q - 1} \;\dot{\to}\; \sum_{m=0}^{n-1} e^{am} .$$

But

$$\sum_{m=0}^{n-1} e^{am} = \frac{e^{an} - 1}{e^a - 1},$$

and so

$$F^*(q) = \frac{e^q}{(e^q - 1)(e^q - e^a)} \;\dot{\to}\; \frac{1}{1 - e^a}(1 - e^{an}) . \tag{2.63}$$

Figure 2.19 shows the lattice function (2.63) for $a = -0{\cdot}5$ and $a = 0{\cdot}5$.

EXAMPLE 2. Find the original of

$$F^*(q) = \frac{e^q}{(e^q - 1)^2 (e^q - e^a)} .$$

We have from the previous example that

$$F^*(q) = \frac{e^q}{(e^q - 1)(e^q - e^a)} \;\dot{\longrightarrow}\; \frac{1}{1 - e^a} (1 - e^{an}) .$$

We find, using Theorem 5 once more, that,

$$\frac{e^q}{(e^q - 1)^2 (e^q - e^a)} \;\dot{\longrightarrow}\; \frac{1}{1 - e^a} \sum_{m=0}^{n-1} (1 - e^{am}) .$$

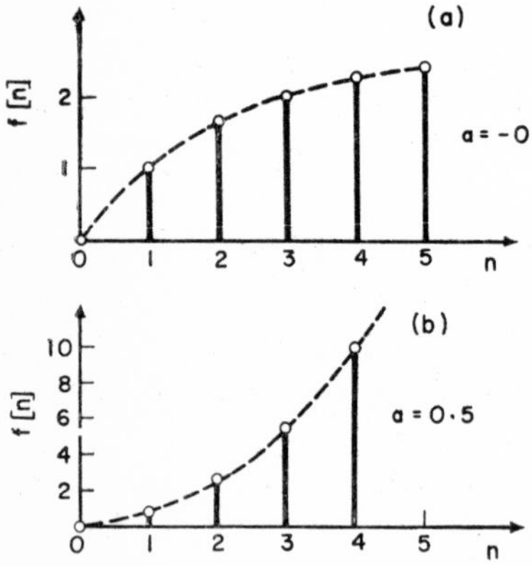

FIG. 2.19. The lattice function $\frac{1-e^{an}}{1-e^a}$ for (*a*) $a = -0{\cdot}5$, and (*b*) $a = +0{\cdot}5$.

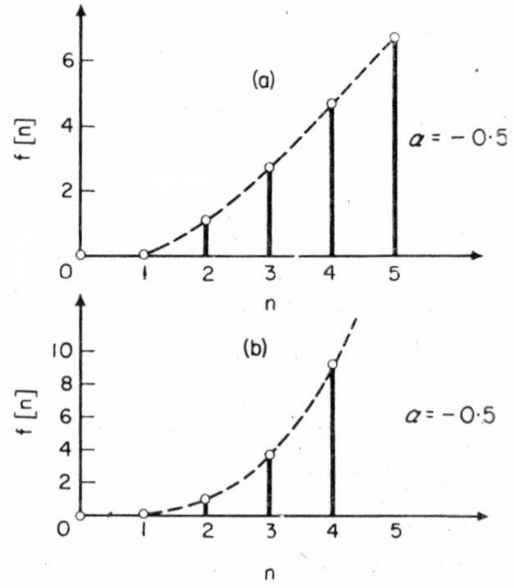

FIG. 2.20. The lattice function $\frac{n}{1-e^a} - \frac{1-e^{an}}{(1-e^a)^2}$ for (*a*) $a = -0{\cdot}5$, and (*b*) $a = +0{\cdot}5$.

However

$$\sum_{m=0}^{n-1} 1 = n, \qquad \sum_{m=0}^{n-1} e^{am} = \frac{e^{an} - 1}{e^a - 1},$$

and so

$$F^*(q) = \frac{e^q}{(e^q - 1)^2 (e^q - e^a)} \;\dot{\longrightarrow}\; \frac{n}{1 - e^a} - \frac{1 - e^{an}}{(1 - e^a)^2} .$$

The corresponding lattice functions for $a = -0{\cdot}5$ and $a = 0{\cdot}5$ are shown in Fig. 2.20.

Theorem 5 permits the sum of a lattice function to be found very easily.

EXAMPLE 1. Evaluate the series

$$\sum_{m=0}^{n-1} m .$$

As the image of n equals $\dfrac{e^q}{(e^q - 1)^2}$ (see 2.56), we have from the theorem on the image of a sum (Theorem 5) that

$$\frac{e^q}{(e^q - 1)^3} \mathrel{\dot{\longrightarrow}} \sum_{m=0}^{n-1} m .$$

However, from (2.57)

$$\frac{e^q}{(e^q - 1)^3} \mathrel{\dot{\longrightarrow}} \frac{n^{(2)}}{2\,!} = \frac{n(n-1)}{2\,!} ,$$

and so

$$\sum_{m=0}^{n-1} m = \frac{n(n-1)}{2!} ,$$

which, of course, is to be expected as the left side is the formula for the sum of an arithmetical progression. We shall now give a less trivial example.

EXAMPLE 2. Evaluate the series

$$\sum_{m=0}^{n-1} m^2 .$$

We have from (2.59)

$$\frac{e^q}{(e^q - 1)^3} (e^q + 1) \mathrel{\dot{\longrightarrow}} n^2 ,$$

and so, using the theorem on the transformation of a sum

$$\frac{e^q}{(e^q - 1)^4} (e^q + 1) = \frac{e^q}{(e^q - 1)^4} e^q + \frac{e^q}{(e^q - 1)^4} \mathrel{\dot{\longrightarrow}} \sum_{m=0}^{n-1} m^2 .$$

However, from (2.58),

$$\frac{e^q}{(e^q - 1)^4} \mathrel{\dot{\longrightarrow}} \frac{n^{(3)}}{3\,!} = \frac{n(n-1)\,(n-2)}{3\,!} ,$$

and from the original-translation theorem (see 2.39)

$$\frac{e^q}{(e^q - 1)^4} e^q \mathrel{\dot{\longrightarrow}} \frac{(n+1)^{(3)}}{3\,!} = \frac{(n+1)\, n(n-1)}{3\,!} ,$$

and so

$$\sum_{m=0}^{n-1} m^2 = \frac{n^{(3)}}{3\,!} + \frac{(n+1)^{(3)}}{3\,!} = \frac{n(n-1)\,(2n-1)}{3\,!} .$$

The last two theorems show that the *multiplier* $(e^q - 1)$ *plays in the discrete Laplace transformation the role of q or p in the usual Laplace* *transformation;* it sets up the relationship between the formal operational method in the theory of difference equations and the discrete Laplace transformation.

These properties, along with the original-translation theorem, form the basis of the method for solving difference equations.

THEOREM 6. MULTIPLICATION OF THE ORIGINAL BY n^k.

On differentiating the fundamental relationship

$$F^*(q) = \sum_{n=0}^{\infty} e^{-qn} f[n]$$

k times with respect to q, we obtain

$$\frac{d^k F^*(q)}{dq^k} = \sum_{n=0}^{\infty} e^{-qn} (-1)^k n^k f[n],$$

which gives

$$D\{n^k f[n]\} = (-1)^k \frac{d^k F^*(q)}{dq^k}. \tag{2.64}$$

Thus *multiplication of the original by* n^k *corresponds to the k-th order derivative of the image with respect to* $(-q)$.

EXAMPLE 1. Let $f[n] = n^2$. We obtain, on applying Theorem 6 to (2.59),

$$D\{n^3\} = -\frac{d}{dq}\left[\frac{e^q}{(e^q-1)^3}(e^q+1)\right] = \frac{e^q}{(e^q-1)^4}(e^{2q}+4e^q+1).$$

EXAMPLE 2. Let $f[n] = n^3$. Applying Theorem 6 to the preceding example gives

$$D\{n^4\} = -\frac{d}{dq}\left[\frac{e^q}{(e^q-1)^4}(e^{2q}+4e^q+1)\right] =$$

$$= \frac{e^q}{(e^q-1)^5}(e^{3q}+11e^{2q}+11e^q+1).$$

EXAMPLE 3. Let $f[n] = n^k$. Applying Theorem 6 to the image of the constant lattice function gives

$$D\{n^k\} = (-1)^k \frac{d^k}{dq^k}\left[\frac{e^q}{e^q-1}\right].$$

Using the formula for the derivative of a quotient, this expression can be written as

$$D\{n^k\} = \frac{e^q}{(e^q-1)^{k+1}} R_k(e^q), \tag{2.65}$$

where

$$
\begin{aligned}
R_0(e^q) &= 1\,,\\
R_1(e^q) &= 1\,,\\
R_2(e^q) &= e^q + 1\,,\\
R_3(e^q) &= e^{2q} + 4e^q + 1\,,\\
R_4(e^q) &= e^{3q} + 11e^{2q} + 11e^q + 1\,,\\
&\ldots\ldots\ldots\ldots\ldots\ldots
\end{aligned}
\tag{3M}
$$

In the general case $R_k(e^q)$ can be written in the form of a determinant:

$$
R_k(e^q) = k!\begin{vmatrix}
1 & 1-e^q & 0 & \ldots 0\\
\frac{1}{2!} & 1 & 1-e^q & \ldots 0\\
\frac{1}{3!} & \frac{1}{2!} & 1 & \ldots 0\\
\ldots & \ldots & \ldots & \ldots\\
\frac{1}{k!} & \frac{1}{(k-1)!} & \frac{1}{(k-2)!} & \ldots 1
\end{vmatrix}. \tag{2.66}
$$

THEOREM 7. MULTIPLICATION OF THE ORIGINAL BY $n^{(k)}$.

By differentiating the fundamental relationship

$$F^*(q) = \sum_{n=0}^{\infty} e^{-qn} f[n]$$

k times with respect to e^{-q}, we find

$$\frac{d^k F^*(q)}{de^{-qk}} = \sum_{n=0}^{\infty} n(n-1)\ldots(n-k+1)\, e^{-q(n-k)} f[n].$$

Using the notation for the factorial function $n^{(k)} = n(n-1)\ldots(n-k+1)$, and multiplying both sides of the equality by e^{-qk}, we obtain

$$e^{-qk}\frac{d^k F^*(q)}{de^{-qk}} = \sum_{n=0}^{\infty} e^{-qn} n^{(k)} f[n].$$

from which

$$D\{n^{(k)} f[n]\} = e^{-qk}\frac{d^k F^*(q)}{de^{-qk}}. \tag{2.67}$$

Thus *multiplication of the original by* $n^{(k)}$ *corresponds to the k-th derivative of the image with respect to* e^{-q} *multiplied by* e^{-qk}.

THEOREM 8. DIVISION OF THE ORIGINAL BY n^k.

Suppose the lattice function $f[n]$ satisfies the condition

$$f[0] = 0 \quad \text{and} \quad \lim_{n \to 0} \frac{f[n]}{n} = 0 .$$

In this case the fundamental relationship (2.19) can be written in the form

$$F^*(q) = \sum_{n=1}^{\infty} e^{-qn} f[n] .$$

Integrating both sides of this equality from q to ∞ gives

$$\int_q^{\infty} F^*(q)\, dq = \sum_{n=1}^{\infty} e^{-qn} \frac{f[n]}{n} . \tag{2.68}$$

Repeating the integration k times gives

$$\int_q^{\infty} \ldots \int_q^{\infty} F^*(q)\, (dq)^k = \sum_{n=1}^{\infty} e^{-qn} \frac{f[n]}{n^k} . \tag{2.69}$$

Consequently

$$D\left\{\frac{f[n]}{n^k}\right\} = \int_q^{\infty} \ldots \int_q^{\infty} F^*(q)\, (dq)^k . \tag{2.70}$$

Dividing the original by n^k corresponds to integrating the image k times from q to ∞.

EXAMPLE. Let $f[n] = 1[n-1]$, the constant delayed lattice function (Fig. 2.16); $f[0] = 0$. The image of $1[n-1]$ equals $\frac{1}{(e^q - 1)}$. From Theorem 8 we have

$$D\left\{\frac{1[n-1]}{n}\right\} = \int_q^{\infty} \frac{dq}{e^q - 1} = \ln \frac{e^q}{e^q - 1} . \tag{2.71}$$

The lattice function $\frac{1[n-1]}{n}$ is shown in Fig. 2.21.

If $\lim_{n \to 0} \frac{f[n]}{n} =$ cons. i. e. is not equal to zero, then by adding this constant to both parts of (2.68) we obtain

$$\int_q^{\infty} F^*(q)\, dq + \lim_{n \to 0} \frac{f[n]}{n} = \sum_{n=0}^{\infty} e^{-qn} \frac{f[n]}{n} .$$

THEOREM 9. DIFFERENTIATION WITH RESPECT TO A PARAMETER.

Let the original and the image contain a parameter λ which does not depend on n or q.

$$F^*(q, \lambda) \xrightarrow{\cdot} f[n, \lambda]$$

or, explicitly,

$$F^*(q, \lambda) = \sum_{n=0}^{\infty} e^{-qn} f[n, \lambda]. \tag{2.72}$$

We find on differentiating (2.72) with respect to λ

$$\frac{\partial F^*(q, \lambda)}{\partial \lambda} \xrightarrow{\cdot} \frac{\partial f[n, \lambda]}{\partial \lambda}, \tag{2.73}$$

i.e. **differentiation with respect to a parameter is commutative in the discrete Laplace transformation.**

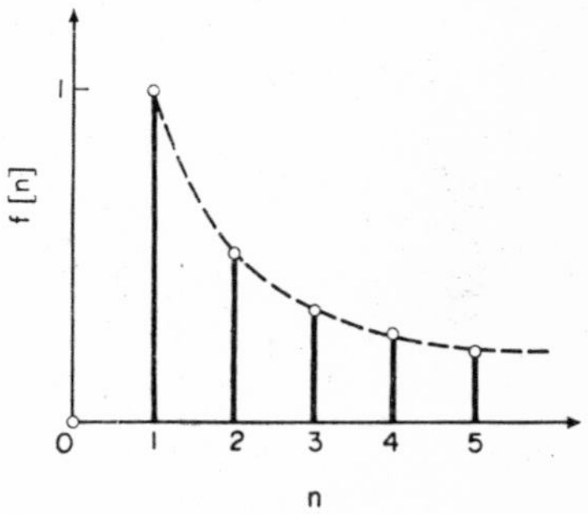

FIG. 2.21. The lattice function $\frac{1\,[n-1]}{n}$.

EXAMPLE.

$$D\{e^{an}\} = \frac{e^q}{e^q - e^a}.$$

Here $\lambda = a$, and so from Theorem 9 we have

$$D\left\{\frac{\partial e^{an}}{\partial a}\right\} = D\{ne^{an}\} = \frac{\partial}{\partial a}\left[\frac{e^q}{e^q - e^a}\right] = \\ = \frac{e^q\, e^a}{(e^q - e^a)^2}. \tag{2.74}$$

The image of the displaced lattice function corresponding to the derivative of a continuous function can be found using this theorem.

In fact, consider $f(\bar{t}) = f(n + \varepsilon) = f[n, \varepsilon]$. The derivative of $f(\bar{t})$ with respect to $\bar{t}$ equals

$$\frac{df(\bar{t})}{d\bar{t}} = \frac{df(n+\varepsilon)}{d(n+\varepsilon)} = \frac{df(n+\varepsilon)}{d\varepsilon} = \frac{df[n, \varepsilon]}{d\varepsilon}.$$

Using (2.73) with $\lambda = \varepsilon$, we obtain

$$\frac{\partial F^*(q, \varepsilon)}{\partial \varepsilon} \xrightarrow{\cdot} \left(\frac{df(\bar{t})}{d\bar{t}}\right)_{\bar{t}=n+\varepsilon},$$

i.e. *the derivative with respect to ε of the image of a displacement lattice function corresponds to the displaced lattice function of the derivative of $f(\bar{t})$.*

THEOREM 10. INTEGRATION WITH RESPECT TO A PARAMETER.

Integrating (2.72) with respect to the parameter and taking, on the right-hand side, the integral sign within the summation sign, we obtain

$$\int_{\lambda_0}^{\lambda} F^*(q, \lambda)\, \mathrm{d}\lambda = \sum_{n=0}^{\infty} \mathrm{e}^{-qn} \left[\int_{\lambda_0}^{\lambda} f[n, \lambda]\, \mathrm{d}\lambda \right],$$

from which

$$\int_{\lambda_0}^{\lambda} F^*(q, \lambda)\, \mathrm{d}\lambda \;\dot{\longrightarrow}\; \int_{\lambda_0}^{\lambda} f[n, \lambda]\, \mathrm{d}\lambda\,. \tag{2.75}$$

i.e. *integration with respect to a parameter is commutative in the discrete Laplace transformation.*

EXAMPLE.

$$D\,\{\mathrm{e}^{\alpha n}\} = \frac{\mathrm{e}^q}{\mathrm{e}^q - \mathrm{e}^\alpha}\,.$$

Here $\lambda = \alpha$, and from Theorem 10 we have

$$D\left\{\int_0^{\alpha} \mathrm{e}^{\alpha n}\, \mathrm{d}\alpha\right\} = D\left\{\frac{\mathrm{e}^{\alpha n} - 1}{n}\right\} = \int_0^{\alpha} \frac{\mathrm{e}^q\, \mathrm{d}\alpha}{\mathrm{e}^q - \mathrm{e}^\alpha}\,.$$

However

$$\int \frac{\mathrm{d}\alpha}{a - \mathrm{e}^\alpha} = \frac{1}{a}\,[\alpha - \ln(a - \mathrm{e}^\alpha)]\,,$$

and so

$$D\left\{\frac{\mathrm{e}^{\alpha n} - 1}{n}\right\} = \alpha - \ln\frac{\mathrm{e}^q - \mathrm{e}^\alpha}{\mathrm{e}^q - 1}\,. \tag{2.76}$$

We now use this theorem and the theorem on the image of a sum (Theorem 5) to find the image of the displaced lattice function of an integral, which is defined by

$$\varphi\,[n, \varepsilon] = \int_0^{n+\varepsilon} f(\bar{t})\, \mathrm{d}\bar{t}\,.$$

We write $\varphi\,[n, \varepsilon]$ in the form

$$\varphi\,[n, \varepsilon] = \sum_{m=0}^{n-1} \int_0^1 f\,[m, \varepsilon]\, \mathrm{d}\varepsilon + \int_0^{\varepsilon} f\,[n, \varepsilon]\, \mathrm{d}\varepsilon\,.$$

The first term on the right side of this expression gives the area under the curve from 0 to n, and the second the area from n to $n + \varepsilon$. We apply the discrete Laplace transformation to this expression:

$$\sum_{m=0}^{n-1} D\left\{\int_0^1 f\,[m, \varepsilon]\, \mathrm{d}\varepsilon\right\} + D\left\{\int_0^{\varepsilon} f\,[n, \varepsilon]\, \mathrm{d}\varepsilon\right\}.$$

However, from Theorem 10, this can be rewritten in the form

$$\int_0^1 D\left\{\sum_{m=0}^{n-1} f[m, \varepsilon]\right\} d\varepsilon + \int_0^\varepsilon D\{f[n, \varepsilon]\} d\varepsilon.$$

Remembering that

$$F^*(q, \varepsilon) \doteq f[n, \varepsilon],$$

we obtain using Theorem 5

$$\varphi[n, \varepsilon] \doteq \frac{1}{e^q - 1} \int_0^1 F^*(q, \varepsilon)\, d\varepsilon + \int_0^\varepsilon F^*(q, \varepsilon)\, d\varepsilon. \qquad (2.77)$$

THEOREM 11. PRODUCT OF IMAGES (CONVOLUTION THEOREM).

In applications this is one of the most important of the theorems. It enables the original of a product of images to be found if the originals of the factors of the product are known.

Let

$$F_1^*(q) = \sum_{m=0}^{\infty} e^{-qm} f_1[m]; \qquad F_2^*(q) = \sum_{n=0}^{\infty} e^{-qn} f_2[n].$$

Now form the product

$$F_1^*(q)\, F_2^*(q) = \sum_{m=0}^{\infty} e^{-qm} f_1[m] \sum_{n=0}^{\infty} e^{-qn} f_2[n].$$

On multiplying the series on the right side of the equality for $\operatorname{Re} q > \sigma_c$, where σ_c is the greater of the two abscissae of convergence, we obtain

$$F_1^*(q)\, F_2^*(q) = \sum_{n=0}^{\infty} e^{-qn} \left[\sum_{m=0}^{n} f_1[m] f_2[n-m]\right] =$$

$$= \sum_{n=0}^{\infty} e^{-qn} \left[\sum_{m=0}^{n} f_1[n-m] f_2[m]\right],$$

since for $n < m$ the lattice functions equal zero.

Thus, in the usual notation, we have

$$F_1^*(q)\, F_2^*(q) \doteq \sum_{m=0}^{n} f_1[m] f_2[n-m] = \sum_{m=0}^{n} f_1[n-m] f_2[m]. \qquad (2.78)$$

We now give an alternative proof of this theorem which is based on the original-translation theorem. Multiply

$$F_1^*(q) = \sum_{m=0}^{\infty} e^{-qm} f_1[m]$$

by $F_2^*(q)$ to obtain

$$F_1^*(q)\,F_2^*(q) = \sum_{m=0}^{\infty} \mathrm{e}^{-qm}\,F_2^*(q)\,f_1[m]\,.$$

However, from the original-translation theorem (Theorem 2)

$$\mathrm{e}^{-qm}\,F_2^*(q) \doteq \begin{cases} 0 & \text{when } n < m\,, \\ f_2[n-m] & \text{when } n \geqslant m\,, \end{cases}$$

and thus

$$F_1^*(q)\,F_2^*(q) \doteq \sum_{m=0}^{n} f_1[m]\,f_2[n-m]\,.$$

By replacing the variable $n - m$ by n_1 in the right side of this expression we arrive at the second form of the convolution theorem; the second form also follows directly as there is nothing to choose between $f_1[n]$ and $f_2[n]$ in the course of the proof.

The convolution theorem is often used to find the original of an image which can be split up into the product of simpler images.

Example 1. Find the original corresponding to

$$F^*(q) = \frac{\mathrm{e}^q}{(\mathrm{e}^q - \mathrm{e}^a)\,(\mathrm{e}^q - \mathrm{e}^{a_1})}\,.$$

This image is the product of the two images (2.45) and (2.29):

$$F_1^*(q) = \frac{1}{\mathrm{e}^q - \mathrm{e}^a} \doteq \mathrm{e}^{a(n-1)} \quad (n \geqslant 1) \quad \text{and} \quad F_2^*(q) = \frac{\mathrm{e}^q}{\mathrm{e}^q - \mathrm{e}^{a_1}} \doteq \mathrm{e}^{a_1 n}\,. \quad (n \geqslant 0)$$

We find using the convolution theorem

$$F^*(q) = F_1^*(q)\,F_2^*(q) \doteq \sum_{m=1}^{n} \mathrm{e}^{a(m-1)}\,\mathrm{e}^{a_1(n-m)} = \mathrm{e}^{a_1(n-1)} \sum_{m=1}^{n} \mathrm{e}^{(a-a_1)(m-1)}\,.$$

However

$$\sum_{m=1}^{n} \mathrm{e}^{(a-a_1)(m-1)} = \frac{1 - \mathrm{e}^{(a-a_1)n}}{1 - \mathrm{e}^{a-a_1}} = \frac{\mathrm{e}^{a_1} - \mathrm{e}^{an}\,\mathrm{e}^{-a_1(n-1)}}{\mathrm{e}^{a_1} - \mathrm{e}^a}\,,$$

and so finally

$$F^*(q) = \frac{\mathrm{e}^q}{(\mathrm{e}^q - \mathrm{e}^a)\,(\mathrm{e}^q - \mathrm{e}^{a_1})} \doteq \frac{1}{\mathrm{e}^{a_1} - \mathrm{e}^a}\,(\mathrm{e}^{a_1 n} - \mathrm{e}^{an})\,. \tag{2.79}$$

The lattice function corresponding to this image is shown in Fig. 2.22 for $a_1 = -0{\cdot}5$, $a = -1$.

Example 2. Find the original of

$$F^*(q) = \frac{\mathrm{e}^q}{(\mathrm{e}^q - \mathrm{e}^a)\,(\mathrm{e}^q - \mathrm{e}^{a_1})^2}\,.$$

Writing $F^*(q)$ as the product of the two images

$$F_1^*(q) = \frac{1}{e^q - e^{\alpha_1}} \doteq\!\!\rightarrow e^{\alpha_1(n-1)}$$

and

$$F_2^*(q) = \frac{e^q}{(e^q - e^{\alpha})(e^q - e^{\alpha_1})} \doteq\!\!\rightarrow \frac{1}{e^{\alpha_1} - e^{\alpha}}(e^{\alpha_1 n} - e^{\alpha n}),$$

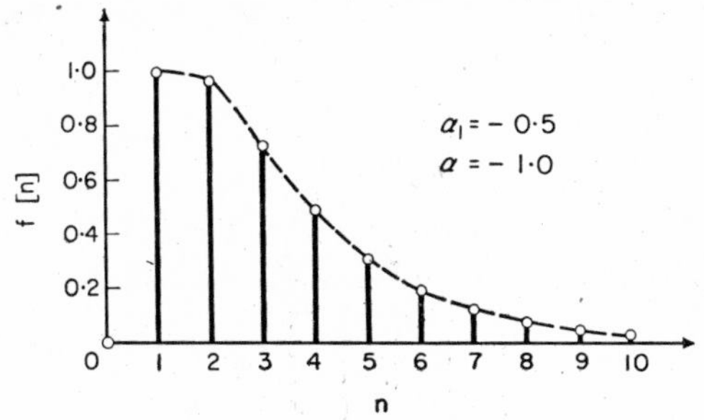

FIG. 2.22. The lattice function $(e^{\alpha_1} - e^{\alpha})^{-1} (e^{\alpha_1 n} - e^{\alpha n})$ for $\alpha_1 = -0{\cdot}5$ and $\alpha = -1$.

we find, as above, that

$$F^*(q) = F_1^*(q)\,F_2^*(q) \doteq\!\!\rightarrow \sum_{m=1}^{n} e^{\alpha_1(m-1)}\,\frac{e^{\alpha_1(n-m)} - e^{\alpha(n-m)}}{e^{\alpha_1} - e^{\alpha}} =$$

$$= \frac{1}{e^{\alpha_1} - e^{\alpha}}\left\{\sum_{m=1}^{n} e^{\alpha_1(n-1)} - e^{\alpha n}\sum_{m=1}^{n} e^{-\alpha m + \alpha_1(m-1)}\right\}.$$

Carrying out the summation in the previous manner gives

$$F^*(q) = \frac{e^q}{(e^q - e^{\alpha})(e^q - e^{\alpha_1})^2} \doteq\!\!\rightarrow \frac{n e^{\alpha_1(n-1)}}{e^{\alpha_1} - e^{\alpha}} - \frac{e^{\alpha_1 n} - e^{\alpha n}}{(e^{\alpha_1} - e^{\alpha})^2}. \qquad (2.80)$$

The corresponding lattice function for $\alpha_1 = 0{\cdot}5$ and $\alpha = -1$ is shown in Fig. 2.23.

THEOREM 12. IMAGE OF A LATTICE FUNCTION WITH A RELATIVE PERIOD $\lambda \neq 1$

The lattice functions $f[n]$ considered above had a relative repetition period of unity (Fig. 2.24*a*). In a number of cases we require to consider lattice functions $f_\lambda[n] = f[\lambda n]$, which have a relative repetition period $\lambda \neq 1$. Such lattice functions are shown Fig. 2.24 *b* and *c* for $\lambda > 1$, and $\lambda < 1$ respectively. To find the image of $f[\lambda n]$, we replace in the image of $f[n]$ (2.19)

$$D\{f[n]\} = \sum_{n=0}^{\infty} e^{-qn} f[n] = F^*(q)$$

n by λn. We then obtain

$$D\{f[\lambda n]\} = \sum_{n=0}^{\infty} e^{-q\lambda n} f[\lambda n] = F_\lambda^*(\lambda q). \tag{2.81}$$

Here $q = pT$, where T is the absolute (i.e. real-time) repetition period of the lattice function $f[n]$. The absolute repetition period of $f[\lambda n]$ equals λT.

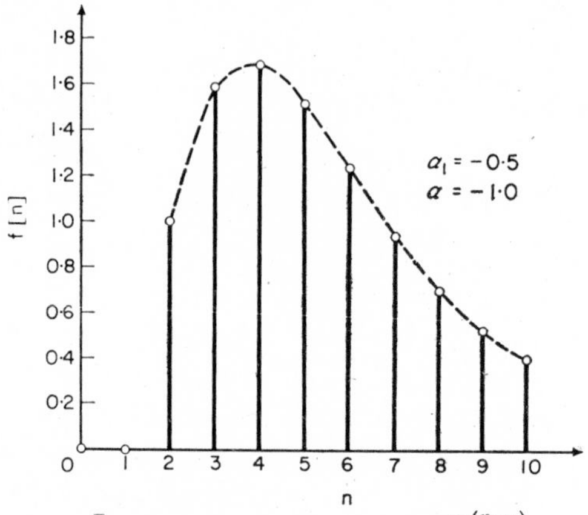

FIG. 2.23. The lattice function $\dfrac{n e^{a_1(n-1)}}{e^{a_1} - e^{a}} - \dfrac{e^{a_1 n} - e^{an}}{(e^{a_1} - e^{a})^2}$ for $a_1 = -0{\cdot}5$ and $a = -1$.

Thus, *the image of the lattice function $f[\lambda n]$ is obtained by replacing, in the image of $f[n]$, the argument q by λq and the parameter T by λT.*

EXAMPLE 1. Consider the lattice function

$$f[n] = e^{a_1 T n}.$$

The image of this function equals

$$F^*(q) = \frac{e^q}{e^q - e^{a_1 T}}.$$

From Theorem 12 the image of the lattice function

$$f[\lambda n] = e^{a_1 T \lambda n}$$

is given by

$$F_\lambda^*(\lambda q) = \frac{e^{\lambda q}}{e^{\lambda q} - e^{a_1 T \lambda}}.$$

As is illustrated in Fig. 2.24 the lattice functions $f_\lambda[n] = f[\lambda n]$ for different values of λ correspond to different values of the same continuous function.

EXAMPLE 2. Consider the function $f[n] = a_1 Tn$. Its image equals

$$F^*(q) = a_1 T \frac{e^q}{(e^q - 1)^2}.$$

From Theorem 12 the image of the lattice function

$$f[\lambda n] = a_1 T \lambda n$$

is given by

$$F^*_\lambda(\lambda q) = a_1 T \lambda \frac{e^{\lambda q}}{(e^{\lambda q} - 1)^2}.$$

If λ is a whole number, the image $F^*_\lambda(\lambda q)$ can be expressed in terms of the image $F^*(q)$. To see this, we replace q by $q + j\,2\pi\nu/\lambda$ in the expression defining the discrete Laplace transformation. Then

$$F^*\left(q + j\frac{2\pi\nu}{\lambda}\right) = \sum_{n=0}^{\infty} f[n]\, e^{-qn - j\frac{2\pi\nu}{\lambda}n}.$$

Adding these equalities for $\nu = 0, 1, 2, \ldots, (\lambda - 1)$, we obtain

$$\sum_{\nu=0}^{\lambda-1} F^*\left(q + j\frac{2\pi\nu}{\lambda}\right) = $$

$$= \sum_{n=0}^{\infty}\left[\sum_{\nu=0}^{\lambda-1} e^{-j\frac{2\pi\nu}{\lambda}}\right] f[n]\, e^{-qn}.$$

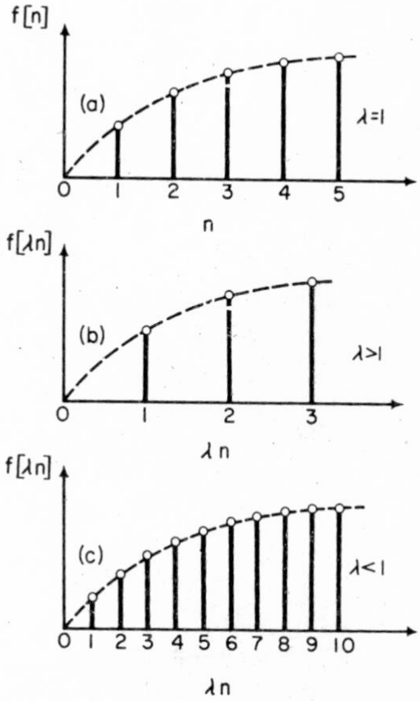

FIG. 2.24. Change of argument of a lattice function; (a) $\lambda = 1$, (b) $\lambda > 1$, and (c) $\lambda < 1$.

However, as is easily shown,

$$\sum_{\nu=0}^{\lambda-1} e^{-j\frac{2\pi\nu}{\lambda}n} = \frac{1 - e^{-j2\pi n}}{1 - e^{-\frac{j2\pi n}{\lambda}}} = \begin{cases} \lambda & \text{for } n = \lambda r, \\ 0 & \text{for } n \neq \lambda r, \end{cases}$$

where r is a whole number. Consequently, on replacing r by n,

$$\sum_{\nu=0}^{\lambda-1} F^*\left(q + j\frac{2\pi\nu}{\lambda}\right) = \lambda \sum_{n=1}^{\infty} f[\lambda n]\, e^{-q\lambda n} = \lambda F^*_\lambda(\lambda q),$$

from which we obtain

$$F^*_\lambda(\lambda q) = \frac{1}{\lambda}\sum_{\nu=0}^{\lambda-1} F^*\left(q + j\frac{2\pi\nu}{\lambda}\right). \tag{2.82}$$

This relationship gives the image of a more 'rare' lattice function with a relative period λ in terms of the image of the lattice function with relative period unity.

EXAMPLE. Find $D\{e^{-a2n}\}$. Noting that

$$D\{e^{-an}\} = \frac{e^q}{e^q - e^{-a}},$$

we obtain from formula (2.82) for $\lambda = 2$

$$D\{e^{-a2n}\} = \frac{1}{2}\left[\frac{e^q}{e^q - e^{-a}} + \frac{e^{q+j\pi}}{e^{q+j\pi} - e^{-a}}\right] = \frac{e^{2q}}{e^{2q} - e^{-2a}},$$

which agrees with the previous result for $a_1 T = a$.

The theorems given above are concerned with the correspondence between operations in the original and image domains. We shall now give a few theorems in which, for certain limiting values of the variables, the equality of original and image is established.

THEOREM 13. SUM OF THE DISCRETA, OR ORDINATES, OF A LATTICE FUNCTION.

Suppose the abscissa of convergence of $f[n]$ is negative $\sigma_c < 0$. Then, putting $q = 0$ in the fundamental relationship (2.19), we have

$$F^*(0) = \lim_{q \to 0} F^*(q) = \sum_{n=0}^{\infty} f[n]. \tag{2.83}$$

The right side of equation (2.83) is the sum of the ordinates of the lattice function. Thus, *the sum of the ordinates or discreta of a lattice function equals the value of the image at* $q = 0$.

EXAMPLE. Let $f[n] = e^{-\beta n}$. Then

$$F^*(q) = \frac{e^q}{e^q - e^{-\beta}}, \qquad \sigma_c < 0.$$

From Theorem 13 we have

$$\sum_{n=0}^{\infty} e^{-\beta n} = F^*(0) = \frac{1}{1 - e^{-\beta}},$$

which, of course, is obviously correct.

THEOREM 14. THE FINAL VALUE OF A LATTICE FUNCTION.

We apply the previous theorem to the first difference $\Delta f[n]$. As the image of this difference equals

$$D\{\Delta f[n]\} = (e^q - 1)\, F^*(q) - e^q f(0),$$

where

$$F^*(q) \stackrel{\cdot}{\longrightarrow} f[n].$$

we have from Theorem 13

$$\sum_{n=0}^{\infty} \Delta f[n] = \lim_{q\to 0} (\mathrm{e}^q - 1)\, F^*(q) - f(0).$$

However

$$\sum_{n=0}^{\infty} \Delta f[n] = \sum_{n=0}^{\infty} (f[n+1] - f[n]) = \lim_{n\to\infty} f[n] - f[0],$$

and so

$$\lim_{n\to\infty} f[n] = \lim_{q\to\infty} (\mathrm{e}^q - 1)\, F^*(q). \qquad (2.84)$$

EXAMPLE 1.

$$\frac{\mathrm{e}^q}{\mathrm{e}^q - 1} \stackrel{\cdot}{\longrightarrow} 1\,[n]; \qquad \lim_{n\to\infty} 1\,[n] = \lim_{q\to 0} (\mathrm{e}^q - 1) \frac{\mathrm{e}^q}{\mathrm{e}^q - 1} = 1.$$

EXAMPLE 2.

$$\frac{\mathrm{e}^q}{\mathrm{e}^q - \mathrm{e}^{-a}} \stackrel{\cdot}{\longrightarrow} \mathrm{e}^{-an}; \qquad \lim_{n\to\infty} \mathrm{e}^{-an} = \lim_{q\to 0} (\mathrm{e}^q - 1) \frac{\mathrm{e}^q}{\mathrm{e}^q - \mathrm{e}^{-a}} = 0.$$

THEOREM 15. THE INITIAL VALUE OF A LATTICE FUNCTION.

Consider the difference

$$\Delta f[n-1] = f[n] - f[n-1].$$

Its image, using the original-translation theorem (Theorem 2), equals

$$D\{\Delta f[n-1]\} = \mathrm{e}^{-q}\left[(\mathrm{e}^q - 1)\, F^*(q) - \mathrm{e}^q f[0]\right] =$$

$$= (1 - \mathrm{e}^{-q})\, F^*(q) - f[0]. \qquad (2.85)$$

Let q tend to infinity. Then, remembering that

$$\lim_{q\to\infty} \{D(\Delta f[n-1]\} = \lim_{q\to\infty} \sum_{n=0}^{\infty} \mathrm{e}^{-qn} \Delta f[n-1] = 0,$$

we obtain from (2.85)

$$f[0] = \lim_{n\to 0} f[n] = \lim_{q\to\infty} (1 - \mathrm{e}^{-q})\, F^*(q) = \lim_{q\to\infty} F^*(q). \qquad (2.86)$$

EXAMPLE.

$$\frac{\mathrm{e}^q}{\mathrm{e}^q - \mathrm{e}^{-a}} \stackrel{\cdot}{\longrightarrow} \mathrm{e}^{-an}; \qquad \lim_{n\to 0} \mathrm{e}^{-an} = \lim_{q\to\infty} \frac{\mathrm{e}^q}{\mathrm{e}^q - \mathrm{e}^{-a}} = 1.$$

The above rules and theorems are basic in the theory of the discrete Laplace transformation. Not only do they permit the number of correspondences between originals and images to be increased, but they also enable us to study the properties of the originals by using their images which, in many problems, can be obtained without difficulty.

The correspondence between operations in the original and image domains is given in Table A1.* Table A2 gives originals and the corresponding images; some of these have been deduced in the present section as examples illustrating the theorems.

2.4. Solution of the simplest difference equations

Difference equations can be solved using the discrete Laplace transformation with the same convenience as when applying the usual Laplace transformation to the solution of differential equations.

Difference equations are solved using the following procedure. When the discrete Laplace transformation is applied to a linear difference equation with constant coefficients we obtain, using the theorems on linearity, original-translation and image of a difference, an algebraic equation for the image of the required lattice function. This equation contains all the boundary conditions and can easily be solved for the image.

The next stage consists in finding the original of the image obtained in this way. In the simplest cases this can be done using already known relationships between images and originals. In other cases, when this cannot be done, a general method is used to find the original corresponding to the image; this method is presented in subsequent sections.

We give a simple example to illustrate the method of solving difference equations by means of the discrete Laplace transformation. Let

$$\Delta y[n] = n \tag{2.87}$$

and for

$$n = 0, \quad y[0] = y_0.$$

Apply the discrete Laplace transformation to both sides of the equation:

$$D\{\Delta y[n]\} = D\{n\}.$$

* Tables denoted by the letter A will be found in the Appendix at the end of Volume II.

Write

$$D\{y[n]\} = Y^*(q).$$

Then, using the theorem for the image of a first difference, we have

$$D\{\Delta y[n]\} = (e^q - 1)Y^*(q) - e^q y[0].$$

Using the relationship (2.56) and remembering that $y[0] = y_0$, we can write this equation in the form

$$(e^q - 1)Y^*(q) - e^q y_0 = \frac{e^q}{(e^q - 1)^2}.$$

Solving the latter for $Y^*(q)$ gives

$$Y^*(q) = \frac{e^q}{(e^q - 1)^3} + \frac{e^q}{e^q - 1} y_0. \tag{2.88}$$

Using relationships (2.57) and (2.58) we obtain on transforming from the image to the original

$$y[n] = \binom{n}{2} + y_0 = \frac{n(n-1)}{2} + y_0. \tag{2.89}$$

It is easily seen from a simple check that this solution satisfies equation (2.87) and the initial conditions.

Consider now the equation

$$\Delta^{k+1} y[n] = 0 \tag{2.90}$$

with the initial conditions $\Delta^\nu y[0] = a_\nu (\nu = 0, 1, \ldots, k)$. Applying a discrete Laplace transformation to this equation, and remembering from (2.54) that

$$D\{\Delta^{k+1} y[n]\} = (e^q - 1)^{k+1} Y^*(q) - e^q \sum_{\nu=0}^{k} (e^q - 1)^{k-\nu} \Delta^\nu y[0],$$

we obtain

$$(e^q - 1)^{k+1} Y^*(q) = e^q \sum_{\nu=0}^{k} (e^q - 1)^{k-\nu} \Delta^\nu y[0]$$

or

$$Y^*(q) = \sum_{\nu=0}^{k} \frac{e^q}{(e^q - 1)^{\nu+1}} \Delta^\nu y[0]. \tag{2.91}$$

However, from (2.58),

$$\frac{e^q}{(e^q - 1)^{\nu+1}} \overset{\bullet}{\longrightarrow} \binom{n}{\nu} = \frac{n^{(\nu)}}{\nu!},$$

and so, on transforming from image to original, we have

$$y[n] = \sum_{\nu=0}^{k} \frac{n^{(\nu)}}{\nu!} \Delta^{\nu} y[0]. \tag{2.92}$$

This expression is the well-known Newton interpolation formula for integral values of the argument.+ The differences $\Delta^{\nu} y[0]$ can be expressed, using formula (2.4), in terms of the values of the function $y[\nu] = y_{\nu}$.

We note that the above formula can be considered as defining the values of the function in terms of its differences, i.e. as the inverse of (2.4) for $n = 0$.

We now go on to consider certain technical problems which give rise to difference equations.

The ladder network. We obtained in § 2.1 difference equations governing the currents and voltages in a ladder network consisting of N identical meshes formed from T-sections (Fig. 2.10):

$$\left.\begin{aligned} (\mathbf{z}_1 + \mathbf{z}_2)\, i[n] - \mathbf{z}_2\, i[n+1] - u[n] = 0\,, \\ \mathbf{z}_2\, i[n] - (\mathbf{z}_1 + \mathbf{z}_2)\, i[n+1] - u[n+1] = 0\,. \end{aligned}\right\} \tag{2.93}$$

We denote the images of the lattice functions $i[n]$ and $u[n]$ by $I^*(q)$ and $U^*(q)$; using the original-translation theorem (Theorem 2) we have

$$\left.\begin{aligned} D\{i[n+1]\} = e^q I^*(q) - e^q i[0]\,, \\ D\{u[n+1]\} = e^q U^*(q) - e^q u[0]\,, \end{aligned}\right\} \tag{2.94}$$

where $i[0]$ and $u[0]$ are the boundary values, i.e. the values of $i[n]$ and $u[n]$ for $n = 0$.

We obtain on applying the discrete Laplace transformation to (2.93)

$$(\mathbf{z}_1 + \mathbf{z}_2)\, I^*(q) - \mathbf{z}_2\, e^q \left[I^*(q) - i[0]\right] - U^*(q) = 0\,,$$

$$\mathbf{z}_2\, I^*(q) - (\mathbf{z}_1 + \mathbf{z}_2)\, e^q \left[I^*(q) - i[0]\right] - e^q \left[U^*(q) - u[0]\right] = 0$$

or

$$[\mathbf{z}_1 + \mathbf{z}_2 - \mathbf{z}_2 e^q]\, I^*(q) - U^*(q) = -\,\mathbf{z}_2 e^q i[0]\,,$$

$$[\mathbf{z}_2 - (\mathbf{z}_1 + \mathbf{z}_2) e^q]\, I^*(q) - e^q U^*(q) = -\,(\mathbf{z}_1 + \mathbf{z}_2) e^q i[0] - e^q u[0]\,.$$

+ See, for example, Sh. E. Mikeladze (2; 1953).

On solving this linear system of algebraic equations for the images, we find:

$$I^*(q) = \frac{e^q[e^q - (1 + \mathbf{z}_1/\mathbf{z}_2)]\, i[0] - e^q(u[0]/\mathbf{z}_2)}{e^{2q} - 2(1 + \mathbf{z}_1/\mathbf{z}_2)\, e^q + 1}, \tag{2.95}$$

$$U^*(q) = \frac{e^q[e^q - (1 + \mathbf{z}_1/\mathbf{z}_2)]\, u[0] - \mathbf{z}_2 e^q[(1 + \mathbf{z}_1/\mathbf{z}_2)^2 - 1]\, i[0]}{e^{2q} - 2(1 + \mathbf{z}_1/\mathbf{z}_2)\, e^q + 1}. \tag{2.96}$$

Writing

$$1 + \frac{\mathbf{z}_1}{\mathbf{z}_2} = \cosh\chi \tag{2.97}$$

we have

$$\left(1 + \frac{\mathbf{z}_1}{\mathbf{z}_2}\right)^2 - 1 = \frac{\mathbf{z}_1}{\mathbf{z}_2}\left(2 + \frac{\mathbf{z}_1}{\mathbf{z}_2}\right) = \cosh^2\chi - 1 = \sinh^2\chi, \tag{2.98}$$

and the expressions for the images can be rewritten in the form

$$I^*(q) = \frac{e^q(e^q - \cosh\chi)\, i[0] - e^q(u[0]/\mathbf{z}_2)}{e^{2q} - 2e^q\cosh\chi + 1}, \tag{2.99}$$

$$U^*(q) = \frac{e^q(e^q - \cosh\chi)\, u[0] - e^q\sinh^2\chi\, \mathbf{z}_2\, i[0]}{e^{2q} - 2e^q\cosh\chi + 1}. \tag{2.100}$$

Using (2.33) and (2.34), we obtain on transforming from the images to the originals

$$i[n] = i[0]\cosh\chi n - \frac{u[0]}{\mathbf{z}_2\sinh\chi}\sinh\chi n,$$

$$u[n] = u[0]\cosh\chi n - i[0]\,\mathbf{z}_2\sinh\chi\sinh\chi n,$$

or

$$i[n] = i[0]\cosh\chi n - u[0]\,\mathbf{Y}\sinh n, \tag{2.101}$$

$$u[n] = u[0]\cosh\chi n - i[0]\,\mathbf{Z}\sinh\chi xn, \tag{2.102}$$

where we have written

$$\mathbf{Z} = \frac{1}{\mathbf{Y}} = \mathbf{z}_2\sinh\chi = \mathbf{z}_2\sqrt{\left[\frac{\mathbf{z}_1}{\mathbf{z}_2}\left(2 + \frac{\mathbf{z}_1}{\mathbf{z}_2}\right)\right]}\,. \tag{2.103}$$

Z and **Y** are called the iterative impedance and the iterative admittance, respectively, of the ladder network.

The solutions (2.101), (2.102) contain the boundary conditions $i[0]$, $u[0]$, the values of which depend on the conditions at the beginning and end of the ladder network.

We now consider a particular case of the general solution (2.101), (2.102). Suppose the ladder network is driven by a sinusoidal voltage generator, the amplitude of the voltage being $u_g = u[0]$, and suppose the last mesh (the N-th) is closed by a short-circuit (short-circuit operation). Thus $u[N] = 0$.

Using this condition and putting $n = N$ in (2.102), we obtain

$$0 = u_g \cosh \chi N - i[0] \mathbf{Z} \sinh \chi N ,$$

therefore
$$i[0] = \frac{u_g \cosh \chi N}{\mathbf{Z} \sinh \chi N} = u[0] \mathbf{Y} \coth \chi N. \tag{2.104}$$

We find, on substituting this value for $i[0]$ in (2.101) and (2.102),

$$i[n] = u_g \mathbf{Y} (\coth \chi N \cosh \chi n - \sinh \chi n) = u_g \mathbf{Y} \frac{\cosh \chi (N - n)}{\sinh \chi N} \tag{2.105}$$

and

$$u[n] = u_g (\cosh \chi n - \coth \chi N \sinh \chi n) = u_g \frac{\sinh \chi (N - n)}{\sinh \chi N} . \tag{2.106}$$

If the N-th mesh is open-circuited (no-load operation), we have for $n = N$

$$i[N] = 0$$

and from (2.101) we obtain

$$i[0] = u_g \mathbf{Y} \frac{\sinh \chi N}{\cosh \chi N} = u_g \mathbf{Y} \tanh \chi N.$$

Substituting this value of $i[0]$ in (2.101) and (2.102), we obtain

$$i[n] = u_g \mathbf{Y} (\tanh \chi N \cosh \chi n - \sinh \chi n) = u_g \mathbf{Y} \frac{\sinh \chi (N - n)}{\cosh \chi N} , \tag{2.107}$$

$$u[n] = u_g (\cosh \chi n - \tanh \chi N \sinh \chi n) = u_g \frac{\cosh \chi (N - n)}{\cosh \chi N} . \tag{2.108}$$

These expressions give the currents and voltages in any mesh $n \leqslant N$. The currents and voltages can be expressed explicitly in terms of the mesh parameters. This will be done below in a more complex example.

Voltage distribution in a chain of high-voltage insulators. A chain of high-voltage insulators consists of insulators attached to each other by metallic rods. The first insulator is attached by a rod to the mast, which is earthed. The final insulator is connected to the high-voltage a. c. (of angular frequency ω) line. We calculate the voltage distribution along the chain.+

+ See also G. Karman, M. Biot. (2; 1948).

The equivalent circuit of the chain, neglecting insulator leakage, is shown in Fig. 2.25. Here C_1 denotes the capacitance between neighbouring rods, and C_2 the capacitance to earth. This equivalent circuit is a particular case of the general ladder network considered above and the formulae obtained there are applicable. However, we shall examine this case on its own merits as this gives the required results more quickly. We number the meshes starting from the mast.

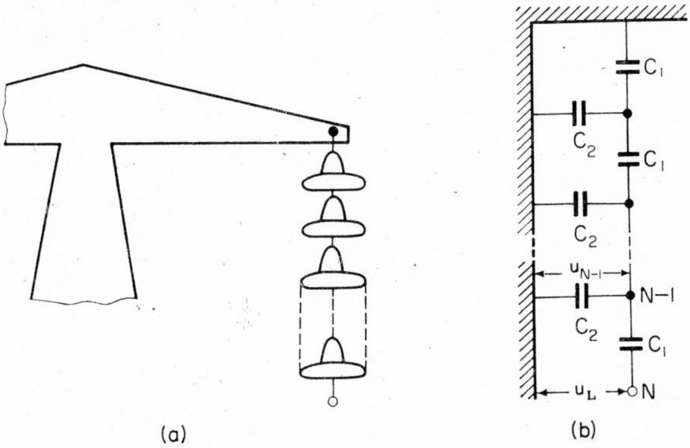

FIG. 2.25. A chain of insulators (*a*) and its equivalent circuit (*b*).

Kirchhoff's nodal current equation gives, for the $(n+1)$ th node on writing voltages in complex form,

$$j\,\omega\,C_1\,(u\,[n+2]-u\,[n+1])=$$
$$=j\,\omega\,C_1\,(u\,[n+1]-u\,[n]+j\,\omega\,C_2\,u\,[n+1]\,,$$

or, dividing by $j\,\omega\,C_1$

$$u\,[n+2]-2\left(1+\frac{C_2}{2C_1}\right)u\,[n+1]+u\,[n]=0\,, \qquad (2.109)$$

where $u[n]$ is the required lattice function.

Now consider the boundary conditions. At the beginning of the chain (at the mast) we have $u[0]=0$. At the end of the chain (on the line) $n=N$ and we have $u[N]=u_L$, where u_L is the line voltage with respect to earth. Let $U^*(q)$ denote the image of $u[n]$. Then, using the original-translation theorem, we have

$$\left.\begin{aligned} D\{u\,[n+1]\}&=\mathrm{e}^q\,U^*\,(q)-\mathrm{e}^q\,u\,[0],\\ D\{u\,[n+2]\}&=\mathrm{e}^{2q}\,U^*\,(q)-\mathrm{e}^{2q}\,u\,[0]-\mathrm{e}^q\,u\,[1]\,.\end{aligned}\right\} \qquad (2.110)$$

Applying the discrete Laplace transformation to (2.109) and using the boundary condition $u[0] = 0$, we obtain

$$\left[e^{2q} - 2\left(1 + \frac{C_2}{2C_1}\right) e^q + 1\right] U^*(q) = e^q u[1],$$

from which

$$U^*(q) = \frac{e^q}{e^{2q} - 2(1 + C_2/2C_1) e^q + 1} u[1]. \tag{2.111}$$

Introducing the notation

$$\left.\begin{aligned} \cosh \chi &= 1 + \frac{C_2}{2C_1}, \\ \sinh \chi &= \sqrt{(\cosh^2 \chi - 1)} = \sqrt{\left[\frac{C_2}{C_1}\left(1 + \frac{C_2}{4C_1}\right)\right]}. \end{aligned}\right\} \tag{2.112}$$

we can rewrite (2.111) as

$$U^*(q) = \frac{e^q \sinh \chi}{e^{2q} - 2e^q \cosh \chi + 1} \cdot \frac{u[1]}{\sinh \chi}.$$

Transforming from image to original using (2.33), we obtain

$$u[n] = u[1] \frac{\sinh \chi n}{\sinh \chi}. \tag{2.113}$$

It only remains to express $u[1]$ in terms of the known boundary condition $u[N] = u_L$. For $n = N$ we obtain from (2.113)

$$u[1] = u_L \frac{\sinh \chi}{\sinh \chi N}.$$

Substituting this value into (2.113) gives finally

$$u[n] = u_L \frac{\sinh \chi n}{\sinh \chi N}. \tag{2.114}$$

If $C_2/2C_1$ is small then χ is small, and so $\sinh \chi N \approx \chi N$, $\sinh \chi n \approx \chi n$. In this case $u[n]$ is given approximately by

$$u[n] \approx u_L \frac{n}{N}, \tag{2.115}$$

i.e. the voltage on the insulators varies linearly; the voltage drop across each insulator is the same. If $C_2/2C_1$ is not small, the voltage drop across insulators near the line is considerably greater than across those further away. For a given χ there will be a certain value of N above which the addition of insulators will have practically no effect on the voltage drop across the insulators near the line.

The above problem illustrates that in some cases a good choice of origin considerably reduces the labour necessary to get the final solution.

The gain of an N-stage amplifier. A circuit diagram of an N-stage amplifier is shown in Fig. 2.26*a*. A sinusoidal voltage of amplitude u_{gen} is fed to the input of the amplifier from a generator of internal impedance $\mathbf{z}_{gen}$. The anode load $\mathbf{z}_a$ of each stage is the same and takes the form of a two-terminal network, a tuned circuit, for example.

The impedance between the grid and anode of each valve is denoted by $\mathbf{z}_1$. These impedances (not shown on the circuit diagram) characterise the effect of the anode circuit on the grid circuit. As is well known the gain of an N-stage amplifier is defined as the ratio of the amplifier output voltage to the input voltage or generator e.m.f. If the anode circuit has no effect on the grid circuit, i.e. $\mathbf{z}_1 = \infty$,

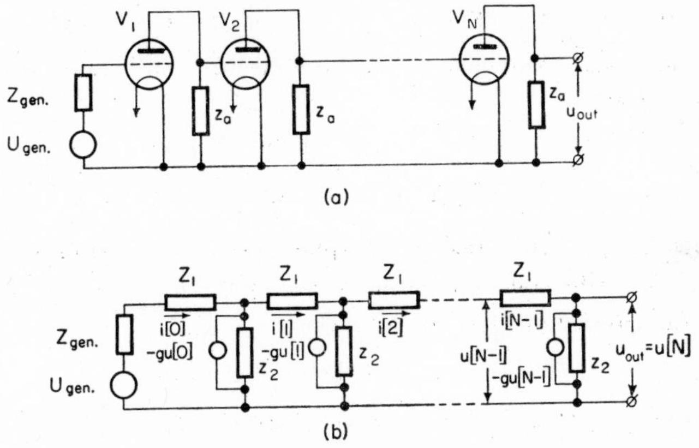

FIG. 2.26. An N-stage amplifier (a) and its equivalent circuit (b).

the gain of the N-stage amplifier equals the gain of a single stage raised to the power N, as the stages are identical. If $\mathbf{z}_1 \neq \infty$ the calculation of the gain is difficult, especially for a large number of stages, if carried out by the usual method of solving the system of linear equations corresponding to the equivalent N-mesh ladder network. Considerable simplification results if difference equations are used.+

We replace the valves by current generators of internal conductance $1/r_a$, where r_a is the valve internal impedance. The equivalent circuit of the N-stage amplifier then takes the form shown in Fig. 2.26*b*, where g is the valve mutual conductance and

$$\mathbf{z}_2 = \frac{r_a \mathbf{z}_a}{r_a + \mathbf{z}_a}$$

+ See also Faust, Beak (2; 1946); Stone (2; 1947(2)).

is the parallel combination of the load and internal impedance of a valve.

The equivalent circuit (Fig. 2.26b) is a ladder network, differing however, from that considered previously by having equivalent current generators $gu[n]$. By writing down the voltage equation for the n-th mesh and the current equation for the n-th node, we easily obtain

$$u[n] = \mathbf{z}_1 i[n] + u[n+1],$$

$$i[n] = i[n+1] + \frac{u[n+1]}{\mathbf{z}_2} + gu[n],$$

or

$$\left.\begin{aligned} \mathbf{z}_1 i[n] + u[n+1] - u[n] = 0, \\ \mathbf{z}_2 i[n+1] - \mathbf{z}_2 i[n] + u[n+1] + g\mathbf{z}_2 u[n] = 0. \end{aligned}\right\} \quad (2.116)$$

It is easily seen from the equivalent circuit that the boundary conditions satisfy

$$n = 0: \quad u_g = u[0] + \mathbf{z}_2 i[0], \quad (2.117)$$

$$n = N: \quad i[N] = 0. \quad (2.118)$$

We now apply the discrete Laplace transformation to the above system of difference equations, just as before, and we obtain the following equations for the images

$$\left.\begin{aligned} \mathbf{z}_1 I^*(q) + (\mathrm{e}^q - 1) U^*(q) = \mathrm{e}^q u[0], \\ \mathbf{z}_2(\mathrm{e}^q - 1) I^*(q) + (\mathrm{e}^q + g\mathbf{z}_2) U^*(q) = \mathbf{z}_2 \mathrm{e}^q i[0] + \mathrm{e}^q u[0], \end{aligned}\right\} \quad (2.119)$$

which can be solved to give

$$I^*(q) = \frac{(\mathrm{e}^q - 1)\,\mathrm{e}^q i[0] - [(1 + g\mathbf{z}_2)/\mathbf{z}_2]\,\mathrm{e}^q u[0]}{\mathrm{e}^{2q} - 2(1 + \mathbf{z}_1/2\mathbf{z}_2)\,\mathrm{e}^q + 1 - g\mathbf{z}_1}, \quad (2.120)$$

$$U^*(q) = \frac{[\mathrm{e}^q - (1 + \mathbf{z}_1/\mathbf{z}_2)]\,\mathrm{e}^q u[0] - \mathbf{z}_1 \mathrm{e}^q i[0]}{\mathrm{e}^{q2} - 2(1 + \mathbf{z}_1/2\mathbf{z}_2)\,\mathrm{e}^q + 1 - g\mathbf{z}_1}. \quad (2.121)$$

We put

$$A = \sqrt{(1 - g\mathbf{z}_1)}; \quad \cosh\chi = \frac{1}{A}\left(1 + \frac{\mathbf{z}_1}{2\mathbf{z}_2}\right),$$

$$\sinh\chi = \frac{1}{A}\sqrt{\left[\left(1 + \frac{\mathbf{z}_1}{2\mathbf{z}_2}\right)^2 - A^2\right]} = \frac{1}{A}\sqrt{\left[\frac{\mathbf{z}_1}{\mathbf{z}_2} + \left(\frac{\mathbf{z}_1}{2\mathbf{z}_2}\right)^2 + g\mathbf{z}_1\right]}. \quad (2.122)$$

Then (2.120) and (2.121) can be written

$$I^*(q) = \frac{(\mathrm{e}^q - A\cosh\chi)\,\mathrm{e}^q i[0] + \mathrm{e}^q\left[(\mathbf{z}_1/2\mathbf{z}_2)\,i[0] - \{(1 + g\mathbf{z}_2)/\mathbf{z}_2\}\,u[0]\right]}{\mathrm{e}^{2q} - 2A\mathrm{e}^q\cosh\chi + A^2}, \quad (2.123)$$

$$U^*(q) = \frac{(\mathrm{e}^q - A\cosh\chi)\,\mathrm{e}^q u[0] - \mathrm{e}^q\left[(\mathbf{z}_1/2\mathbf{z}_2)\,u[0] + \mathbf{z}_1 i[0]\right]}{\mathrm{e}^{2q} - 2A\mathrm{e}^q\cosh\chi + A^2}. \quad (2.124)$$

Using transformations (2.48), (2.49) with $e^\lambda = A$, we find on transforming to the originals

$$i[n] = A^n\left(i[0]\cosh\chi n + \frac{(\mathbf{z}_1/2\mathbf{z}_2)\, i[0] - \{(1+g/\mathbf{z}_2)\,\mathbf{z}_2\}\, u[0]\sinh\chi n}{A\sinh\chi}\right), \quad (2.125)$$

$$u[n] = A^n\left(u[0]\cosh\chi n - \frac{(\mathbf{z}_1/2\mathbf{z}_2)\, u[0] + \mathbf{z}_1 i[0]\sinh\chi n}{A\sinh\chi}\right). \quad (2.126)$$

We return to boundary conditions in order to find the quantities $i[0]$, and $u[0]$ appearing in these expressions. We assume in the following that $\mathbf{z}_{gen.} = \mathbf{z}_2{}^*$. Putting $n = N$ in (2.125), we can write the boundary conditions (2.117), (2.118) in the form

$$\mathbf{z}_2 i[0] + u[0] = u_{gen.},$$

$$\left(\cosh\chi N + \frac{\mathbf{z}_1}{2\mathbf{z}_2}\frac{\sinh\chi N}{A\sinh\varkappa}\right) i[0] - \left(\frac{1+g\mathbf{z}_2}{\mathbf{z}_2}\frac{\sinh\chi N}{A\sinh\chi}\right) u[0] = 0.$$

$i[0]$ and $u[0]$ are obtained from these equations:

$$i[0] = u_{gen.}\frac{\{(1+g\mathbf{z}_2)/\mathbf{z}_2\}\sinh\lambda N}{A\sinh\chi\cosh\chi N + (\mathbf{z}_1/2\mathbf{z}_2 + 1 + g\mathbf{z}_2)\sinh\chi N}, \quad (2.127)$$

$$u[0] = u_{gen.}\frac{A\sinh\chi\cosh\chi N + (\mathbf{z}_1/2\mathbf{z}_2)\sinh\chi N}{A\sinh\chi\cosh\chi N + (\mathbf{z}_1/2\mathbf{z}_2 + 1 + g\mathbf{z}_2)\sinh\chi N}. \quad (2.128)$$

The current and voltage in any stage can be obtained from equations (2.125) and (2.126), along with (2.127), (2.128). We are interested in the output voltage, i.e. in $u[N]$.

Putting $n = N$ in (2.126) and introducing the expressions for $i[0]$ and $u[0]$ from (2.127) and (2.128), we obtain after some manipulation

$$u[N] = u_{gen}\frac{A^{N+1}\sinh\chi}{A\sinh\chi\cosh\chi N + (A\cosh\chi + g\mathbf{z}_2)\sinh\chi N}, \quad (2.129)$$

which gives the gain of the N-stage amplifier in the form

$$\frac{u[N]}{u_{gen.}} = \frac{A^{N+1}\sinh\chi}{A\sinh\chi(N+1) + g\mathbf{z}_2\sinh\chi N}. \quad (2.130)$$

The gain (2.130) can be expressed in terms of the amplifier parameters $\mathbf{z}_1$, $\mathbf{z}_2$ and g. To do this we use the formula+

$$\sinh\chi n = \sum_{\nu=1}^{[n+1]/2}\binom{n}{2\nu-1}\cosh^{n-2\nu+1}\chi\,\sinh^{2\nu-1}\chi, \quad (2.131)$$

+ See footnote on next page.

where $\binom{n}{2\nu - 1} = \frac{n!}{(2\nu - 1)!\,(n - 2\nu + 1)!}$ are the binomial coefficients. Putting $n = N$ and then $n = N + 1$ in this formula, substituting the resulting expressions for $\sinh \chi N$ and $\sinh \chi (N + 1)$ in (2.130), then replacing A, $\cosh \chi$ and $\sinh \chi$ by their values from (2.122), we obtain finally

$$\frac{u[N]}{u_{gen.}} = \frac{(1 - g\mathbf{z}_1)^N}{\Xi(N + 1) + g\mathbf{z}_2\,\Xi(N)}, \tag{2.132}$$

where

$$\Xi(N) = \sum_{\nu=1}^{(N+1)/2} \binom{N}{2\nu - 1} \left(1 + \frac{\mathbf{z}_1}{2\mathbf{z}_2}\right)^{N-2\nu+1} \left[\frac{\mathbf{z}_1}{\mathbf{z}_2} + \left(\frac{\mathbf{z}_1}{2\mathbf{z}_2}\right)^2 + g\mathbf{z}_1\right]^{2\nu-1}.$$

This expression for the gain is given in Table 2.1 for $N = 1, 2, 3, 4$.

As $\mathbf{z}_1 \to \infty$, corresponding to zero anode-grid feedback, we obtain from (2.132) (see also Table 2.1) the well-known result

$$\frac{u[N]}{u_{gen.}} = (-1)^N (g\mathbf{z}_2)^N. \tag{2.133}$$

In this case the gain of the N-stage amplifier is the N-th power of the gain of a single stage.

TABLE 2. 1.

The Gain of an N-stage Amplifier

Number of stages	Gain
1	$\frac{(1 - g\mathbf{z}_1)\,\mathbf{z}_2}{2\mathbf{z}_2 + \mathbf{z}_1 + g\mathbf{z}_2^2}$
2	$\frac{(1 - g\mathbf{z}_1)^2\mathbf{z}_2^2}{(\mathbf{z}_1 + 3\mathbf{z}_2 + 2g\mathbf{z}_2^2)\,(\mathbf{z}_1 + \mathbf{z}_2)}$
3	$\frac{(1 - g\mathbf{z}_1)^3\,\mathbf{z}_2^3}{\mathbf{z}_1^3 + 3\mathbf{z}_1^2\mathbf{z}_2(2 + g\mathbf{z}_2) + \mathbf{z}_1 z_2^2(10 + 8g\mathbf{z}_2 + g^2\mathbf{z}_2^2) + \mathbf{z}_2^3(4 + 3g\mathbf{z}_2)}$
4	$\frac{(1 - g\mathbf{z}_1)^4\,\mathbf{z}_2^4}{(\mathbf{z}_1^2 + 3\mathbf{z}_1\mathbf{z}_2 + \mathbf{z}_2^2 + g\mathbf{z}_1\mathbf{z}_2^2)\,(\mathbf{z}_1^2 + 5\mathbf{z}_1\mathbf{z}_2 + 3g\mathbf{z}_1\mathbf{z}_2^2 + 5\mathbf{z}_2^2 + 4g\mathbf{z}_2^3)}$

Knowledge of the gain enables us to investigate the stability of the N-stage amplifier, which can be disturbed by the anode-grid feedback.[+] We shall not go into this here, however.

[+] See Faust, Beek (2; 1946); A. A. Kolosov (2; 1945).

Electrical circuit with periodically switched parameters. We previously obtained a difference equation (2.18) for an electrical circuit with step-wise changing parameters (Fig. 2.11a)

$$u_C[n+1] - e^{-\beta_{av}} u_C[n] = R. \tag{2.134}$$

Here we have written

$$\left.\begin{aligned} \beta_{av} &= \beta'\gamma + \beta''(1-\gamma), \\ R &= u_0(1 - e^{-\beta'\gamma})\, e^{-\beta''(1-\gamma)}. \end{aligned}\right\} \tag{2.135}$$

Equation (2.134) gives the voltage on the capacitor at discrete moments of time. We shall assume that $u_C[0] = 0$. Denoting

$$D\{u_C[n]\} = U_C^*(q),$$

we have from the original-translation theorem (Theorem 2)

$$D\{u_C[n+1]\} = e^q U_C^*(q) - e^q u_C[0].$$

Applying the discrete Laplace transformation to (2.134), remembering that $u_C[0] = 0$ and that

$$D\{R\} = \frac{Re^q}{e^q - 1},$$

we obtain

$$(e^q - e^{-\beta_{av}})\, U_C^*(q) = \frac{Re^q}{e^q - 1}$$

or

$$U_C^*(q) = \frac{Re^q}{(e^q - e^{-\beta_{av}})(e^q - 1)}. \tag{2.136}$$

The original of this expression is obtained using the previously obtained transformation (2.63), and we finally obtain

$$u_C[n] = R\frac{1}{1 - e^{-\beta_{av}}}(1 - e^{-\beta_{av} n}). \tag{2.137}$$

The voltage on the capacitor at any moment of time is obtained by substituting (2.137) into the previously obtained relationships (2.16) and (2.17). This gives

$$u_C(\bar{t}) = u_0 + \left(R\frac{1 - e^{-\beta_{av} n}}{1 - e^{-\beta_{av}}} - u_0\right) e^{-\beta'(\bar{t}-n)}, \qquad n \leqslant \bar{t} \leqslant n+\gamma,$$

$$u_C(\bar{t}) = \left[u_0 + \left(R\frac{1 - e^{-\beta_{av} n}}{1 - e^{-\beta_{av}}} - u_0\right) e^{-\beta'\gamma}\right] e^{-\beta''(\bar{t}-n-\gamma)}, \quad n+\gamma \leqslant \bar{t} \leqslant n+1.$$

The voltage on the capacitor is obtained in the form of a displaced lattice function by putting in this expression $\bar{t} = n + \varepsilon$, where n is an integer and $\varepsilon \leqslant 1$:

$$\left.\begin{aligned} u_C(n+\varepsilon) = u_C[n,\varepsilon] &= u_0 + \left(R\,\frac{1-e^{-\beta_{av}n}}{1-e^{-\beta_{av}}} - u_0\right) e^{-\beta'\varepsilon}, \\ &\qquad 0 \leqslant \varepsilon \leqslant \gamma \\ u_C(n+\varepsilon) = u_C[n,\varepsilon] &= \left[u_0 + \left(R\,\frac{1-e^{-\beta_{av}n}}{1-e^{-\beta_{av}}} - u_0\right) e^{-\beta'\gamma}\right] e^{-\beta''(\varepsilon-\gamma)}, \\ &\qquad \gamma \leqslant \varepsilon \leqslant 1. \end{aligned}\right\} \tag{2.138}$$

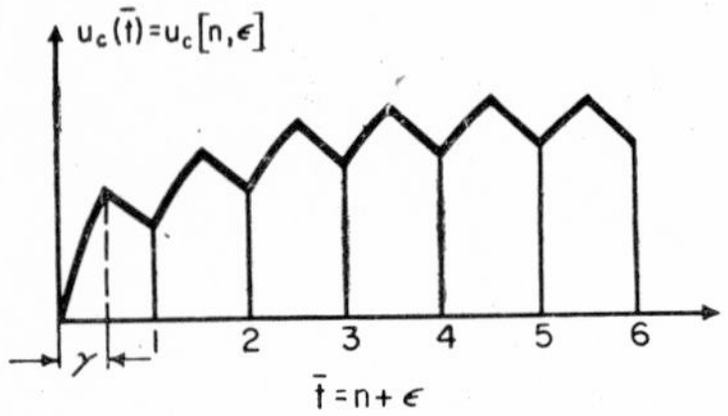

FIG. 2.27. The voltage $u_c(\bar{t})$ on the capacitor in the charge-discharge circuit.

These formulae give, for $n = 0, 1, 2, \ldots$ and $0 \leqslant \varepsilon \leqslant 1$, the voltage on the capacitor at any instant of time. The variation of $u_C[n, \varepsilon]$ with $\bar{t}$ is shown in Fig. 2.27. As n increases u_C tends to a steady, periodic saw-tooth voltage u_{Cs} whose equation is obtained from (2.138) by letting $n \to \infty$; this equation takes the form

$$\left.\begin{aligned} u_{Cs}[n,\varepsilon] = u_C[\infty,\varepsilon] &= u_0 + \left(\frac{R}{1-e^{-\beta_{av}}} - u_0\right) e^{-\beta'\varepsilon}, \\ &\qquad 0 \leqslant \varepsilon \leqslant \gamma, \\ u_{Cs}[n,\varepsilon] = u_C[\infty,\varepsilon] &= \left[u_0 + \left(\frac{R}{1-e^{-\beta_{av}}} - u_0\right)\right] e^{-\beta''(\varepsilon-\gamma)}, \\ &\qquad \gamma \leqslant \varepsilon \leqslant 1. \end{aligned}\right\} \tag{2.139}$$

2.5. Solution of linear difference equations of arbitrary order

We have examined above first and second order difference equations, and also systems of two linear first order difference equations which arise when solving problems on ladder networks and systems with periodically switched parameters.

We now consider a difference equation of arbitrary order, say the l-th, which we write in the form

$$a_0 y[n] + a_1 y[n+1] + \ldots + a_l y[n+l] = f[n] \tag{2.140}$$

with the boundary conditions

$$y[0] = y_0, \quad y[1] = y_1, \ldots, y[l-1] = y_{l-1}. \tag{2.141}$$

Apply the discrete Laplace transformation to (2.140). Using the original-translation theorem (Theorem 2) we have

$$D\{y[n+k]\} = e^{kq} Y^*(q) - \sum_{r=0}^{k-1} y[r]\, e^{-(r-k)q},$$

and so (2.140) transforms into

$$\begin{aligned}(a_0 + a_1 e^q + a_2 e^{2q} + \ldots + a_l e^{lq}) Y^*(q) = F^*(q) + \\ + (a_1 e^q + a_2 e^{2q} + \ldots + a_l e^{lq}) y_0 + \\ + (a_2 e^q + a_3 e^{2q} + \ldots + a_l e^{(l-1)q}) y_1 + \\ \ldots\ldots\ldots\ldots\ldots\ldots \\ a_l e_q y_{l-1}.\end{aligned} \tag{2.142}$$

We denote

$$\left.\begin{aligned} a_0 + a_1 e^q + a_2 e^{2q} + \ldots + a_l e^{lq} &= G^*(q), \\ a_1 e^q + a_2 e^{2q} + \ldots + a_l e^{lq} &= H_1^*(q), \\ a_2 e^q + \ldots + a_l e^{(l-1)q} &= H_2^*(q), \\ \ldots\ldots\ldots\ldots\ldots \\ a_l e^q &= H_l^*(y). \end{aligned}\right\} \tag{2.143}$$

The image $Y^*(q)$ can then be put in the form

$$Y^*(q) = \frac{F^*(q)}{G^*(q)} + \sum_{k=1}^{l} \frac{H_k^*(q)}{G^*(q)} y_{k-1} \tag{2.144}$$

or, grouping under the summation sign coefficients with the same e^{kq},

$$Y^*(q) = \frac{F^*(q)}{G^*(q)} + \sum_{k=1}^{l} \frac{A_k e^{kq}}{G^*(q)} = \frac{F^*(q)}{G^*(q)} + \frac{E^*(q)}{G^*(q)}, \tag{2.145}$$

where $E^*(q) = A_1 e^q + A_2 e^{2q} + \ldots + A_l e^{lq}$ and the A_k are given by

$$\left.\begin{aligned} A_1 &= a_1 y_0 + a_2 y_1 + \ldots + a_{l-1} y_{l-2} + a_l y_{l-1}, \\ A_2 &= a_2 y_0 + a_3 y_1 + \ldots + a_l y_{l-2}, \\ &\ldots\ldots\ldots\ldots\ldots \\ A_l &= a_l y_0. \end{aligned}\right\} \tag{2.146}$$

The problem is now to obtain the original (lattice function) corresponding to the above image. To do this we require the so-called expansion formulae, which we now proceed to deduce.

We assume that the image $Y^*(q)$ can be reduced to the form

$$Y^*(q) = \frac{H^*(q)}{G^*(q)}, \tag{2.147}$$

where

$$\left.\begin{aligned} G^*(q) &= a_0 + a_1 e^q + \ldots + a_l e^{lq}, \\ H^*(q) &= b_0 + b_1 e^q + \ldots + b_{l'} e^{l'q} \end{aligned}\right\} \tag{2.148}$$

i.e. $G^*(q)$ and $H^*(q)$ are polynomials in e^q, and the degree $^{l'q}$ does not exceed the degree l. We also assume that the equation

$$G^*(q) = 0$$

has only simple roots e^{q_ν} ($\nu = 1, 2, \ldots, l$), different from unity. In this case+

$$\left[\frac{dG^*(q)}{de^q}\right]_{q=q_\nu} = \dot{G}^*(q_y) \neq 0. \tag{2.149}$$

The image $Y^*(q)$ can be expanded into a sum of simple fractions

$$Y^*(q) = \frac{H^*(q)}{G^*(q)} = \sum_{\nu=1}^{l} \frac{c_\nu}{e^q - e^{q_\nu}}. \tag{2.150}$$

Here $c_\nu (\nu = 1, 2, \ldots, l)$ are constant coefficients; they can be found in the following manner. Multiply both sides of (2.150) by $(e^q - e^{q_\mu})$ where μ is any integer from 1, 2, ..., l; we then obtain

$$\frac{H^*(q)}{G^*(q)}(e^q - e^{q_\mu}) = c_\mu + (^q - e^{q_\mu}) \sum_{\substack{\nu=1 \\ \nu\neq\mu}}^{l} \frac{c^\nu}{(e^q - e^{q_\nu})}. \tag{2.151}$$

Now put $q = q_\mu$. The sum having the factor $(e^q - e^{q_\mu})$ becomes zero, and so the right side becomes equal to c_ν. The left side of the equality becomes indeterminate, however, for $e^q = e^{q_\mu}$; as, for this value, $G^*(q)$ equals zero. The indeterminancy can be resolved in the usual manner giving, from (2.151),

$$c_\mu = \frac{H^*(q)}{\left[\frac{dG^*(q)}{de^q}\right]_{q=q_\mu}} = \frac{H^*(q_\mu)}{\dot{G}^*(q_\mu)}. \tag{2.152}$$

In this way the expansion (2.150) can be written in the form

$$Y^*(q) = \frac{H^*(q)}{G^*(q)} = \sum_{\nu=1}^{l} \frac{H^*(q_\nu)}{\dot{G}^*(q_\nu)} \frac{1}{e^q - e^{q_\nu}}. \tag{2.153}$$

Using relationship (2.45)

$$\frac{1}{e^q - e^{q_\nu}} \xrightarrow{\cdot} \begin{cases} e^{q\nu(n-1)}, & (n \geqslant 1), \\ 0, & (n < 1), \end{cases}$$

+ The dot above G^* implies differentiation with respect to e^q.

and the linearity theorem (Theorem 1), the original $y[n]$ corresponding to $Y^*(q)$ is easily seen to be

$$y[n] = \sum_{\nu=1}^{l} \frac{H(q_\nu)}{\dot{G}(q_\nu)} e^{q_\nu(n-1)}, \quad (n \geqslant 1), \tag{2.154}$$

or

$$y[n] = \sum_{\nu=1}^{l} \frac{H^*(q_\nu)}{e^{q_\nu} \dot{G}^*(q_\nu)} e^{q_\nu n}, \quad (n \geqslant 1). \tag{2.155}$$

This formula enables us to find the original corresponding to an image of the form (2.147).

Consider an image $Y_1^*(q)$ having a slightly different form, namely

$$Y_1^*(q) = \frac{H^*(q)}{G^*(q)} \frac{e^q}{e^q - 1}. \tag{2.156}$$

$\dfrac{e^q}{e^q - 1}$ is the image of the constant lattice function $1[n]$. The image (2.156) differs from (2.147) in having an additional pole for $q = 0$, i.e. for $e^q = 1$. We shall often come across this type of image in future work.

The original $y_1[n]$ is found using the convolution theorem (Theorem 11). Since

$$\frac{H^*(q)}{G^*(q)} \stackrel{\cdot}{\longrightarrow} y[n], \qquad \frac{e^q}{e^q - 1} \stackrel{\cdot}{\longrightarrow} 1[n],$$

we have, using the convolution theorem,

$$y_1[n] = \sum_{m=0}^{n} y[m]\, 1[n-m] = \sum_{m=1}^{n} y[m],$$

as $y[0] = 0$, and $1[n-m] = 1$ always for $n \geqslant m$.

On substituting $y[n]$ from (2.155) and changing the order of summation, we obtain

$$y_1[n] = \sum_{\nu=1}^{l} \frac{H^*(q_\nu)}{e^{q_\nu} \dot{G}^*(q_\nu)} \sum_{m=1}^{n} e^{q_\nu m}.$$

However

$$\sum_{m=1}^{n} e^{q_\nu m} = \frac{e^{q_\nu} (1 - e^{q_\nu n})}{1 - e^{q_\nu}},$$

and so

$$y_1[n] = \sum_{\nu=1}^{l} \frac{H^*(q_\nu)}{(1 - e^{q_\nu}) \dot{G}^*(q_\nu)} - \sum_{\nu=1}^{l} \frac{H^*(q_\nu)}{(1 - e^{q_\nu}) \dot{G}^*(q_\nu)} e^{q_\nu n}. \tag{2.157}$$

We obtain by putting $q = 0$ in (2.153)

$$\frac{H^*(0)}{G^*(0)} = \sum_{\nu=1}^{l} \frac{H^*(q_\nu)}{G^*(q_\nu)} \frac{1}{1 - e^{q_\nu}}.$$

Consequently, (2.157) can be rewritten as

$$y_1[n] = \frac{H^*(0)}{G^*(0)} - \sum_{\nu=1}^{l} \frac{H^*(q_\nu)}{(1 - e^{q_\nu})\,\dot{G}^*(q_\nu)}\, e^{q_\nu n}. \tag{2.158}$$

This formula is the analogue of the well-known Heaviside expansion formula.

Consider finally an image $Y_2^*(q)$ of the form

$$Y_2^*(q) = \frac{H^*(q)}{G^*(q)} \frac{e^q}{e^q - e^{j\bar{\omega}}}. \tag{2.159}$$

$e^q/(e^q - e^{j\bar{\omega}})$ is the image of $e^{j\bar{\omega}n} = \cos\bar{\omega}\,n + j\sin\bar{\omega}\,n$, i.e. the complex harmonic lattice function, and has a purely imaginary pole at $q = j\,\bar{\omega}$. Using the convolution theorem, as before, we obtain

$$y_2[n] = \sum_{m=0}^{n} y[m]\, e^{j\bar{\omega}(n-m)} = \sum_{m=1}^{n} y[m]\, e^{j\bar{\omega}(n-m)}.$$

Here, as previously, we have assumed $y[0] = 0$. We obtain on substituting $y[n]$ from (2.155) and changing the order of summation:

$$y_2[n] = e^{j\bar{\omega}n} \sum_{\nu=1}^{l} \frac{H^*(q_\nu)}{e^{q_\nu}\dot{G}^*(q_\nu)} \sum_{m=1}^{n} e^{(q_\nu - j\bar{\omega})m}.$$

However

$$\sum_{m=1}^{n} e^{(q_\nu - j\bar{\omega})m} = e^{q_\nu} \frac{1 - e^{(q_\nu - j\bar{\omega})n}}{e^{j\bar{\omega}} - e^{q_\nu}}$$

and therefore

$$y_2[n] = \left(\sum_{\nu=1}^{l} \frac{H^*(q_\nu)}{(e^{j\bar{\omega}} - e^{q_\nu})\,\dot{G}^*(q_\nu)} \right) e^{j\bar{\omega}n} - \sum_{\nu=1}^{l} \frac{H^*(q_\nu)}{(e^{j\bar{\omega}} - e^{q_\nu})\,\dot{G}^*(q_\nu)}\, e^{q_\nu n}. \tag{2.160}$$

We get on putting $q = j\,\bar{\omega}$ in (2.153)

$$\frac{H^*(j\bar{\omega})}{F^*(j\bar{\omega})} = \sum_{\nu=1}^{l} \frac{H^*(q_\nu)}{\dot{G}^*(q_\nu)} \frac{1}{e^{j\bar{\omega}} - e^{q_\nu}}. \tag{2.161}$$

Equation (2.160) can now be written

$$y_2[n] = \frac{H^*(j\bar{\omega})}{G^*(j\bar{\omega})}\, e^{j\bar{\omega}n} - \sum_{\nu=1}^{l} \frac{H^*(q)}{(e^{j\bar{\omega}n} - e^{q_\nu})\,\dot{G}^*(q_\nu)}\, e^{q_\nu n}. \tag{2.162}$$

This formula is the analogue of another Heaviside formula which is sometimes called the a.c. switch-on formula. For $\bar{\omega} = 0$ we obtain the previous result.

Formulae (2.155), (2.158) and (2.162) are called *expansion formulae*, by analogy with the nomenclature used in the usual Laplace transformation. These formulae hold provided the equation $G^*(q) = 0$ does not have repeated roots. These expansion formulae can be obtained in a more general form, which covers the case of repeated roots, by a limiting transition or by the general method to be described later. We note that formulae (2.158) and (2.162) can be obtained in exactly the same manner as formula (2.155). We leave this as an exercise for the reader.

We now return to our search for the solution for the l-th order difference equation. We showed (2.145) that the image of this solution has the form

$$Y^*(q) = \frac{F^*(q)}{G^*(q)} + \frac{E^*(q)}{G^*(q)}. \tag{2.163}$$

We assume that all the roots of $G^*(q) = 0$ are simple. From expansion formula (2.159) we find

$$\frac{1}{G^*(q)} \doteq\!\!\rightarrow \sum_{\nu=1}^{l} \frac{1}{e^{q_\nu} \dot{G}^*(q_\nu)} e^{q_\nu n} = \psi[n], \tag{2.164}$$

$$\frac{E^*(q)}{G^*(q)} \doteq\!\!\rightarrow \sum_{\nu=1}^{l} \frac{E^*(q_\nu)}{e^{q_\nu} \dot{G}^*(q_\nu)} e^{q_\nu n} = \psi_1[n]. \tag{2.165}$$

We have from the convolution theorem (Theorem 11)

$$\frac{1}{G^*(q)} F^*(q) \doteq\!\!\rightarrow \sum_{m=0}^{n} \psi[m] f[n-m], \tag{2.166}$$

since

$$F^*(q) \doteq\!\!\rightarrow f[n],$$

where $f[n]$ is the right side of the difference equation.

Thus, on transforming from image to original, we obtain the solution of the l-th order difference equation, taking into account the boundary conditions, in the form

$$y[n] = \sum_{m=0}^{n} \psi[m] f[n-m] + \psi_1[n]. \tag{2.167}$$

If all the boundary values equal zero

$$y_0 = y_1 = \ldots = y_{l-1} = 0,$$

then from (2.146) $A_k = 0$ $(k = 1, 2, \ldots, l)$, $E^*(q) = 0$, and therefore $\psi_1(n) \equiv 0$. In this case we have from (2.167)

$$y[n] = \sum_{m=0}^{n} \psi[m] f[n-m]. \tag{2.168}$$

The method for solving a linear difference equation of arbitrary order has been described above. Systems of linear difference equations can be solved analogously. The discrete Laplace transformation is applied to the system of difference equations. This gives a system of linear algebraic equations in the images of certain variables. Solving this system of linear algebraic equations gives the images of the corresponding variables in the form (2.144). The required originals are obtained from the images using the expansion formulae and the procedure described above.

2.6. Inverse discrete Laplace transformation: reduction formula

Given a lattice function $f[n]$, the fundamental relationship

$$F^*(q) = \sum_{n=0}^{\infty} e^{-qn} f[n] \tag{2.169}$$

enables its image $F^*(q)$ to be calculated. Relationship (2.169), which we may write briefly as

$$F^*(q) = D\{f[n]\}, \tag{2.170}$$

and for the displaced lattice function as

$$F^*(q, \varepsilon) = D\{f[n, \varepsilon]\}, \tag{2.171}$$

defines the problem of the direct discrete Laplace transformation, or briefly, the *direct transformation.*

For a given image, the general relationship giving the original is written conventionally as

$$f[n] = D^{-1}\{F^*(q)\}, \tag{2.172}$$

and for the displaced lattice function as

$$f[n, \varepsilon] = D^{-1}\{F^*(q, \varepsilon)\}. \tag{2.173}$$

This relationship defines the problem of the inverse discrete Laplace transformation, or briefly, the *inverse transformation.*

The aim of the inverse transformation is thus to find the lattice function $f[n]$ which satisfies (2.169) for a given image $F^*(q)$.

We have, essentially, considered only the direct transformation in the preceding sections and only for certain particular cases have we shown how to find the original of a given image. A general method of carrying out the inverse transformation is given in this section.

It was pointed out earlier that an image $F^*(q)$ is a function of e^q. However, e^q has the property that for $q = 2\pi kj$,

$$e^{2\pi kj} = 1$$

for any integer k. Thus

$$e^{q+2\pi kj} = e^q$$

and consequently, for any integer k,

$$F^*(q + 2\pi kj) = F^*(q).$$

This means that an image $F^*(q)$ is a periodic function along the imaginary axis of the complex plane $q = \sigma + j\,\bar{\omega}$, with a period of 2π. Due to this periodicity $F^*(q)$ can always be considered in the strip $-\pi < \text{Im}\, q \leqslant \pi$, i.e. for $-\pi < \bar{\omega} \leqslant \pi$ (Fig. 2.28).

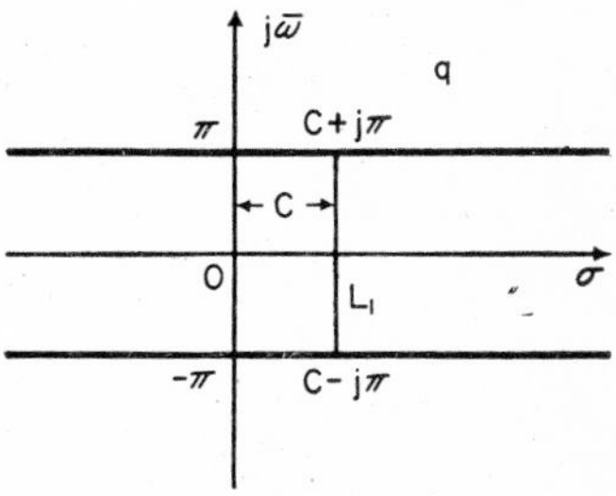

FIG. 2.28. The strip $-\pi < \bar{\omega} \leqslant \pi$. Path of integration L_1.

In general $F^*(q)$ may have singular points inside the strip, for example poles, at which $F^*(q)$ becomes infinite. To each complex pole $q_\nu = \sigma_\nu + j\,\bar{\omega}_\nu$ in the strip $-\pi < \text{Im}\, q \leqslant \pi$ there always corresponds a conjugate pole $q_{\nu+1} = \sigma_\nu - j\,\bar{\omega}_\nu$, since the coefficients appearing in $F^*(q)$ are always real. It was for this reason that this particular strip was chosen in the first place. The imaginary parts of all other poles differ by an amount $\pm 2\pi kj$. Poles such that $q_{\nu,\,\nu+1} = \sigma_\nu \pm j\,\pi$, i.e. $\bar{\omega} = \pi$, lie on the boundary of the strip. In this case only one of these poles must be considered, namely, $q_\nu = \sigma_\nu + j\,\pi$. In future, when speaking of the singularities of an image $F^*(q)$, we shall mean those singularities lying inside the fundamental strip, without stating this every time.

We assume that the singularities q_ν of $F^*(q)$ lie to the left of a straight-line segment L_1, of length $2\,\pi$ and situated at a distance c to the right of the imaginary axis (Fig. 2.28). c is an arbitrary positive constant which is greater than the abscissa of convergence.

Multiply both sides of (2.169) by e^{qm} (where m is an integer) and then integrate them along L_1 i.e. from $c - j\pi$ to $c + j\pi$:

$$\int_{c-j\pi}^{c+j\pi} F^*(q)\, e^{qm}\, dq = \int_{c-j\pi}^{c+j\pi} \left\{ \sum_{n=0}^{\infty} e^{-qn} f[n] \right\} e^{qm} dq =$$

$$= \sum_{n=0}^{\infty} f[n] \int_{c-j\pi}^{c+j\pi} e^{-q(n-m)}\, dq. \tag{2.174}$$

Interchanging the operations of integration and summation is justified as c is greater than the abscissa of convergence of $f[n]$. If $n \neq m$ then

$$\int_{c-j\pi}^{c+j\pi} e^{-q(n-m)} = \left[-\frac{e^{-q(n-m)}}{n-m} \right]_{c-j\pi}^{c+j\pi} = \frac{e^{-c(n-m)}}{n-m} \left[e^{j\pi(n-m)} - e^{-j\pi(n-m)} \right] = 0.$$

If $n = m$, then

$$\int_{c-j\pi}^{c+j\pi} dq = (c + j\pi) - (c - j\pi) = 2\pi j\,,$$

and thus (2.174) gives

$$\int_{c-j\pi}^{c+j\pi} F^*(q)\, e^{qm}\, dq = f[m]\, 2\pi j\,,$$

or, replacing the variable m by n we have finally

$$f[n] = \frac{1}{2\pi j} \int_{c-j\pi}^{c+j\pi} F^*(q)\, e^{qn}\, dq\,, \tag{2.175}$$

and for the displaced lattice function

$$f[n, \varepsilon] = \frac{1}{2\pi j} \int_{c-j\pi}^{c+j\pi} F^*(q, \varepsilon)\, e^{qn}\, dq. \tag{2.176}$$

These formulae, called *inversion formulae,* solve the problem of the inverse transformation. They are analogous to the inversion formula of the usual Laplace transformation. Obviously, integration along the straight-line segment L_1 can be replaced by integration along any curve Γ lying to the right of L_1 (Fig. 2.29a). This follows from Cauchy's theorem, which states that the integral round a closed contour of a function with no singularities inside the contour equals zero.+ It can also be seen that the values of the integrals (2.175),

+ See A. I. Markushevich (2; 1950).

(2.176) are unchanged if the curve Γ (or the segment L_1) is displaced to the right (Fig. 2.29*b*); this is due to the periodicity of the integrand, as a result of which the values of the integrals along the boundary segments of the strip (*ad* and *bc*) are equal in absolute value and opposite in sign.

We assume that the function $F^*(q)$ is uniformly bounded in $\bar{\omega} = \operatorname{Im} q$, $(-\pi < \bar{\omega} \leqslant \pi)$ as $\operatorname{Re} q = c \to \infty$, i.e.

$$\lim_{\operatorname{Re} q \to \infty} |F^*(q)| < A .$$

We can then show that for negative values of n

$$f[n] \equiv 0 . \qquad (2.177)$$

This is proved as follows. Since the value of the integral does not

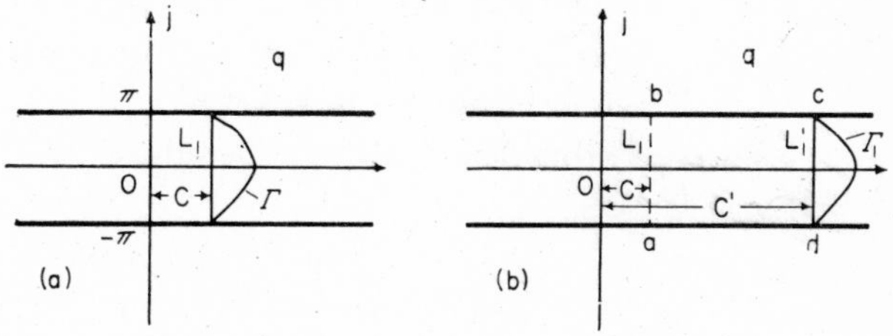

FIG. 2.29. Change of path of integration.

change on shifting the path of integration L_1 to the right, (2.175) can be written in the form

$$f[n] = \frac{1}{2\pi j} \int_{c'-j\pi}^{c'+j\pi} F^*(q)\, e^{qn}\, dq = \frac{1}{2\pi j} \int_{L_1'} F^*(q)\, e^{qn}\, dq .$$

Noting, that for a sufficiently large c' on the segment L' $(q = c' + j\bar{\omega})$, we have

$$|F^*(q)| < A \,|\, e^{qn} | = | e^{c'n + j\bar{\omega}n} | = e^{c'n}, \quad |dq| = |d(c' + j\bar{\omega})| = d\bar{\omega},$$

and so in this case

$$\left| \frac{1}{2\pi j} \int_{L_1'} F^*(q)\, e^{qn}\, dq \right| < \frac{1}{2\pi} \int_{L_1'} |F^*(q)|\,|e^{qn}|\,|dq| \leqslant \frac{A e^{c'n}}{2\pi} \int_{L_1'} d\bar{\omega} = A e^{c'n} .$$

As $c' \to \infty$ the right side of (2.178) tends to zero if $n < 0$. Hence

$$\lim_{\operatorname{Re} q = c' \to \infty} \frac{1}{2\pi j} \int_{L_1'} F^*(q)\, e^{qn}\, dq = 0 ,$$

and so, from (2.175), we see that for $n < 0$

$$f[n] \equiv 0 .$$

We now proceed to the evaluation of the integral (2.175) for $n \geqslant 0$. Calculation can be simplified by changing the variable. Put

$$e^q = z . \qquad (2.179)$$

Then $F^*(q) = F(z)$, $dz = e^q \, dq$ and consequently (2.175) becomes

$$f[n] = \frac{1}{2\pi j} \int_{L_1} F^*(q) \, e^{qn} \, dq = \frac{1}{2\pi j} \int_{\Gamma_0} F(z) \, z^{n-1} \, dz . \qquad (2.180)$$

The path of integration L_1 in the q-plane (Fig. 2.29) is converted into a circle Γ_0 of radius e^c in the z-plane (Fig. 2.30). The poles q_ν of the function $F(q)$, which lie to the left of the segment L_1, correspond to poles $z_\nu = e^{q_\nu}$ of the function $F(z)$ lying inside the circle Γ_0.

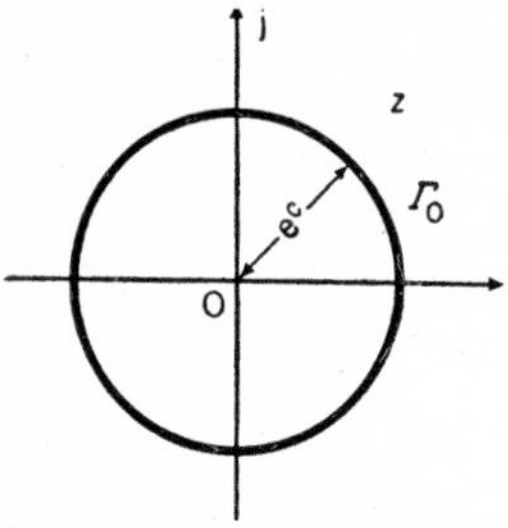

FIG. 2.30. Path of integration in the z-plane.

From the theory of residues+ we have

$$\int_{\Gamma_0} F(z) \, z^{n-1} \, dz = 2\pi j \sum_\nu \mathrm{Res}_{z_\nu} [F(s) \, z^{n-1}], \qquad (2.181)$$

where $\mathrm{Res}_{z_\nu} [F(z) z^{n-1}]$ is the residue of the function $F(z) z^{n-1}$ at the pole $z = z_\nu$. Reverting from the variable q back to the variable z in the last expression, the inversion formula can be written in the form

$$f[n] = \frac{1}{2\pi j} \int_{L_1} F^*(q) \, e^{qn} \, dq = \sum_\nu \mathrm{Res}_{q_\nu} [F^*(q) \, e^{q(n-1)}] . \qquad (2.182)$$

If q_ν is a simple pole, the corresponding residue equals

$$\mathrm{Res}_q \, [F^*(q) \, e^{q(n-1)}] = \lim_{q \to q_\nu} \{F^*(q) \, (e^q - e^{q_\nu}) \, e^{q(n-1)}\}. \qquad (2.183)$$

If q_ν is a pole of order r_ν, the corresponding residue equals

$$\mathrm{Res}_{q_\nu} [F^*(q) \, e^{q(n-1)}] = \frac{1}{(r_\nu - 1)!} \lim_{q \to q_\nu} \frac{d^{r_\nu - 1}}{de^{q(r_\nu - 1)}} \{F^*(q) \, (e^q - e^{q_\nu})^{r_\nu} \, e^{q(n-1)}\}. \qquad (2.184)$$

Hence the computation of the original using formula (2.182) reduces to evaluating the residues $\mathrm{Res}_{q_\nu} [F^*(q) e^{q(n-1)}]$.

The inversion formula will now be applied to a few simple examples.

+ See A. I. Markushevich (2; 1950).

EXAMPLE 1. Let

$$F^*(q) = \frac{e^q}{e^q - e^a}.$$

In this case $F^*(q)$ has one simple pole at $q_1 = a$ in the strip $-\pi < \text{Im } q < \pi$. From (2.183)

$$\text{Res}_{q_1}[F^*(q)\, e^{q(n-1)}] = \lim_{q\to a} \left\{\frac{e^q}{e^q - e^a}(e^q - e^a)\, e^{q(n-1)}\right\} = \lim_{q\to a} e^{qn} = e^{an},$$

and consequently, from (2.182), we obtain

$$D^{-1}\{F^*(q)\} = f[n] = e^{an},$$

which agrees with the result obtained previously by another method.

EXAMPLE 2. Let

$$F^*(q) = \frac{e^q}{(e^q - e^a)^2}.$$

In the strip $-\pi < \text{Im } q \leqslant \pi$ the image $F^*(q)$ has one pole, of order $r_1 = 2$, at $q_1 = a$. We have from (2.184)

$$\text{Res}_{q_1}[F^*(q)\, e^{q(n-1)}] = \frac{1}{(2-1)!} \lim_{q\to a} \frac{d}{de^q}\left\{\frac{e^q}{(e^q - e^a)^2}(e^q - e^a)^2\, e^{q(n-1)}\right\} =$$

$$= \lim_{q\to a} \frac{d}{de^q} e^{qn} = n e^{a(n-1)},$$

and consequently, from (2.182), we obtain

$$D^{-1}\{F^*(q)\} = f[n] = n e^{a(n-1)}.$$

The inversion supplies the general solution to the problem of the inverse transformation and enables the original of a given image to be found.

Using the inversion formula (2.182), let us find the original corresponding to an image of the form

$$Y^*(q) = \frac{H^*(q)}{G^*(q)}, \tag{2.185}$$

where $H^*(q)$ and $G^*(q)$ are polynomials in (2.148). We assume that $Y^*(q)$ has poles

q_1 of order r_1,

q_2 of order r_2,

. . . .

q_s of order r_s.

These poles are the roots of $G^*(q) = 0$ in the strip $-\pi < \text{Im } q \leqslant \pi$, and moreover $r_1 + r_2 + \ldots + r_s = l$. The residues $\operatorname{Res}_{q_\nu} [Y^*(q)\, e^{q(n-1)}]$ are determined by (2.184) and equal

$$= \frac{1}{(r_\nu - 1)!} \lim_{q \to q_\nu} \frac{d^{r_\nu - 1}}{de^{q(r_\nu - 1)}} \left\{ \frac{H^*(q)}{G^*(q)} (e^q - e^{q_\nu})^{r_\nu} e^{q(n-1)} \right\} =$$

$$= \frac{1}{(r_\nu - 1)!} \frac{d^{r_\nu - 1}}{de^{q(r_\nu - 1)}} \left\{ \frac{H^*(q)}{G^*(q)} (e^q - e^{q_\nu})^{r_\nu} e^{q(n-1)} \right\}_{q = q_\nu} . \qquad (2.186)$$

On applying to (2.186) the formula for the repeated differentiation of two functions

$$\frac{H^*(q)}{e^q\, G^*(q)} (e^q - e^{q_\nu})^{r_\nu} \text{ and } e^{qn} ,$$

we obtain

$$\operatorname{Res}_{q_\nu} [Y^*(q)\, e^{q(n-1)}] = \sum_{\mu=0}^{r_\nu - 1} c_{\nu\mu} \frac{n^{(\mu)}}{\mu!} e^{q_\nu (n-\mu)} , \qquad (2.187)$$

where

$$n^{(\mu)} = n(n-1) \ldots (n - \mu + 1), \quad n^{(0)} = 1 , \qquad (2.188)$$

is the factorial function and

$$c_{\nu\mu} = \frac{1}{(r_\nu - \mu - 1)!} \frac{d^{r_\nu - \mu - 1}}{de^{q(r_\nu - \mu - 1)}} \left\{ \frac{H^*(q)}{e^q\, G^*(q)} (e^q - e^{q_\nu})^{r_\nu} \right\}_{q = q_\nu} . \qquad (2.189)$$

The final expression for the original is obtained by substituting (2.187) in (2.182):

$$y[n] = \sum_{\nu=1}^{s} \sum_{\mu=0}^{r_\nu - 1} c_{\nu\mu} \frac{n^{(\mu)}}{\mu!} e^{q_\nu (n-\mu)} . \qquad (2.190)$$

For the particular case when the poles are simple ($s = l$, $r_\nu = 1$, $\mu = 0$), we have from (2.189)

$$c_{\nu 0} = \frac{H^*(q_\nu)}{e^{q_\nu}\, \dot{G}^*(q_\nu)} ,$$

and (2.190) reduces to the expansion formula which we have already met:

$$y[n] = \sum_{\nu=1}^{l} \frac{H^*(q_\nu)}{e^{q_\nu}\, \dot{G}^*(q_\nu)} e^{q_\nu n} .$$

The expansion formulae for an image with a zero-order or purely imaginary pole are obtained similarly. A most important theorem on the multiplication of originals can be easily proved using the expansion formulae.

THEOREM 16. MULTIPLICATION OF ORIGINALS

Denote by σ_{c_1}, σ_{c_2} and σ_c the abscissae of convergence of the lattice functions $f_1[n]$, $f_2[n]$ and $f_1[n]\,f_2[n]$ respectively.

From the definition of the discrete Laplace transformation

$$D\{f_1[n]\,f_2[n]\} = \sum_{n=0}^{\infty} e^{-qn} f_1[n]\,f_2[n]\,, \qquad (2.191)$$

where $\sigma_c < \sigma$; $\sigma = \operatorname{Re} q$. Substitute in (2.191)

$$f_1[n] = \frac{1}{2\pi j} \int_{c_1-j\pi}^{c_1+j\pi} F_1^*(s)\, e^{sn}\, ds\,,$$

where $\sigma_{c_1} < c_1$; then, on changing the order of integration and summation, we obtain

$$D\{f_1[n]\,f_2[n]\} = \frac{1}{2\pi j} \int_{c_1-j\pi}^{c_1+j\pi} F_1^*(s) \left[\sum_{n=0}^{\infty} e^{-(q-s)n} f_2[n]\right] ds,$$

where $\sigma_c < \sigma$, $\sigma_{c_1} < c_1$. By the definition of the discrete Laplace transformation

$$\sum_{n=0}^{\infty} e^{-(q-s)n} f_2[n] = F_2^*(q-s), \qquad \sigma_{c_2} < \sigma - \operatorname{Re} s\,,$$

and so

$$D\{f_1[n]\,f_2[n]\} = \frac{1}{2\pi j} \int_{c-j\pi}^{c+j\pi} F_1^*(s)\, F_2^*(q-s)\, ds \qquad (2.192)$$

$$(\sigma_c, \ \sigma_{c_1} + \sigma_{c_2} < \sigma; \ \sigma_{c_1} < c < \sigma - \sigma_{c_2})\,.$$

As it makes no difference which image we start off with we must also have

$$D\{f_1[n]\,f_2[n]\} = \frac{1}{2\pi j} \int_{c-j\pi}^{c+j\pi} F_1^*(q-s)\, F_2^*(s)\, ds \qquad (2.193)$$

$$(\sigma_c, \ \sigma_{c_2} + \sigma_{c_1} < \sigma; \ \sigma_{c_2} < c < \sigma - \sigma_{c_1})\,.$$

This theorem enables the image of the product of two lattice functions to be calculated when the image of each function is known; it is the dual of the convolution theorem (Theorem 11).

Using the same method as before we can show that

$$D\{f_1[n]\,f_2[n]\} = \sum_{\nu} \operatorname{Res}_{s_\nu} [F_1^*(s)\, F_2^*(q-s)]\,, \qquad (2.194)$$

where the residues are taken at the singularities, s_ν of the function $F_1^*(s)$.

We now use this theorem to find the image of the product of two lattice functions, one of which is the solution of a difference equation, the other being arbitrary. Let

$$F_1^*(q) = Y^*(q) = \frac{H^*(q)}{G^*(q)} \stackrel{\cdot}{\longrightarrow} y[n],$$

and

$$F_2^*(q) \stackrel{\cdot}{\longrightarrow} f_2[n].$$

Assuming for simplicity that $Y^*(q)$ has only simple poles $q_\nu = s$ $\nu = 1, 2, \ldots, l$), we have, using (2.194)

$$D\{y[n] f_2[n]\} = \sum_{\nu=1}^{l} \frac{H^*(q_\nu)}{e^{q_\nu} \dot{G}^*(q_\nu)} F_2^*(q - q_\nu). \tag{2.195}$$

Here the notation s_ν has been replaced by q_ν. In particular, if

$$f_2[n] = y[n],$$

i.e.

$$F_2^*(q) = Y^*(q) = \frac{H^*(q)}{G^*(q)},$$

then formula (2.195) gives the image of the squared lattice function as

$$D\{y^2[n]\} = \sum_{\nu=1}^{l} \frac{H^*(q_\nu)}{e^{q_\nu} \dot{G}^*(q_\nu)} \frac{H^*(q - q_\nu)}{G^*(q - q_\nu)}. \tag{2.196}$$

In all the formulae obtained q plays the role of a parameter.

The sum of the squares of the lattice function ordinates can easily be found using (2.196) along with the theorem of the sum of the discreta or ordinates of a lattice function (Theorem 13). Assuming that the abscissa of convergence of $y[n]$ is negative ($\sigma_c < 0$), formula (2.196) gives for $q = 0$

$$\sum_{n=0}^{\infty} y^2[n] = \sum_{\nu=1}^{l} \frac{H^*(q_\nu)}{e^{q_\nu} \dot{G}^*(q_\nu)} \frac{H^*(-q_\nu)}{G^*(-q_\nu)}. \tag{2.197}$$

In general, by applying Theorem 13 to (2.192), the sum of the products of the ordinates of two lattice functions $f_1[n]$ and $f_2[n]$ is given by

$$\sum_{n=0}^{\infty} f_1[n] f_2[n] = \frac{1}{2\pi j} \int_{c-j\pi}^{c+j\pi} F_1^*(s) F_2^*(-s)\, ds \tag{2.198}$$

and when

$$f_1[n] = f_2[n] = f[n],$$

i.e.

$$F_1^*(q) = F_2^*(q) = F(q),$$

$$\sum_{n=0}^{\infty} f^2[n] = \frac{1}{2\pi j} \int_{c-j\pi}^{c+j\pi} F^*(s)\, F^*(-s)\, ds. \tag{2.199}$$

Expression (2.197) gives

$$I_2 = \sum_{n=0}^{\infty} y^2[n]$$

in terms of the image $Y^*(q)$ if the poles q_ν of the latter are known.

It is possible, however, to find I_2 directly in terms of the coefficients of $Y^*(q)$, thus avoiding the computation of the poles. Let

$$Y^*(q) = \frac{b_l e^{ql} + b_{l-1} e^{q(l-1)} + \dots + b_1 e^q + b_0}{a_l e^{ql} + a_{l-1} e^{q(l-1)} + \dots + a_1 e^q + a_0} = \frac{H^*(q)}{G^*(q)}.$$

The case $l_1 < l$ is obtained by equating the coefficients $b_l, b_{l-1}, \dots, b_{l_1+1}$ to zero. We put $e^{q\nu} = z_\nu$ in (2.197) to simplify the calculation; then

$$H^*(q_\nu) = H(z_\nu), \quad H^*(-q_\nu) = H\left(\frac{1}{z_\nu}\right),$$

$$\dot{G}^*(q_\nu) = \dot{G}(z_\nu), \quad G^*(-q_\nu) = G\left(\frac{1}{z_\nu}\right),$$

and we obtain

$$I_2 = \sum_{n=0}^{\infty} y^2[n] = \sum_{\nu=1}^{l} \frac{H(z_\nu)\, H(1/z_\nu)}{z_\nu\, \dot{G}(z_\nu)\, G(1/z_\nu)}, \tag{2.200}$$

where now the dot over G denotes differentiation with respect to z. I_2 can also be expressed in the form of an integral (2.199)

$$I_2 = \frac{1}{2\pi} \int_{\Gamma_0} \frac{H(z)\, H(1/z)}{z\, G(z) G(1/z)}\, dz, \tag{2.201}$$

where Γ_0 is the contour of integration $|z| = 1$;

$$H(z) = \sum_{\mu=1}^{l} b_\mu z^\mu, \quad G(z) = \sum_{\mu=0}^{l} a_\mu z^\mu.$$

We introduce the auxiliary function

$$I_2[n] = \frac{1}{2\pi j} \int_{\Gamma_0} \frac{1}{z^{n+1}} \frac{H(z)\, H(1/z)}{G(z)\, G(1/z)}\, dz$$

or

$$I_2[n] = \frac{1}{2\pi j} \int_{\Gamma_0} \frac{1}{z^{n+1}} \frac{\sum_{\mu=0}^{l} b_\mu z^\mu \sum_{\mu=0}^{l} b_\mu z^{l-\mu}}{\sum_{\mu=0}^{l} a_\mu z^\mu \sum_{\mu=0}^{l} a_\mu z^{l-\mu}} dz.$$

Then

$$I_2[0] = I_2 .$$

To evaluate $I_2[n]$ we construct the sum

$$S[n] = \sum_{\mu=0} a_\mu I_2[n-\mu] = \frac{1}{2\pi j} \int_{\Gamma_0} \frac{1}{z^{n+1}} \frac{\sum_{\mu=0}^{l} b_\mu z^\mu \sum_{\mu=0}^{l} b_\mu z^{l-\mu}}{\sum_{\mu=0}^{l} a_\mu z^{l-\mu}} dz. \quad (2.202)$$

We write

$$\psi(z) = \frac{\sum_{\mu=0}^{l} b_\mu z^\mu \sum_{\mu=0}^{l} b_\mu z^{l-\mu}}{\sum_{\mu=0}^{l} a_\mu z^{l-\mu}},$$

where $\psi(z)$ is a function which is regular in the circle $|z| \leqslant 1$. We put $\psi(z)$ into a more convenient form. We first note that

$$\sum_{\mu=0}^{l} b_\mu z^\mu \sum_{\mu=0}^{l} b_\mu z^{l-\mu} = \sum_{\mu=0}^{2l} g_\mu z^\mu ,$$

where

$$g_\mu = g_{2l-\mu} = \sum_{r=0}^{\mu} b_r b_{l-\mu+r} \quad (b_i \equiv 0 \text{ when } i > l).$$

Then

$$\psi(z) = \frac{\sum_{\mu=0}^{2l} g_\mu z^\mu}{\sum_{\mu=0}^{l} a_\mu z^{l-\mu}} = \frac{\sum_{\mu=0}^{2l} g_\mu z^\mu}{\sum_{\mu=0}^{l} a_{l-\mu} z^\mu} = \sum_{k=0}^{\infty} \gamma_k z^k .$$

We find, on dividing out the polynomials, that the coefficients γ_k obey the recurrence relationship+

$$\gamma_k = \frac{1}{a_l}\left[g_k - \sum_{\mu=0}^{k-1} \gamma_\mu a_{l+\mu-k}\right], \quad (2.203)$$

or, explicitly,

$$\gamma_k = \frac{1}{a_l^{k+1}} \begin{vmatrix} a_l & 0 & \cdots g_0 \\ a_{l-1} & a_l & \cdots g_1 \\ a_{l-2} & a_{l-1} & \cdots g_2 \\ \cdot & \cdot & \cdot \\ a_{l-k} & a_{l-k+1} & \cdots g_k \end{vmatrix} . \quad (2.204)$$

+ γ_k can also be found by the method described later on in § 5.5 of vol. II

Consequently, we find from (2.202)

$$S[n] = \sum_{\mu=0}^{l} a_\mu I_2[n-\mu] =$$

$$= \frac{1}{2\pi j} \int_{\Gamma_0} \frac{1}{z^{n+1}} \psi(z)\, dz = \frac{1}{n!} \psi^{(n)}(0) = \gamma_n$$

and therefore, for $n = 0, 1, 2, \ldots, l$, we obtain the system of equations

$$\sum_{\mu=0}^{l} a_\mu I_2[n-\mu] = \gamma_n, \quad n = 0, 1, 2, \ldots, l.$$

Remembering that $I_2[n]$ is an even function, i. e.

$$I_2[-n] = I_2[n],$$

this system of equations can be written out fully in the form

$$\begin{array}{l} a_0 I_2[0] + a_1 I_2[1] + a_2 I_2[2] + \ldots + a_{l-1} I_2[l-1] + a_l I_2[l] = \gamma_0, \\ a_1 I_2[0] + (a_0 + a_2) I_2[1] + a_3 I_2[2] + \ldots + a_l I_2[l-1] + 0 = \gamma_1, \\ a_2 I_2[0] + (a_1 + a_3) I_2[1] + (a_0 + a_4) I_2[2] + \ldots + 0 + 0 = \gamma_2, \\ \ldots\ldots\ldots\ldots\ldots\ldots\ldots\ldots\ldots\ldots\ldots\ldots \\ a_l I_2[0] + a_{l-1} I_2[1] + a_{l-2} I_2[2] + \ldots + a_1 I_2[l-1] + a_0 I_2[l] = \gamma_l, \end{array}$$

These equations can be solved for

$$I_2[0] = I_2$$

the solutions being

$$I_2 = \frac{\Delta_1}{\Delta} = \frac{\begin{vmatrix} \gamma_0 & a_1 & a_2 & \ldots & a_{l-2} & a_{l-1} & a_l \\ \gamma_1 & a_0 + a_2 & a_3 & \ldots & a_{l-1} & a_l & 0 \\ \gamma_2 & a_1 + a_3 & a_0 + a_4 & \ldots & a_l & 0 & 0 \\ \cdot & \cdot & \cdot & \ldots & \cdot & \cdot & \cdot \\ \cdot & \cdot & \cdot & \ldots & \cdot & \cdot & \cdot \\ \cdot & \cdot & \cdot & \ldots & \cdot & \cdot & \cdot \\ \gamma_l & a_{l-1} & a_{l-2} & \ldots & a_2 & a_1 & a_0 \end{vmatrix}}{\begin{vmatrix} a_0 & a_1 & a_2 & \ldots & a_{l-2} & a_{l-1} & a_l \\ a_1 & a_0 + a_2 & a_3 & \ldots & a_{l-1} & a_l & 0 \\ a_2 & a_1 + a_3 & a_0 + a_4 & \ldots & a_l & 0 & 0 \\ \cdot & \cdot & \cdot & \ldots & \cdot & \cdot & \cdot \\ \cdot & \cdot & \cdot & \ldots & \cdot & \cdot & \cdot \\ \cdot & \cdot & \cdot & \ldots & \cdot & \cdot & \cdot \\ a_l & a_{l-1} & a_{l-2} & \ldots & a_2 & a_1 & a_0 \end{vmatrix}}. \tag{2.205}$$

Consequently, without having to calculate the poles, we have found I_2 in terms of the coefficients of $Y^*(q)$.

We now write out the values of I_2 for $l = 1$, $l = 2$ and $l = 3$.

$l = 1$:

$$I_2 = \frac{\begin{vmatrix} \gamma_0 & a_1 \\ \gamma_1 & a_0 \end{vmatrix}}{\begin{vmatrix} a_0 & a_1 \\ a_1 & a_0 \end{vmatrix}} = \frac{\gamma_0 a_0 - \gamma_1 a_1}{a_0^2 - a_1^2}, \tag{2.206}$$

where

$$\gamma_0 = \frac{g_0}{a_1} = \frac{b_0 b_1}{a_1}; \quad \gamma_1 = \frac{g_1 a_1 - g_0 a_0}{a_1^2} = \frac{(b_0^2 + b_1^2) a_1 - b_0 b_1 a_0}{a_1^2}.$$

$l = 2$:

$$I_2 = \frac{\begin{vmatrix} \gamma_0 & a_1 & a_2 \\ \gamma_1 & a_0 + a_2 & 0 \\ \gamma_2 & a_1 & a_0 \end{vmatrix}}{\begin{vmatrix} a_0 & a_1 & a_2 \\ a_1 & a_0 + a_2 & 0 \\ a_2 & a_1 & a_0 \end{vmatrix}} = \frac{(a_0 + a_2)(a_0 \gamma_0 - a_2 \gamma_2) + a_1 \gamma_1 (a_2 - a_0)}{(a_0 - a_2)(a_0 - a_1 + a_2)(a_0 + a_1 + a_2)}, \tag{2.207}$$

where

$$\gamma_0 = \frac{g_0}{a_2} = \frac{b_0 b_2}{a_2}; \quad \gamma_1 = \frac{g_1}{a_2} - \frac{a_1 g_0}{a_2^2} = \frac{b_0 b_1 + b_1 b_2}{a_2} - \frac{a_1 b_0 b_2}{a_2^2};$$

$$\gamma_2 = \frac{g_2}{a_2} - \frac{a_0 g_0 + a_1 g_1}{a_2^2} + \frac{a_1^2 g_0}{a_2^3} = \frac{b_0^2 + b_1^2 + b_2^2}{a_2^2} -$$

$$- \frac{a_0 b_0 b_2 + a_1 (b_0 b_1 + b_1 b_2)}{a_2^2} + \frac{a_1^2 b_0 b_2}{a_2^3}.$$

$l = 3$:

$$I_2 = \frac{\begin{vmatrix} \gamma_0 & a_1 & a_2 & a_3 \\ \gamma_1 & a_0 + a_2 & a_3 & 0 \\ \gamma_2 & a_1 + a_3 & a_0 & 0 \\ \gamma_3 & a_2 & a_1 & a_0 \end{vmatrix}}{\begin{vmatrix} a_0 & a_1 & a_2 & a_3 \\ a_1 & a_0 + a_2 & a_3 & 0 \\ a_2 & a_1 + a_3 & a_0 & 0 \\ a_3 & a_2 & a_1 & a_0 \end{vmatrix}}, \tag{2.208}$$

where

$$\gamma_0 = \frac{g_0}{a_3} = \frac{b_0 b_3}{a_3}; \quad \gamma_1 = \frac{g_1}{a_3} - \frac{a_2 g_0}{a_3^2} = \frac{b_0 b_2 + b_1 b_3}{a_3} - \frac{a_2 b_0 b_3}{a_3^2};$$

$$\gamma_2 = \frac{g_2}{a_2} - \frac{a_1 g_0 + a_2 g_1}{a_3^2} + \frac{a_2^2 g_0}{a_3^3} =$$

$$= \frac{1}{a_3}(b_0 b_1 + b_1 b_2 + b_2 b_3) - \frac{1}{a_3^2}(a_1 b_0 b_3 + a_2 b_0 b_2 + a_2 b_1 b_3) + \frac{a_2^2}{a_3^3} b_0 b_3;$$

$$\gamma_3 = \frac{g_3}{a_3} - \frac{1}{a_3^2}(a_0g_0 + a_1g_1 + a_2g_2) +$$

$$+ \frac{a_2}{a_3^3}(2\,a_1g_0 + a_2g_1) - \frac{a_2^3}{a_3^4}g_0 = \frac{1}{a_3}(b_0^2 + b_1^2 + b_2^2 + b_3^2) -$$

$$- \frac{1}{a_3^2}[a_0b_0b_3 + a_1b_0b_2 + a_1b_1b_3 + a_2(b_0b_1 + b_1b_2 + b_2b_3)] +$$

$$+ \frac{a_2}{a_3^3}(2\,a_1b_0b_3 + a_2b_0b_2 + a_2b_1b_3) - \frac{a_2^3}{a_3^4}b_0b_3\,.$$

The coefficients γ_k simplify greatly if $b_0 = 0$ or $b_l = 0$. Although formula (2.205) has been deduced for the case when $G(z) = 0$ has simple roots it also holds for the case of higher order roots, since the roots are continuous functions of the coefficients a_k+.

In the above we have always considered the lattice function $f[n]$. We emphasise that all the relationships obtained hold also for the displaced lattice function $f[n, \varepsilon]$, where ε is a parameter. In this case it is only necessary to replace $f[n]$ by $f[n, \varepsilon]$ and $F^*(q)$ by $F^*(q, \varepsilon)$.

2.7. Relationship between the discrete Laplace transformation, Fourier series and Laurent series

Assume that the lattice function $f[n]$ has a negative abscissa of convergence σ_c. We may then, in the formulae for the direct and inverse Laplace transformation

$$F^*(q) = \sum_{n=0}^{\infty} e^{-qn} f[n]$$

and

$$f[n] = \frac{1}{2\pi j}\int_{c-j\pi}^{c+j\pi} F^*(q)\, e^{qn}\, dq$$

put $q = j\bar{\omega}$ and $c = 0$. We then obtain

$$F^*(j\bar{\omega}) = \sum_{n=0}^{\infty} e^{-j\bar{\omega}n} f[n] =$$

$$= \sum_{n=0}^{\infty} f[n]\cos n\bar{\omega} - j\sum_{n=1}^{\infty} f[n]\sin n\bar{\omega}\,, \qquad (2.209)$$

+ O. M. Kryzhanovskii has derived the expression for I_2 in a slightly different form (2; 1953).

and

$$f[n] = \frac{1}{2\pi j} \int_{-j\pi}^{j\pi} F^*(j\bar{\omega})\, e^{j\bar{\omega}n}\, d(j\bar{\omega}) = \frac{1}{2\pi} \int_{-\pi}^{\pi} F^*(j\bar{\omega})\, e^{j\bar{\omega}n}\, d\bar{\omega}\,. \quad (2.210)$$

We call $F^*(j\bar{\omega})$ the spectrum of the lattice function $f[n]$.

The real and imaginary parts of the spectrum $F^*(j\bar{\omega})$ are denoted by $B_F^*(\bar{\omega})$ and $M_F^*(\bar{\omega})$, so that

$$F^*(j\bar{\omega}) = B_F^*(\bar{\omega}) + jM_F^*(\bar{\omega})\,.$$

We then have from (2.209)

$$\left.\begin{aligned} B_F^*(\bar{\omega}) &= \sum_{n=0}^{\infty} f[n] \cos \bar{\omega}\, n, \\ M_F^*(\bar{\omega}) &= -\sum_{n=1}^{\infty} f[n] \sin \bar{\omega}\, n. \end{aligned}\right\} \quad (2.211)$$

Thus $B_F^*(\bar{\omega})$ and $M_F^*(\bar{\omega})$ are respectively even and odd periodic functions of $\bar{\omega}$.

Substituting $F^*(j\bar{\omega}) = B_F^*(\bar{\omega}) + jM_F^*(\bar{\omega})$ and $e^{j\bar{\omega}n} = \cos \bar{\omega}n + j \sin \bar{\omega}n$ in (2.210) and separating real and imaginary parts, we obtain

$$f[n] = \frac{1}{2\pi} \int_{-\pi}^{\pi} \{B_F^*(\bar{\omega}) \cos \bar{\omega}\, n - M_F^*(\bar{\omega}) \sin \bar{\omega}\, n\}\, d\bar{\omega} +$$

$$+ \frac{j}{2\pi} \int_{-\pi}^{\pi} \{B_F^*(\bar{\omega}) \sin \bar{\omega}\, n + M_F^*(\bar{\omega}) \cos \bar{\omega}\, n\}\, d\bar{\omega}\,.$$

Since $B_F^*(\bar{\omega})$ and $M_F^*(\bar{\omega})$ are respectively even and odd functions of $\bar{\omega}$, the integrand in the first expression will be an even function of $\bar{\omega}$ and the integrand in the second an odd function of $\bar{\omega}$. The second integral thus equals zero. The lower limit in the first integral can be replaced by 0 provided we multiply the integral by 2. We thus obtain

$$f[n] = \frac{1}{\pi} \int_{0}^{\pi} \{B_F^*(\bar{\omega}) \cos \bar{\omega}\, n - M_F^*(\bar{\omega}) \sin \bar{\omega}\, n\}\, d\bar{\omega}. \quad (2.212)$$

Putting $(-n)$ for n in (2.212) gives

$$0 = \frac{1}{\pi} \int_{0}^{\pi} \{B_F^*(\bar{\omega}) \cos \bar{\omega}\, n + M_F^*(\bar{\omega}) \sin \bar{\omega}\, n\}\, d\bar{\omega}\,, \quad (2.213)$$

since we proved in § 2.6 that $f[n] \equiv 0$ for negative values of n (see [2. 177]). Finally, on adding and subtracting (2.213) and (2.212), we obtain

$$\left.\begin{aligned} f[n] &= \frac{2}{\pi}\int_0^\pi B_F^*(\bar\omega)\cos\bar\omega n\,\mathrm{d}\bar\omega\,, \\ f[n] &= -\frac{2}{\pi}\int_0^\pi M_F^*(\bar\omega)\sin\bar\omega n\,\mathrm{d}\bar\omega\,. \end{aligned}\right\} \tag{2.214}$$

From expressions (2.214) and (2.211) we conclude that, for $\sigma_c < 0$, the lattice function is related to the real and imaginary parts of the image with $q = j\bar\omega$ by the usual (and not the integral) Fourier transformation. In other words, the *values of the lattice function equal the Fourier coefficients of the real or imaginary parts of its spectrum.*

We obtain from (2.199) for $s = j\bar\omega$

$$I_2 = \sum_{n=0}^{\infty} f^2[n] = \frac{1}{2\pi}\int_{-\pi}^{\pi} F^*(j\bar\omega)\,F^*(-j\bar\omega)\,\mathrm{d}\bar\omega\,,$$

or, since

$$F^*(j\bar\omega)\,F^*(-j\bar\omega) = |F^*(j\omega)|^2 = B_F^{*2}(\bar\omega) + M_F^{*2}(\bar\omega)\,,$$

we have, remembering that the latter expression is even,

$$I_2 = \sum_{n=0}^{\infty} f^2[n] = \frac{1}{\pi}\int_0^\pi |F^*(j\bar\omega)|^2\,\mathrm{d}\bar\omega =$$

$$= \frac{1}{\pi}\int_0^\pi \left[B_F^{*2}(\bar\omega) + M_F^{*2}(\bar\omega)\right]\mathrm{d}\bar\omega\,, \tag{2.215}$$

i.e. *the sum of the squares of the ordinates of a lattice function is proportional to the area under its spectrum squared.* This relationship is the Lyapunov-Parceval equality, well known from the theory of Fourier series.

The above relationships hold only when the abscissa of convergence of the lattice function is negative.

The discrete Laplace transformation can be considered as a generalised Fourier transformation in the sense that it does not impose such strict conditions ($\sigma_c < 0$) on the transformed lattice function.

We now put $e^q = \mathbf{z}$ in the formula for the direct Laplace transformation, giving

$$F^*(\ln \mathbf{z}) = F(\mathbf{z}) = \sum_{n=0}^{\infty} f[n] \frac{1}{\mathbf{z}^n}. \tag{2.216}$$

The function $F(\mathbf{z})$ can be considered as the principal part of a Laurent series, the coefficients being $f[n]$. Carrying out this change of variable in the inversion formula gives

$$f[n] = \frac{1}{2\pi j} \int_{\Gamma_0} F(z) \frac{d\mathbf{z}}{\mathbf{z}^{-n+1}}, \tag{2.217}$$

where Γ_0 is a circle of radius $e^{c'}$. The last formula is the well-known expression for the coefficients of a Laurent series.

The transformations effected by expressions (2.216), (2.217) are called in foreign literature the *direct and inverse z-transformations.*

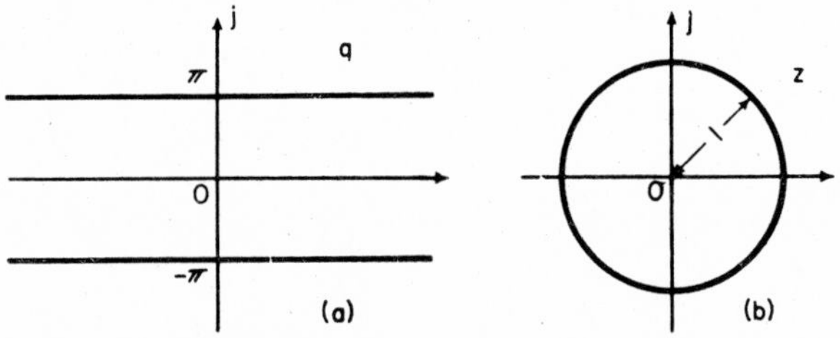

FIG. 2.31. The strip $-\pi < \omega \leqslant \pi$ (*a*), and the circle $|z| \leqslant 1$ (*b*).

All z-transformation theorems can be obtained from the theorems of the discrete Laplace transformation by making the simple change of variable $z = e^q$. Also, the image $F(z)$ is obtained from $F^*(q)$ by making the same change of variable. The transformation $z = e^q$ implies that the image in the z-transformation is a function of z and that the circle $|z| = 1$ (Fig. 2.31*b*) plays the role of the strip $-\pi < \operatorname{Im} q \leqslant \pi$ (Fig. 2.31*a*).

Although the expression for the image of a z-transformation looks slightly simpler and the images themselves are not multivalued but single valued, the discrete Laplace transformation proves more convenient whenever it is required to draw an analogy between continuous functions and lattice functions, i.e. between continuous systems and pulse systems. Moreover, many theorems of the discrete Laplace transformation have a simpler form. These were the considerations which decided the use of the discrete Laplace transformation in this book although, as was said above, there is no basic difference between the discrete Laplace transformation and the z-transformation.

The series which defines the discrete Laplace transformation can be considered as a special case of the Dirichlet series. In several works† the following transformation is used to solve difference equations

$$F^*(s) = \sum_{n=0}^{\infty} a^{ns} f[n] .$$

This transformation is obtained by making the simple change of variable $q = s \ln a$ in the discrete Laplace transformation.

Finally, difference equations can be solved by a method based on a purely operational point of view;‡ this method has been developed recently by Ya. Mikusinskii in connection with the solution of differential equations.

Formulae (2.214) can be used to obtain an approximate solution of a difference equation. For this purpose we replace q by $j\bar{\omega}$ in the image of the difference equation solution, separate real and imaginary parts

$$Y^*(j\bar{\omega}) = B_Y^*(\bar{\omega}) + jM_Y^*(\bar{\omega}) ,$$

then use the first of relationships (2.214) which, in the present case, is written as

$$y[n] = \frac{2}{\pi} \int_0^{\pi} B_Y^*(\bar{\omega}) \cos \bar{\omega} n \, d\bar{\omega} . \tag{2.218}$$

If $B_Y^*(\bar{\omega})$ is given graphically, then $y[n]$ can be calculated from this expression using any approximate method of integration.

Similarly relationship (2.215), which is written in the present instance as

$$I_2 = \sum_{n=0}^{\infty} y^2[n] = \frac{1}{\pi} \int_0^{\pi} |Y^*(j\bar{\omega})|^2 d\bar{\omega} =$$

$$= \frac{1}{\pi} \int_0^{\pi} [B_Y^{*2}(\bar{\omega}) + M_Y^{*2}(\bar{\omega})] \, d\bar{\omega} , \tag{2.219}$$

can be used to find the approximate value of the sum of the squares of the discreta if $B_Y^*(\bar{\omega})$ and $M_Y^*(\bar{\omega})$ are given graphically.

We shall consider these problems in more detail in § 5.5.

† See, for example, Tomlinson (2; 1953); Sagrov, Higgins (2; 1956).
‡ See, for example, Bellert (2; 1957).

2.8. Relationship between the image of a continuous function and the image of the corresponding lattice function

In this section we establish the relationship between the image, or spectrum, of a continuous function and the image, or spectrum, of the corresponding lattice function; this relationship is important in the theory of pulse systems. We also establish the correspondence between operations with these images.

For this purpose let us consider some continuous function $f_T(T\bar{t}) = f(\bar{t})$ of argument $\bar{t} = t/T$, defined in the interval $0 < \bar{t} < \infty$. The image of this function in the sense of the single-sided Laplace transformation is written as

$$F(q) = L\{f(\bar{t})\} = \int_0^\infty e^{-q\bar{t}} f(\bar{t})\, d\bar{t}, \qquad (2.220)$$

where $q = pT$ is the transformation parameter, and

$$F(q) = \frac{1}{T} F_T\left(\frac{q}{T}\right).^{+}$$

The displaced lattice function $f[n, \varepsilon] = f(n + \varepsilon)$ is obtained from the continuous function $f(\bar{t})$ by replacing $\bar{t}$ by $(n + \varepsilon)$ in the latter. The displaced lattice function for $\varepsilon > 0$ is shifted to the right with respect to $f[n, 0] = f[n]$. The image of this discrete lattice function in the sense of the discrete Laplace transformation equals

$$F^*(q, \varepsilon) = D\{f[n, \varepsilon]\} = \sum_{n=0}^{\infty} e^{-qn} f[n, \varepsilon], \qquad (2.221)$$

where ε is considered as a parameter.

In particular we obtain for $\varepsilon = 0$

$$F^*(q, 0) = D\{f[n, 0]\} = \sum_{n=0}^{\infty} e^{-qn} f[n, 0],$$

or, more briefly,

$$F^*(q) = D\{f[n]\} = \sum_{n=0}^{\infty} e^{-qn} f[n].$$

These expressions defining the discrete Laplace transformation have been used repeatedly above.

We now proceed to find the relationship between the image of a lattice function $F^*(q, \varepsilon) = D\{f[n, \varepsilon]\}$ and the image of the correspond-

+ This follows from the similarity theorem of the usual Laplace transformation. If $F_T(p) = L\{f_T(t)\}$, then $\frac{1}{T} F_T\left(\frac{q}{T}\right) = L\{f_T(T\bar{t})\} = L[f(\bar{t})]$. See, for example, M. F. Gardner, D. L. Barnes (2; 1949); G. Doetsch (2; 1958).

ing continuous function $f(\bar{t})$. For this purpose we introduce the functions $f_1(\bar{t})$ and $f_1[n, \varepsilon]$, defined by

$$f_1(\bar{t}) = \frac{1}{2}\left[f(\bar{t}+0) + f(\bar{t}-0)\right]$$

and

$$f_1[n, \varepsilon] = \frac{1}{2}\left[f[n, \varepsilon+0] + f[n, \varepsilon-0]\right].$$

Here $f(\bar{t} \pm 0)$ and $f[n, \varepsilon \pm 0]$ denote the values of the functions to the right and the left of the points $\bar{t} = n + \varepsilon$.

At a point of continuity

$$f_1(\bar{t}) = f(\bar{t}) \text{ and } f_1[n, \varepsilon] = f[n, \varepsilon].$$

At a point of discontinuity the functions $f_1(\bar{t})$ and $f_1[n, \varepsilon]$ give respectively the arithmetical mean of the values of $f(\bar{t})$ and $f[n, \varepsilon]$ to the right and the left of the point of discontinuity. We assume for the moment that $f_1(\bar{t})$, and thus $f_1[n, \varepsilon]$, satisfy the conditions

$$\lim_{\bar{t}\to\pm\infty} f_1(\bar{t}) = 0, \quad \lim_{n\to\pm\infty} f_1[n, \varepsilon] = 0. \tag{2.222}$$

Consider the series

$$\sum_{n=-\infty}^{\infty} f_1(n+\varepsilon) = \sum_{n=-\infty}^{\infty} f_1[n, \varepsilon] = \varphi(\varepsilon). \tag{2.223}$$

The sum of this series is a periodic function of ε with a period equal to unity. This can be seen as follows. By replacing ε by $\varepsilon + m$ in (2.223), where m is an integer, we obtain

$$\varphi(\varepsilon + m) = \sum_{n=-\infty}^{\infty} f_1[n+m, \varepsilon].$$

We have, on putting $n + m = n_1$,

$$\sum_{n=-\infty}^{\infty} f_1[n+m, \varepsilon] = \sum_{n_1=-\infty}^{\infty} f_1[n_1 \varepsilon] = \varphi(\varepsilon),$$

and so

$$\varphi(\varepsilon + m) = \varphi(\varepsilon),$$

i.e. the function $\varphi(\varepsilon)$ is periodic with a period equal to unity.

Write $\varphi(\varepsilon)$ as a Fourier series

$$\varphi(\varepsilon) = \sum_{r=-\infty}^{\infty} \varphi_r \, e^{2\pi j r \varepsilon}. \tag{2.224}$$

The Fourier coefficients φ_r of the function $\varphi(\varepsilon)$ are given by

$$\varphi_r = \int_0^1 \varphi(\varepsilon)\, e^{-2\pi j r \varepsilon}\, d\varepsilon\,, \tag{2.225}$$

or, on substituting $\varphi(\varepsilon)$ from (2.223) and interchanging the order of integration and summation, by

$$\varphi_r = \sum_{n=-\infty}^{\infty} \int_0^1 f_1(n+\varepsilon)\, e^{-2\pi j r \varepsilon}\, d\varepsilon\,.$$

Put $\bar{t} = n + \varepsilon$ in the last equation. Since $e^{2\pi j r n} = 1$, we obtain

$$\varphi_r = \sum_{n=-\infty}^{\infty} \int_n^{n+1} f_1(\bar{t})\, e^{-2\pi j r \bar{t}}\, d\bar{t} = \int_{-\infty}^{\infty} e^{-2\pi j r \bar{t}} f_1(\bar{t})\, d\bar{t}\,.$$

Inserting this value of φ_r in series (2.224), we find

$$\varphi(\varepsilon) = \sum_{r=-\infty}^{\infty} e^{2\pi j r \varepsilon} \int_{-\infty}^{\infty} e^{-2\pi j r \bar{t}} f_1(\bar{t})\, d\bar{t}\,.$$

Comparing this expression with (2.223) gives

$$\sum_{n=-\infty}^{\infty} f_1[n, \varepsilon] = \sum_{r=-\infty}^{\infty} e^{2\pi j r \varepsilon} \int_{-\infty}^{\infty} e^{-2\pi j r \bar{t}} f_1(\bar{t})\, d\bar{t}\,.$$

If, in this latter expression, we replace

$$f_1(\bar{t}) \text{ by } f_1(\bar{t})\, e^{-q|\bar{t}|}$$

and consequently

$$f_1[n, \varepsilon] \text{ by } f_1[n, \varepsilon]\, e^{-q|n+\varepsilon|}\,,$$

where

$$\operatorname{Re} q > 0\,,$$

we have that

$$\sum_{n=-\infty}^{\infty} e^{-q|n+\varepsilon|} f_1[n, \varepsilon] = \sum_{r=-\infty}^{\infty} e^{2\pi j r \varepsilon} \int_{-\infty}^{\infty} e^{-(q|\bar{t}|+2\pi j r \bar{t})} f_1(\bar{t})\, d\bar{t}\,.$$

For this relationship to hold the conditions (2.222) must, obviously, be replaced by the stricter requirements

$$|f_1(\bar{t})| < A e^{\sigma_0 |\bar{t}|}, \qquad |f_1[n, \varepsilon]| < A e^{\sigma_0 |n+\varepsilon|},$$

where A and $\sigma_0 = \operatorname{Re} q > 0$ are constants.

Remembering that for functions of interest

$$f_1(\bar{t}) = f(\bar{t}) \text{ and } f_1[n, \varepsilon] = f[n, \varepsilon] \text{ for } \bar{t} = n + \varepsilon > 0$$

and

$$f_1(\bar{t}) = f(\bar{t}) = f_1[n, \varepsilon] = f[n, \varepsilon] \equiv 0 \text{ for } \bar{t} = n + \varepsilon < 0,$$

and that for $n = 0$ and $\varepsilon = 0$ there is a possible point of discontinuity, giving

$$f_1[0, 0] = \frac{1}{2} f[0, 0]$$

we can write the previously obtained relationship in the form

$$\sum_{n=0}^{\infty}{}' \mathrm{e}^{-qn} f[n, \varepsilon] = \sum_{r=-\infty}^{\infty} \mathrm{e}^{(q+2\pi jr)\varepsilon} \int_0^{\infty} \mathrm{e}^{-(q+2\pi jr)\bar{t}} f(\bar{t})\, \mathrm{d}\bar{t}. \qquad (2.226)$$

The sign $'$ on the summation on the left-hand side indicates that for $\varepsilon = 0$ the first term, which corresponds to $n = 0$, must be multiplied by $^1/_2$.

For $\varepsilon > 0$ the right side of this relationship equals, as can be seen from (2.221), the image of the displaced lattice function $F^*(q, \varepsilon)$. Using the notation given in (2.220) for the image of a continuous function, we can finally write (2.226) in the form

$$F^*(q, \varepsilon) = \sum_{r=-\infty}^{\infty} \mathrm{e}^{(q+2\pi jr)\varepsilon} F(q + 2\pi jr), \qquad (2.227)$$

where ε lies within the interval $0 < \varepsilon \leqslant 1$.

For $\varepsilon = 0$ the left side of (2.226) can be written

$$\frac{1}{2} f[0] + \sum_{n=1}^{\infty} \mathrm{e}^{-qn} f[n] = \sum_{n=0}^{\infty} \mathrm{e}^{-qn} f[n] - \frac{1}{2} f[0] = F^*(q) - \frac{1}{2} f[0],$$

and so in this case the required relationship takes the form

$$F^*(q) = \frac{1}{2} f[0] + \sum_{r=-\infty}^{\infty} F(q + 2\pi jr). \qquad (2.228)$$

The fact that (2.228) does not result from putting $\varepsilon = 0$ in (2.227), provided $f[0] \neq 0$, is due to a well-known property of Fourier series which states that the sum of the series at a point of discontinuity equals the arithmetic mean of the values of the function on each side of the discontinuity.+

Given the image $F(q)$ of a continuous function $f(\bar{t})$, relationships (2.227) and (2.228) determine the image $F^*(q, \varepsilon)$ of the corresponding lattice function $f[n, \varepsilon]$ for any fixed value of ε.

Example. Consider $f(\bar{t}) = 1(\bar{t})$, the unit step function. Its image is

$$F(q) = \frac{1}{T} F_T\left(\frac{q}{T}\right) = \frac{1}{q}.$$

+ See also G. Doetsch (2; 1957). Formula (2.228) in slightly different form is known as Poisson's formula.

From (2.228) we have

$$F^*(q) = \sum_{n=0}^{\infty} 1 \cdot e^{-qn} = \frac{1}{2} + \sum_{r=-\infty}^{\infty} \frac{1}{q + 2\pi jr}.$$

It is known[+] that

$$\sum_{r=-\infty}^{\infty} \frac{1}{q + 2\pi jr} = \frac{1}{q} + \sum_{r=1}^{\infty} \left\{ \frac{1}{q + 2\pi jr} + \frac{1}{q - 2\pi jr} \right\} =$$

$$= \frac{1}{q} + \sum_{r=1}^{\infty} \frac{2q}{q^2 + 4\pi^2 r^2} = \frac{1}{2} \coth \frac{q}{2} = \frac{1}{2} + \frac{1}{e^q - 1},$$

and therefore

$$F^*(q) = \frac{1}{2} + \frac{1}{2} + \frac{1}{e^q - 1} = \frac{e^q}{e^q - 1},$$

which agrees with the previously obtained result (2.28).

We shall now deduce the relationship which, if the image $F^*(q, \varepsilon)$ of the lattice function $f[n, \varepsilon]$ is known, determines the image $F(q)$ of the corresponding continuous function $f(\bar{t})$. We commence by multiplying both sides of (2.227) by $e^{-q\varepsilon}$, giving

$$e^{-q\varepsilon} F^*(q, \varepsilon) = \sum_{r=-\infty}^{\infty} e^{2\pi rj\varepsilon} F(q + 2\pi rj).$$

A comparison of this expression with (2.224) shows that it represents the expansion of $e^{-q\varepsilon} F^*(q, \varepsilon)$ in a Fourier series. The coefficients of this Fourier series equal $F(q + 2\pi jr)$, and thus from (2.225) we have

$$F(q + 2\pi jr) = \int_0^1 e^{-q\varepsilon} F^*(q, \varepsilon) e^{-2\pi jr\varepsilon} \, d\varepsilon.$$

Putting $r = 0$ gives

$$F(q) = \int_0^1 e^{-q\varepsilon} F^*(q, \varepsilon) \, d\varepsilon. \qquad (2.229)$$

This relationship gives the image of a continuous function in terms of the image of the displaced lattice function.

EXAMPLE 1. Consider

$$F^*(q, \varepsilon) = \frac{e^q}{e^q - 1}.$$

Inserting this in (2.229) gives

$$F(q) = \frac{e^q}{e^q - 1} \int_0^1 e^{-q\varepsilon} \, d\varepsilon = \frac{e^q}{e^q - 1} \frac{1 - e^{-q}}{q} = \frac{1}{q}.$$

[+] See, for example, I. M. Ryzhik (2; 1943).

EXAMPLE 2. Consider

$$F^*(q, \varepsilon) = \frac{e^q}{e^q - e^a} e^{a\varepsilon} .$$

Inserting this in (2.229) gives

$$F(q) = \frac{e^q}{e^q - e^a} \int_0^1 e^{-(q-a)\varepsilon} \, d\,\varepsilon = \frac{e^q}{e^q - e^a} \, \frac{1 - e^{-(q-a)}}{q - a} = \frac{1}{q - a} .$$

The images obtained correspond to the unit step and exponential functions.

The relationships between the spectrum of a continuous function $F(j\,\bar{\omega})$ and the spectrum of the displaced lattice function $F(j\bar{\omega}, \varepsilon)$ are obtained by putting $q = j\bar{\omega}$ in (2.229) and (2.227):

$$F(j\,\bar{\omega}) = \int_0^1 e^{-j\bar{\omega}\varepsilon} \, F^*(j\,\bar{\omega}, \varepsilon) \, d\,\varepsilon , \qquad (2.230)$$

$$F^*(j\,\bar{\omega}, \varepsilon) = \sum_{r=-\infty}^{\infty} e^{j(\bar{\omega}+2\pi r)\varepsilon} \, F\,[j(\bar{\omega} + 2\,\pi\, r)] , \qquad (2.231)$$

and in particular if $\varepsilon = 0$ we obtain from (2.228) for $q = j\bar{\omega}$

$$F^*(j\,\bar{\omega}) = \frac{1}{2} f[0] + \sum_{r=-\infty}^{\infty} F\,[j(\bar{\omega} + 2\,\pi\, r)] . \qquad (2.232)$$

It follows from the latter relationship that *the spectrum $F^*(j\,\omega)$ of a lattice function $f[n]$ equals, apart from the constant term $\frac{1}{2}\, f[0]$, the sum of the spectra of the corresponding continuous function which are displaced along the frequency axis by amounts $2\pi\, r$*, where r varies from $-\infty$ to $+\infty$.

This result can also be obtained from simple physical considerations.+ For simplicity we shall assume $f[0] = 0$. Consider a train of amplitude-modulated pulses, the time between successive pulses being T, i.e. the pulse repetition frequency $\omega_0 = 2\pi/T$. The height of these pulses varies in proportion to the values of the modulating function $f_T(t)$, or envelope, at the discrete moments of time $t = nT$ ($n = 0, 1, \ldots$) (Fig. 2.32). These amplitude-modulated pulses correspond to a lattice function $f[nT]$.

The spectral function, or briefly the spectrum, $F(j\,\omega)$ of the envelope is defined by the expression

$$F(j\,\omega) = \int_0^{\infty} e^{-j\omega t} f_T(t) \, d\,t .$$

+ See, for example, the author's own work, [2.1]

If we assume that the pulse duration is sufficiently small compared with the repetition period and that during the time of a pulse the envelope does not change, then the spectrum of each pulse can be written in the form $f[nT]\, e^{-j\omega nT}$, where $f[nT]$ equals the area of the pulse. In this case the amplitude spectrum of each pulse is a constant, equal to the height (or proportional to the area) of the pulse, and the phase spectrum is linear with a slope equal to k times the instant at which the first pulse appears (Fig. 2.33). The spectrum $F^*(j\bar{\omega})$ of the amplitude-modulated pulse train $f[nT]$ is obtained by summing the spectra of the individual pulses

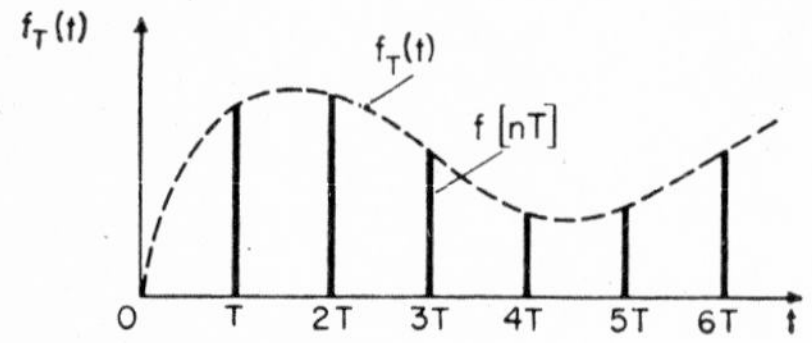

FIG. 2.32. Train of amplitude-modulated pulses.

$$F^*(j\,\omega) = \sum_{n=1}^{\infty} e^{-j\omega nT} f[n\,T]\,,$$

which, on putting $T = 1$ and $\omega = \bar{\omega}$, agrees with the definition of the spectrum of a lattice function (2.209) since $f[0] = 0$.

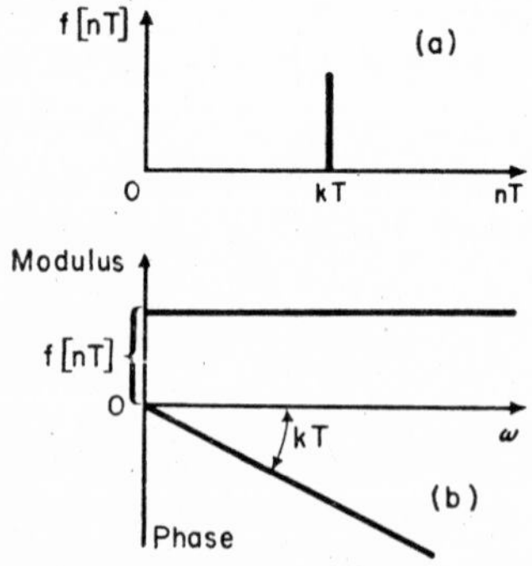

FIG. 2.33. Amplitude spectrum and phase spectrum of a single pulse.

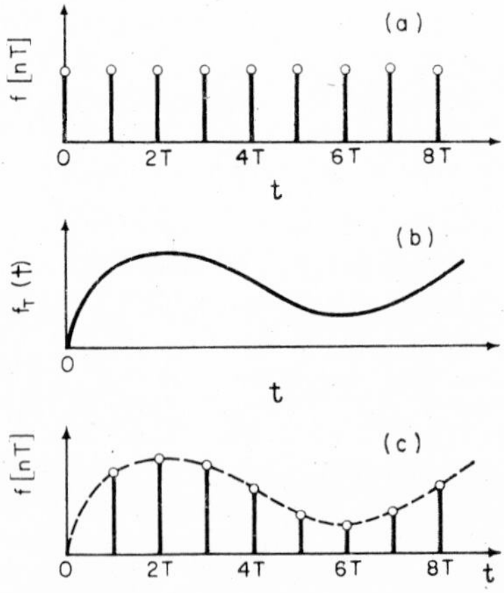

FIG. 2.34. (a) Unmodulated pulse train, (b) continuous signal, (c) modulated pulse train.

On the other hand the unmodulated pulse train $1[nT]$ (Fig. 2.34*a*) can be represented as a Fourier series[+]

$$1\,[nT] = \frac{\omega_0}{2\pi} \sum_{r=-\infty}^{\infty} \mathrm{e}^{jr\omega_0 t}, \quad \omega_0 = \frac{2\pi}{T}.$$

By multiplying both sides of this equality by $f_T(t)$ (Fig. 2.34*b*), we find the expression for the amplitude-modulated pulse train $f_T(t).\ 1\,[nT] = f\,[nT]$ (Fig. 2.34*c*):

$$f\,[nT] = \frac{\omega_0}{2\pi} \sum_{r=-\infty}^{\infty} \mathrm{e}^{jr\omega_0 t} f_T(t)\,.$$

We now transform from functions of time to spectral functions, remembering that the spectrum of $f[nT]$ equals $F^*(j\,\omega)$ and that the spectrum of $\mathrm{e}^{jr\omega_0 t} f_T(t)$ equals $F[j(\omega - r\,\omega_0)]$ — which can easily be seen by substituting $\mathrm{e}^{jr\omega_0 t} f_T(t)$ in the expression defining the spectrum of a continuous function; we obtain

$$F^*(j\,\omega) = \frac{\omega_0}{2\pi} \sum_{r=-\infty}^{\infty} F\,[j(\omega - r\,\omega_0)],$$

which, for $\omega_0 = 2\pi(T = 1)$, $\omega = \bar{\omega}$ and $f[0] = 0$, agrees with the previously obtained relationship (2.232).

Expressions (2.227) and (2.229), which relate the image $F(q)$ of a continuous function with the image $F^*(q, \varepsilon)$ of the corresponding lattice function, set up a correspondence between these functions. If we denote the operations of direct and inverse transformation by $\mathfrak{D}$ and $\mathfrak{D}^{-1}$ respectively, (2.227) and (2.229) can be written in the form

$$F^*(q, \varepsilon) = \mathfrak{D}\{F(q)\}, \tag{2.233}$$

and

$$F(q) = \mathfrak{D}^{-1}\{F^*(q, \varepsilon)\}. \tag{2.234}$$

The simplest cases of the $\mathfrak{D}$ and $\mathfrak{D}^{-1}$ transformations were considered in the examples on p. 172, namely

$$\mathfrak{D}\left\{\frac{1}{q}\right\} = \frac{\mathrm{e}^q}{\mathrm{e}^q - 1} \quad \text{and} \quad \mathfrak{D}\left\{\frac{1}{q - a}\right\} = \frac{\mathrm{e}^q}{\mathrm{e}^q - \mathrm{e}^a}\,\mathrm{e}^{a\varepsilon}. \tag{2.235}$$

We now establish the properties of the $\mathfrak{D}$-transformation (2.233) that play an important part in the theory of pulse systems. These properties supplement the theorems and rules of the discrete Laplace

[+] We recall that the Fourier coefficients are obtained by multiplying the spectral function by $1/T = \omega_0/2\pi$.

transformation given in § 2.3 or, in some cases, present them in a different form. The properties of the H transformation will be given in the form of theorems.

THEOREM 17. LINEARITY OF IMAGES OF CONTINUOUS AND DISCRETE FUNCTIONS.

Let

$$F(q) = \sum_{\nu=1}^{k} a_\nu F_\nu(q) .$$

Applying the $\mathfrak{D}$-transformation to both sides of this expression gives, using (2.227),

$$\mathfrak{D}\{F(q)\} = \mathfrak{D}\left\{\sum_{\nu=1}^{k} a_\nu F_\nu(q)\right\} = \sum_{r=-\infty}^{\infty} \epsilon^{(q+2\pi jr)\varepsilon} \sum_{\nu=1}^{k} a_\nu F_\nu(q + 2\pi jr) .$$

On changing the order of summation in this expression and writing

$$\mathfrak{D}\{F_\nu(q)\} = F_\nu^*(q, \varepsilon) = \sum_{r=-\infty}^{\infty} e^{(q+2\pi jr)\varepsilon} F_\nu(q + 2\pi jr) ,$$

we obtain the final result

$$\mathfrak{D}\left\{\sum_{\nu=1}^{k} a_\nu F_\nu(q)\right\} = \sum_{\nu=1}^{k} a_\nu F_\nu^* (q, \varepsilon) . \tag{2.236}$$

The image of a linear combination of continuous functions corresponds to the linear combination of the images of the corresponding lattice functions, i.e. the $\mathfrak{D}$-transformation is additive. Obviously, Theorem 17 is equivalent to the linearity theorem (Theorem 1).

THEOREM 18. MULTIPLICATION BY e^{-kq} (k is and integer).

Multiply both sides of (2.227) by e^{-kq}, where k is an integer. Then, since

$$e^{-kq} = e^{-k(q+2\pi jr)} \quad (r = \pm 0, 1, 2, \ldots) , \tag{2.237}$$

we obtain

$$e^{-kq} F^*(q, \varepsilon) = \sum_{r=-\infty}^{\infty} e^{(q+2\pi jr)\varepsilon} [e^{-k(q+2\pi jr)} F(q + 2\pi jr)] ,$$

i.e. in the notation of (2.233),

$$\mathfrak{D}\{e^{-kq} F(q)\} = e^{-kq} F^*(q, \varepsilon) . \tag{2.238}$$

Thus, *multiplying* $F(q)$ *by* e^{-kq} *corresponds to multiplying* $F^*(q, \varepsilon)$ *also by* e^{-kq}. This theorem is equivalent to the original-translation theorem (Theorem 2).

THEOREM 19. MULTIPLICATION BY $e^{-\gamma q}$ $(\gamma < 1)$.

Consider

$$\mathfrak{D}\{e^{-\gamma q} F(q)\} = \sum_{r=-\infty}^{\infty} e^{(q+2\pi jr)(\varepsilon-\gamma)} F(q + 2\pi jr) = F^*(q, \varepsilon - \gamma). \quad (2.239)$$

For $\varepsilon < \gamma$, we write (2.239) in the form

$$\mathfrak{D}\{e^{-\gamma q} F(q)\} = \sum_{r=-\infty}^{\infty} e^{(q+2\pi jr)(1+\varepsilon-\gamma)} e^{-q} F(q + 2\pi jr) =$$

$$= e^{-q} F^*(q, 1 + \varepsilon - \gamma). \quad (2.240)$$

Consequently

$$\mathfrak{D}\{e^{-\gamma q} F(q)\} = \begin{cases} e^{-q} F^*(q, 1 + \varepsilon - \gamma), & 0 \leqslant \varepsilon \leqslant \gamma, \\ F^*(q, \varepsilon - \gamma), & \gamma \leqslant \varepsilon \leqslant 1. \end{cases} \quad (2.241)$$

Multiplying the image $F(q)$ by $e^{-\gamma q}$, where $\gamma < 1$, corresponds : to multiplying the image $F^*(q, \varepsilon)$ by e^{-q} and replacing the parameter ε by $1 + \varepsilon\gamma$, when $0 \leqslant \varepsilon \leqslant \gamma$; to replacing the parameter ε by $\varepsilon - \gamma$ when $\gamma \leqslant \varepsilon \leqslant 1$. We obtain from (2.241) for $\gamma = 1$

$$\mathfrak{D}\{e^{-q} F(q)\} = e^{-q} F^*(q, \varepsilon),$$

which agrees with (2.238) for $k = 1$.

THEOREM 20. MULTIPLICATION BY $F_1^*(q, \varepsilon)$.

Let $F(q)$ be the image of a continuous function. We require to find the image of the product

$$F_1^*(q, \varepsilon) F(q).$$

We have

$$\mathfrak{D}\{F_1^*(q, \varepsilon) F(q)\} = \sum_{r=-\infty}^{\infty} e^{(q+2\pi jr)\varepsilon} F_1^*(q + 2\pi jr, \varepsilon) F(q + 2\pi jr).$$

Since $F_1^*(q, \varepsilon)$ is periodic, i.e.

$$F_1^*(q + 2\pi jr, \varepsilon) = F_1^*(q, \varepsilon),$$

we obtain

$$\mathfrak{D}\{F_1^*(q, \varepsilon) F(q)\} = F_1^*(q, \varepsilon) \sum_{r=-\infty}^{\infty} e^{(q+2\pi jr)\varepsilon} F(q + 2\pi jr) =$$

$$= F_1^*(q, \varepsilon) F^*(q, \varepsilon). \quad (2.242)$$

The $\mathfrak{D}$-transformation of the product of $F(q)$ and $F_1^*(q, \varepsilon)$ equals the product of $F^*(q, \varepsilon)$ and $F_1^*(q, \varepsilon)$.

This theorem is a generalisation of Theorem 18 since $F_1^*(q, \varepsilon) = \Phi(e^{-q})$ is a function of e^{-q}.

THEOREM 21. TRANSLATION OF THE INDEPENDENT VARIABLE.

Replace q by $(q \pm \lambda)$ in (2.227). We obtain

$$F^*(q \pm \lambda, \varepsilon) = \sum_{r=-\infty}^{\infty} e^{(q+2\pi jr)\varepsilon} e^{\pm \lambda\varepsilon} F(q \pm \lambda + 2\pi jr),$$

or

$$F^*(q \pm \lambda, \varepsilon) = e^{\pm \lambda\varepsilon} \mathfrak{D}\{F(q \pm \lambda)\}.$$

Consequently

$$e^{\mp \lambda\varepsilon} F^*(q \pm \lambda, \varepsilon) = \mathfrak{D}\{F(q \pm \lambda)\}. \qquad (2.243)$$

A translation of the independent variable of the image $F(q)$ by $\pm\lambda$ corresponds to a similar translation of the independent variable of $F^*(q, \varepsilon)$, the latter being also multiplied by $e^{\mp \varepsilon\lambda}$. This theorem is analogous to the image-translation theorem (Theorem 3).

THEOREM 22. MULTIPLICATION BY q.

We obtain on differentiating both sides of (2.227) with respect to ε

$$\frac{\partial F^*(q, \varepsilon)}{\partial \varepsilon} = \sum_{r=-\infty}^{\infty} e^{(q+2\pi jr)\varepsilon} [(q + 2\pi jr) F(q + 2\pi jr)],$$

i.e.

$$\frac{\partial F^*(q, \varepsilon)}{\partial \varepsilon} = \mathfrak{D}\{q F(q)\}. \qquad (2.244)$$

Multiplying $F(q)$ by q corresponds to differentiating $F^*(q, \varepsilon)$ with respect to ε. If

$$\lim_{q \to \infty} q^\nu F(q) = 0,$$

then differentiating ν times gives

$$\frac{\partial^\nu F^*(q, \varepsilon)}{\partial \varepsilon^\nu} = \mathfrak{D}\{q^\nu F(q)\}, \qquad (2.245)$$

i.e. *multiplying the image $F(q)$ by q corresponds to the ν-th derivative of $F^*(q, \varepsilon)$ with respect to ε.*

This theorem expresses, in another form, the theorem on differentiation with respect to a parameter (Theorem 9). It is not difficult to convince ourselves of this when we remember that multiplying $F(q)$ by q corresponds to differentiating $f(\bar{t})$ with respect to $\bar{t}$ or $f[n, \varepsilon]$ with respect to ε.

THEOREM 23. DIVISION BY q.

Integrating both sides of (2.227) with respect to ε from 0 to ε gives

$$\int_0^\varepsilon F^*(q, \varepsilon)\, d\varepsilon = \sum_{r=-\infty}^{\infty} (e^{(q+2\pi jr)\varepsilon} - 1) \frac{F(q + 2\pi jr)}{q + 2\pi jr}. \tag{2.246}$$

Putting $\varepsilon = 1$ and using (2.237) for $k = -1$, we have

$$\frac{1}{e^q - 1} \int_0^1 F^*(q, \varepsilon)\, d\varepsilon = \sum_{r=-\infty}^{\infty} \frac{F(q + 2\pi jr)}{q + 2\pi jr}. \tag{2.247}$$

Adding (2.246) and (2.247) gives

$$\int_0^\varepsilon F^*(q, \varepsilon)\, d\varepsilon + \frac{1}{e^q - 1} \int_0^1 F^*(q, \varepsilon)\, d\varepsilon = \sum_{r=-\infty}^{\infty} e^{(q+2\pi jr)\varepsilon} \frac{F(q+2\pi jr)}{q + 2\pi jr},$$

i.e.

$$\int_0^\varepsilon F^*(q, \varepsilon)\, d\varepsilon + \frac{1}{e^q - 1} \int_0^1 F^*(q, \varepsilon)\, d\varepsilon = \mathfrak{D}\left\{\frac{F(q)}{q}\right\}. \tag{2.248}$$

Dividing $F(q)$ by q corresponds to integrating $F^*(q, \varepsilon)$ with respect to ε.

Repeating the above process ν times gives

$$\int_0^\varepsilon \cdots \int_0^\varepsilon F^*(q, \varepsilon)\, (d\varepsilon)^\nu + \frac{1}{e^q - 1} \sum_{\eta=0}^{\infty} \frac{\varepsilon^{\nu-\eta-1}}{(\nu - \eta - 1)!} \int_0^1 F^*_{(\eta)}(q, \varepsilon)\, d\varepsilon =$$

$$= \mathfrak{D}\left\{\frac{F(q)}{q^q}\right\}, \tag{2.249}$$

where $F^*_{(\eta)}(q, \varepsilon) = \int_0^\varepsilon F^*_{(\eta-1)}(q, \varepsilon)\, d\varepsilon + \frac{1}{e^q - 1} \int_0^1 F^*_{(\eta-1)}(q, \varepsilon)\, d\varepsilon$

and

$$F_{(0)}(q, \varepsilon) = F^*(q, \varepsilon).$$

This theorem is closely related to the theorem on the image of a sum (Theorem 5) and the theorem on integration with respect to a parameter (Theorem 10). It is known that dividing by q corresponds to integrating $f(\bar{t})$ with respect to $\bar{t}$ or to integrating $f[m, \varepsilon]$ with respect to ε and summing over m. In fact this was done on p. 124 when illustrating Theorem 10.

THEOREM 24. DIFFERENTIATION WITH RESPECT TO q.

On differentiating both sides of (2.227) with respect to q we obtain

$$\frac{dF^*(q,\varepsilon)}{dq} = \sum_{r=-\infty}^{\infty} e^{(q+2\pi jr)\varepsilon} \left\{ \frac{dF(q+2\pi jr)}{d(q+2\pi jr)} + \varepsilon F(q+2\pi jr) \right\},$$

or

$$\frac{dF^*(q,\varepsilon)}{dq} = \mathfrak{D}\left\{ \frac{dF(q)}{dq} \right\} + \varepsilon \mathfrak{D}\{F(q+2\pi jr)\},$$

from which we have

$$\frac{dF^*(q,\varepsilon)}{dq} - \varepsilon F^*(q,\varepsilon) = \mathfrak{D}\left\{ \frac{dF(q)}{dq} \right\}. \tag{2.250}$$

Differentiating $F(q)$ with respect to q corresponds to differentiating $F^*(q, \varepsilon)$ with respect to q and subtracting ε times $F^*(q, \varepsilon)$.

By repeating the above process ν times we can easily show that

$$\sum_{\eta=0}^{\nu} \binom{\nu}{\eta} \frac{d^{\nu-\eta} F^*(q,\varepsilon)}{dq^{\nu-\eta}} (-1)^{\nu-\eta} \varepsilon^{\eta} = \mathfrak{D}\left\{ \frac{d^{\nu} F(q)}{dq} \right\}. \tag{2.251}$$

The number of correspondences can be increased using other relationships between $F(q)$ and $F^*(q, \varepsilon)$. However, those given above are sufficient for our purposes. For convenience they are listed in Table A 4 of the Appendix.

If the image $F(q)$ can be represented as the sum of simple fractions

$$F(q) = \sum_{\nu=1}^{l} c_{\nu} \frac{1}{q - q_{\nu}},$$

where q_{ν} are the poles of $F(q)$, assumed for simplicity to be simple so that

$$c_{\nu} = \lim_{q \to q_{\nu}} [(q - q_{\nu}) F(q)],$$

then $F^*(q, \varepsilon)$ can be expressed in closed form in terms of the coefficients c_{ν}.

We obtain, on applying the $\mathfrak{D}$-transformation to $F(q)$ and using the linearity theorem (Theorem 17)

$$F^*(q,\varepsilon) = \mathfrak{D}\{F(q)\} = \sum_{\nu=1}^{l} c_{\nu} \mathfrak{D}\left\{ \frac{1}{q - q_{\nu}} \right\}.$$

Using (2.235) we have finally

$$F^*(q,\varepsilon) = \sum_{\nu=1}^{l} c_{\nu} \frac{e^{q}}{e^{q} - e^{q_{\nu}}} e^{q_{\nu}\varepsilon}. \tag{2.252}$$

This formula, however, does not show the relationship between $F^*(q, \varepsilon)$ and $F(q)$ in an explicit form.

The relationship between $F^*(q, \varepsilon)$ and $F(q)$ can also be obtained in another form. For this purpose we use the inversion formula of the usual Laplace transformation+

$$f(\bar{t}) = \frac{1}{2\pi j} \int_{c-j\infty}^{c+j\infty} F(s)\, e^{s\bar{t}}\, ds .$$

Putting $\bar{t} = n + \varepsilon$ in this formula and substituting the resulting expression for $f[n, \varepsilon] = f(n + \varepsilon)$ in (2.221), we obtain on changing the order of integration and summation

$$F^*(q, \varepsilon) = \frac{1}{2\pi j} \int_{c-j\infty}^{c+j\infty} \left(\sum_{n=0}^{\infty} e^{-(q-s)n} \right) e^{s\varepsilon} F(s)\, ds,$$

or, since

$$\sum_{n=0}^{\infty} e^{-(q-s)n} = \frac{e^q}{e^q - e^s},$$

we have finally

$$F^*(q, \varepsilon) = \frac{1}{2\pi j} \int_{c-j\infty}^{c+j\infty} \frac{e^q}{e^q - e^s}\, e^{s\varepsilon} F(s)\, ds. \tag{2.253}$$

For $\varepsilon = 0$ we obtain

$$F^*(q, 0) = F^*(q) = \frac{1}{2\pi j} \int_{c-j\infty}^{c+j\infty} \frac{e^q}{e^q - e^s}\, F(s)\, ds . \tag{2.254}$$

In evaluating (2.253) the path of integration (a semi-circle of infinitely large radius) may be chosen either to the right of the straight line c (Fig. 2.35*a*) or to the right of it (Fig. 2.35*b*)

In the first case the calculation reduces to finding the residues at the poles of the function

$$\frac{e^q}{e^q - e^s}\, e^{s\varepsilon},$$

which leads to expression (2.228).

In the second case the calculation reduces to finding the residues at the poles of the function $F(s)$ which leads to expression (2.252).

+ See M. I. Kontorovich (2; 1955); M. F. Gardner, D. L. Barnes (2; 1945); G. Doetsch (2; 1958).

To obtain the relationship between $F(q)$ and $F^*(q, 0)$ we use the inversion formula of the discrete Laplace transformation (2.175),

$$f[n] = \frac{1}{2\pi j} \int\limits_{c-j\pi}^{c+j\pi} F^*(s, 0)\, e^{sn}\, ds.$$

Replacing n by $\bar{t}$ in this expression and substituting in (2.220) we obtain, on changing the order of the integrations,

$$F(q) = \frac{1}{2\pi j} \int\limits_{c-j\pi}^{c+j\pi} F^*(s, 0) \left[\int\limits_{0}^{\infty} e^{-(q-s)\bar{t}}\, d\bar{t} \right] ds\,,$$

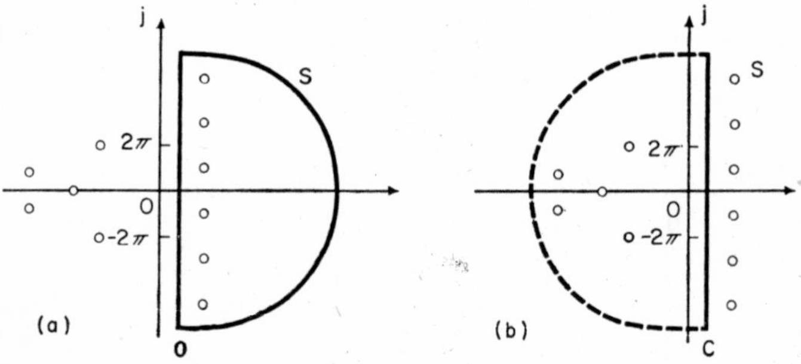

FIG. 2.35. Contours of integration.

which gives the required relationship

$$F(q) = \frac{1}{2\pi j} \int\limits_{c-j\pi}^{c+j\pi} \frac{F^*(s, 0)}{q-s}\, ds\,. \tag{2.255}$$

The relationships deduced above between $F^*(q, \varepsilon)$ and $F(q)$ play an important role in the analysis and synthesis of pulse systems, and when comparing the properties of pulse systems with those of continuous systems.

In the discrete Laplace transformation we meet two types of transformations: the D-transformation, which sets up a correspondence between the lattice function $f[n, \varepsilon]$ and its image $F^*(q, \varepsilon)$; and the $\mathfrak{D}$-transformation, which establishes a correspondence between the image of a continuous function $F(q)$ and the image of the corresponding lattice function $F^*(q, \varepsilon)$.

2.9. Random lattice functions

In contrast to the well-defined types of lattice function considered in the preceding sections, a random lattice function can be characterised only in terms of probability, i.e. it can only be defined by the probability that at some moment of time its value will lie within given limits.

A *random lattice function* $f[n]$ can be formed from a random continuous function $f(\bar{t})$ by replacing $\bar{t} = t/T$ by n (Fig. 2.36) (i.e. in exactly the same manner as for the well-defined type of lattice function).

The ensemble of values of a random lattice function, which we

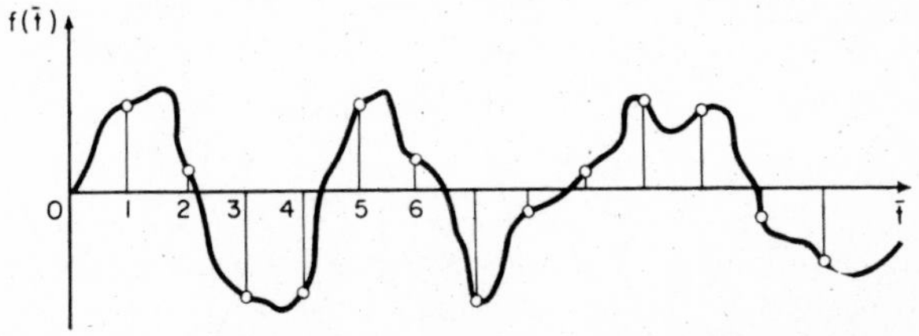

FIG. 2.36. Random continuous and lattice functions.

denote by the symbol $\{ f[n] \}$, is called a random sequence or a discrete random process.

If the probability distribution law is independent of the moments of time $\bar{t} = n$, i.e. to put it otherwise, the statistical properties of the random sequence are independent of the origin chosen, the random sequence is called a *stationary random sequence* or a *discrete stationary random process.*+

A stationary random sequence is characterised physically by the fact that it shows no tendency to increase or decrease as n increases.

The so-called *ergodic hypothesis* holds for a stationary random sequence. This states that a large number of observations, made at arbitrarily chosen moments of time n on one particular system producing a stationary random sequence, have the same statistical properties as a large number of observations made at one instant of time on arbitrarily chosen similar systems.

This theorem enables the statistical or probability characteristics to be found on the basis of a single stationary random sequence which may be obtained, for example, experimentally.

+ See A. M. Yaglom (2; 1952); D. L. Dub (2; 1956).

A discrete random process can be characterised by the mean value of the lattice function $f[n]$ with respect to time, which is defined in the following manner

$$\overline{f[n]} = \lim_{N\to\infty} \frac{1}{2N+1} \sum_{n=-N}^{N} f[n]. \tag{2.256}$$

In conformity with the ergodic hypothesis, the mean value of $f[n]$ with respect to time is the same as the mean value of the ensemble, or mathematical expectation of this quantity. In future work we shall require the mean value of a lattice function with respect to time. A discrete stationary random process is characterised by the deviations from some mean value, the deviations in either direction being equally probable; consequently, the statistical characteristics of a stationary random process, and in particular of a discrete stationary random process, are independent of the choice of origin.

An important characteristic of a discrete random process is the *correlation coefficient*, which characterises the probability of a dependence, or connection, between the values of a lattice function at times separated by m, i.e. between $f[n]$ and $f[n+m]$. This coefficient is defined by

$$r[m] = \frac{\overline{(f[n] - \overline{f[n]})\,(f[n+m] - \overline{f[n+m]})}}{\sqrt{\{(\overline{f^2[n]} - \overline{f[n]}^2)\,(\overline{f^2[n+m]} - \overline{f[n+m]}^2)\}}}, \tag{2.257}$$

where the bars indicate averaging with respect to time of the corresponding functions. If the mean value of a discrete random process equals zero, i.e.

$$\overline{f[n]} = \overline{f[n+m]} = 0,$$

the correlation coefficient $r[m]$ equals

$$r[m] = \frac{\overline{f[n]\,f[n+m]}}{\overline{f^2[n]}}, \tag{2.258}$$

since $\overline{f^2[n]} = \overline{f^2[n+m]}$ is a constant quantity, the mean value of the square of the lattice function.

The *auto-correlation function* is defined by

$$R_{ff}[m] = \lim_{N\to\infty} \frac{1}{2N+1} \sum_{n=-N}^{N} f[n]\,f[n+m]. \tag{2.259}$$

If $\overline{f[n]} = 0$, the auto-correlation function equals the correlation coefficient multiplied by the mean value of the square of the random quantity.

The auto-correlation function $R_{ff}[m]$ is a measure of the dependence between the ordinates of the lattice function, i.e. the discreta of $f[n]$, at different moments of time.

We note a few properties of the auto-correlation function.

(1) On putting $m = 0$ in (2.259) we obtain

$$R_{ff}[0] = \lim_{N\to\infty} \frac{1}{2N+1} \sum_{n=-N}^{N} f^2[n] = \overline{f^2[n]}, \qquad (2.260)$$

i.e. *the value of the auto-correlation function for* $m = 0$ *equals the mean value of the square of the random quantity.*

(2) From the inequality

$$(f[n] \pm f[n+m])^2 \geqslant 0$$

it follows that

$$f^2[n] + f^2[n+m] \geqslant \mp 2 f[n] f[n+m].$$

On taking the mean of both sides of this in equality, and remembering that

$$\overline{f^2[n]} = \overline{f^2[n+m]} = R_{ff}[0],$$

we obtain

$$R_{ff}[0] \geqslant |R_{ff}[m]|,$$

i.e. *the auto-correlation function reaches its largest value at* $m = 0$. The auto-correlation function $R_{ff}[m]$ usually tends to zero as m increases, which shows the weakening of the connection between the discreta at widely separated moments of time.

(3) Since the auto-correlation function is independent of origin, we have

$$R_{ff}[m] = \overline{f[n] f[n+m]} = \overline{f[n-m] f[n]} =$$
$$= \overline{f[n] f[n-m]} = R_{ff}[-m], \qquad (2.261)$$

i.e. *the auto-correlation function is an even function of its argument* m (Fig. 2.37).

In addition to the auto-correlation function, which characterises the dependence or connection at different moments of time between the random values of a single ensemble $\{f[n]\}$, there is also a *cross-correlation function*, which characterises the connection between the random values of two different ensembles $\{f[n]\}$ and $\{\varphi[n]\}$. The cross-correlation function is defined in the following manner

$$R_{f\varphi}[m] = \lim_{N\to\infty} \frac{1}{2N+1} \sum_{n=-N}^{N} f[n]\varphi[n+m] = \overline{f[n]\varphi[n+m]}. \qquad (2.262)$$

From the definition of the cross-correlation function it follows that unlike the auto-correlation function, the *cross-correlation function is non-symmetrical.* i.e.

$$R_{f\varphi}[m] = \overline{f[n]\,\varphi[n+m]} = \overline{f[n-m]\,\varphi[n]} = \overline{\varphi[n]\,f[n-m]} =$$
$$= R_{\varphi f}[-m]\,. \qquad (2.263)$$

If the random quantities $f[n]$ and $\varphi[n]$ are statistically independent, then

$$R_{f\varphi}[m] = \overline{f[n]\,\varphi[n+m]} = 0\,,$$

i.e. *the cross-correlation function of statistically independent random quantities is equal to zero.*

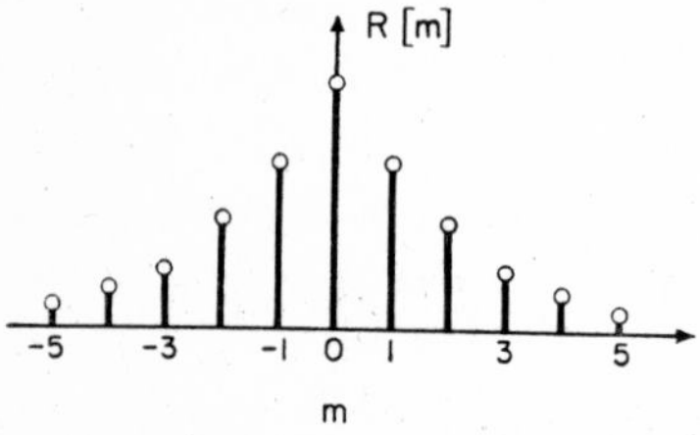

FIG. 2.37. Qualitative form of the correlation function.

We note that if $f[n]$ is not random but a definite lattice function, this does not mean that the auto-correlation function will take its largest value. For example with the periodic function $f[n] = f[n + kN_0]$ $(k = 0, 1, 2, 3, \ldots)$, the auto-correlation function is also a periodic function of the same period N_0 since

$$R_{ff}[m] = \overline{f[n]\,f[n+m]} = \overline{f[n+kN_0]\,f[n+m+kN_0]} =$$
$$= \overline{f[n]\,f[n+m+kN_0]} = R_{ff}[m+kN_0]\,. \qquad (2.264)$$

EXAMPLE 1. Let

$$f[n] = A\sin(\bar{\omega}\,n + \varphi)\,.$$

We have from (2.259)

$$R_{ff}[m] = \lim_{N\to\infty}\frac{1}{2N+1}\sum_{n=-N}^{N} A^2\sin(\bar{\omega}\,n+\varphi)\sin(\bar{\omega}\,n+\bar{\omega}\,m+\varphi) =$$

$$= \lim_{N\to\infty}\frac{1}{2N+1}\sum_{n=-N}^{N}\frac{A^2}{2}\left[\cos\bar{\omega}\,m - \cos(2\,\bar{\omega}\,n+\bar{\omega}\,m+2\varphi)\right].$$

Since

$$\lim_{N\to\infty}\frac{1}{2N+1}\sum_{n=-N}^{N}\frac{A^2}{2}\cos(2\bar{\omega}\,n+\bar{\omega}\,m+2\varphi) = 0\,,$$

we obtain finally

$$R_{ff}[m] = \frac{A^2}{2}\cos\bar{\omega}\,m\,.$$

EXAMPLE 2. If

$$f[n] = A_0 + \sum_{k=1}^{l} A_k \sin(\overline{\omega}_k n + \varphi_k),$$

we obtain from the result of the first example

$$R_{ff}[m] = A_2^0 + \sum_{k=1}^{l} \frac{A_k^2}{2} \cos \overline{\omega}_k m .$$

These examples show that the auto-correlation function of a periodic lattice function does not depend on the phase.

The statistical properties of discrete stationary random processes can be quite fully described in terms of the correlation functions. The correlation functions characterise the time-dependent statistical properties.

We now consider a second characteristic of a discrete random process; it is closely associated with the correlation function and is called the *spectral density.*

The cross spectral density $S^*_{f\Phi}(j\overline{\omega})$, where $\overline{\omega} = \omega T$ is the relative frequency, is defined as the sum of a Fourier series whose coefficients are the values of the cross-correlation function, i.e.

$$S^*_{f\varphi}(j\overline{\omega}) = \sum_{m=-\infty}^{\infty} R_{f\varphi}[m]\, \mathrm{e}^{-j\overline{\omega}m} = \lim_{N\to\infty} \sum_{m=-N}^{N} R_{f\varphi}[m]\, \mathrm{e}^{-j\overline{\omega}m}. \quad (2.265)$$

Substitute in (2.265) the value of the cross-correlation function (2.262) and change the order of the summations; we then obtain

$$S^*_{f\varphi}(j\omega) = \lim_{N\to\infty} \frac{1}{2N+1} \sum_{n=-N}^{N} f[n] \sum_{m=-N}^{N} \varphi[n+m]\, \mathrm{e}^{-j\overline{\omega}m},$$

or, on multiplying by $\mathrm{e}^{-j\overline{\omega}n} . \mathrm{e}^{j\overline{\omega}n} = 1$

$$S^*_{f\varphi}(j\overline{\omega}) = \lim_{N\to\infty} \frac{1}{2N+1} \left\{ \sum_{n=-N}^{N} f[n]\, \mathrm{e}^{j\overline{\omega}n} \right\} \left\{ \sum_{m=-N}^{N} \varphi[n+m]\, \mathrm{e}^{-j\overline{\omega}(n+m)} \right\}.$$

We write

$$\left.\begin{aligned} \sum_{n=-N}^{N} f[n]\, \mathrm{e}^{-j\overline{\omega}m} &= F^*_N(j\overline{\omega}), \\ \sum_{n=-N}^{N} \varphi[n]\, \mathrm{e}^{-j\overline{\omega}n} &= \Phi^*_N(j\overline{\omega}). \end{aligned}\right\} \quad (2.266)$$

Then

$$S^*_{f\varphi}(j\overline{\omega}) = \lim_{N\to\infty} \frac{1}{2N+1} F^*_N(-j\overline{\omega})\, \Phi^*_N(j\overline{\omega}). \quad (2.267)$$

The quantities $F_N^*(-j\bar{\omega})$ and $\Phi_N^*(j\bar{\omega})$ are defined by Fourier sums. In the limit, when $N \to \infty$, they are converted into Fourier series.

In accordance with (2.265), the spectral density is given by

$$S_{ff}^*(\bar{\omega}) = \sum_{m=-\infty}^{\infty} R_{ff}[m]\,\mathrm{e}^{-j\bar{\omega}m}$$

or, since $R_{ff}[m]$ is even,

$$S_{ff}^*(\bar{\omega}) = 2 \sum_{m=0}^{\infty}{}' R_{ff}[m] \cos\bar{\omega}\, m\,, \tag{2.268}$$

where the dash at the summation sign means that the factor 2 is to be omitted for $m = 0$. In this case we have from (2.267)

$$S_{ff}^*(\bar{\omega}) = \lim_{N\to\infty} \frac{1}{2N+1} F_N^*(-j\,\bar{\omega})\, F_N^*(j\,\bar{\omega}) = \lim_{N\to\infty} \frac{1}{2N+1} |\, F_N^*(\bar{\omega})\,|^2. \tag{2.269}$$

The correlation function and the spectral density are closely associated with each other. Given the correlation function, the appropriate spectral density can be calculated using formula (2.265) or (2.268). Since the values of the correlation function are the Fourier coefficients of the spectral density, then

$$R_{f\varphi}[m] = \frac{1}{2\pi} \int_{-\pi}^{\pi} S_{f\varphi}^*(j\,\bar{\omega})\,\mathrm{e}^{j\bar{\omega}m}\,\mathrm{d}\bar{\omega} \tag{2.270}$$

and

$$R_{ff}[m] = \frac{1}{2\pi} \int_{-\pi}^{\pi} S_{ff}^*(\bar{\omega})\,\mathrm{e}^{j\bar{\omega}m}\,\mathrm{d}\bar{\omega} = \frac{1}{\pi} \int_{0}^{\pi} S_{ff}^*(\bar{\omega}) \cos\bar{\omega}\, m\, \mathrm{d}\bar{\omega}\,. \tag{2.271}$$

These formulae are inversion formulae with respect to (2.265) and (2.268).

Table 2.2 gives examples of correlation functions and their corresponding spectral densities.

It is important to note that the correlation functions and spectral densities characterise a discrete stationary random process, i.e. characterise the class of lattice functions having the same statistical properties.

It was shown above (2.260) that the auto-correlation function for $m = 0$ equals the mean value of the square of the random lattice quantity. Using this fact by putting $m = 0$ in (2.271), we obtain an

TABLE 2.2. CORRELATION FUNCTIONS AND SPECTRAL DENSITIES OF STATIONARY RANDOM LATTICE FUNCTIONS

No.	R[m]		$S^*(\bar{\omega})$	
1	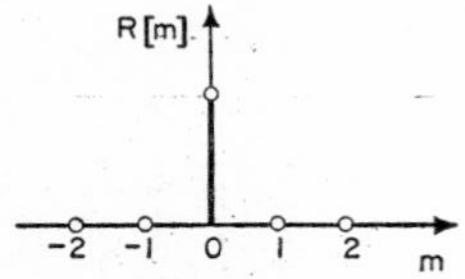	$1, \quad m = 0$ $0, \quad m \neq 0$	1	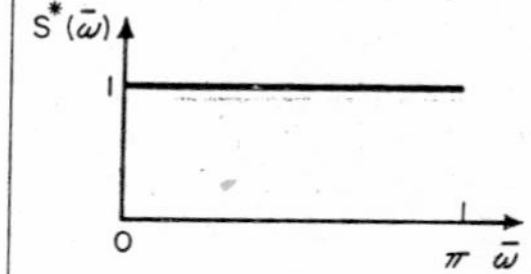
2	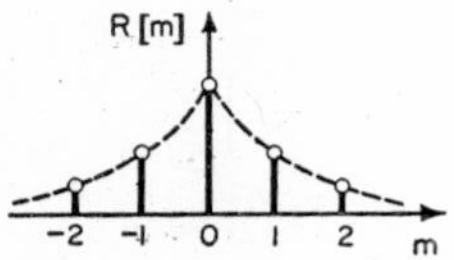	$e^{-\alpha\lvert m\rvert}$	$\dfrac{1 - e^{-2\alpha}}{\lvert e^{j\bar{\omega}} - e^{-\alpha}\rvert^2}$	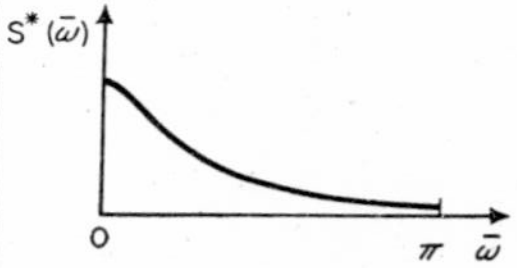
3	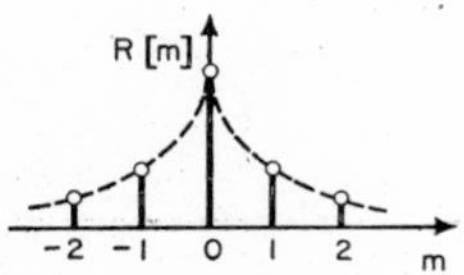	$\dfrac{1 - 2e^{-(\alpha_1+\alpha_2)} + e^{-2\alpha_2}}{1 - e^{-2\alpha_1}}, \quad m = 0$ $\dfrac{(e^{-\alpha_1} - e^{-\alpha_2})(1 - e^{-(\alpha_1+\alpha_2)})}{1 - e^{-2\alpha_1}} \times$ $\times e^{-\alpha_1[\lvert m\rvert - 1]}, \quad m \neq 0$	$\dfrac{\lvert e^{j\bar{\omega}} - e^{-\alpha_2}\rvert^2}{\lvert e^{j\bar{\omega}} - e^{-\alpha_1}\rvert^2}$	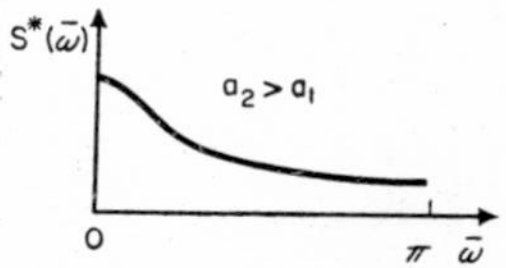

TABLE 2.2. CONTD.

No.	R [m]		$S^*(\bar{\omega})$	
4	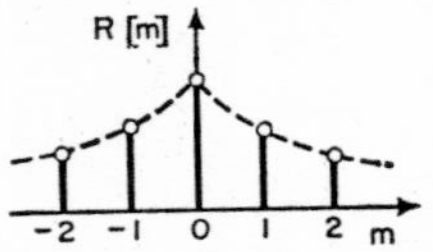	$\frac{1}{(e^{-\alpha_1}-e^{-\alpha_2})(1-e^{-(\alpha_1+\alpha_2)})} \times \left[\frac{e^{-\alpha_1\|m\|+1\|}}{1-e^{-2\alpha_1}} - \frac{e^{-\alpha_2\|m\|+1\|}}{1-e^{-\alpha_2}}\right]$	$\frac{1}{\|e^{-j\omega}-e^{-\alpha_1}\|^2 \|e^{j\omega}-e^{-\alpha_2}\|^2}$	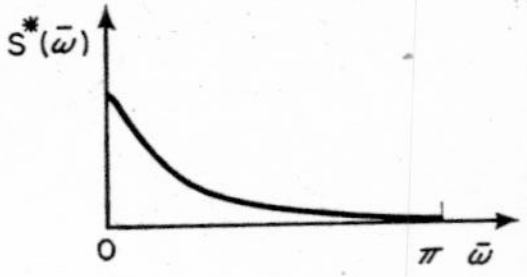
5	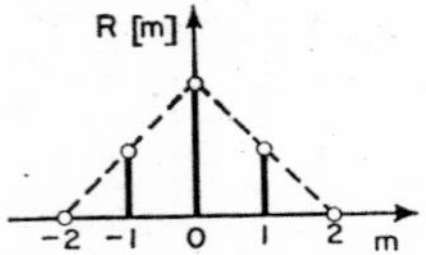	$1-\frac{\|m\|}{m_1}, \quad m < m_1$ $0, \quad m > m_1$	$\frac{1-\cos m_1\bar{\omega}}{2m_1 \sin^2 \frac{\bar{\omega}}{2}}$	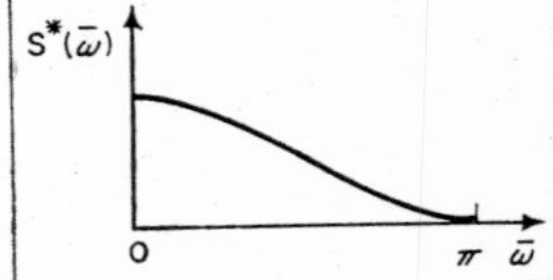
6	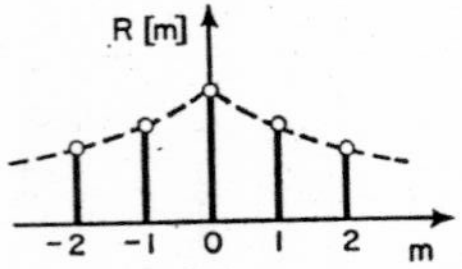	$\frac{1}{m^2+a^2}$	$\frac{\pi \operatorname{ch} a(\pi-\bar{\omega})}{a \operatorname{sh} a\pi}$	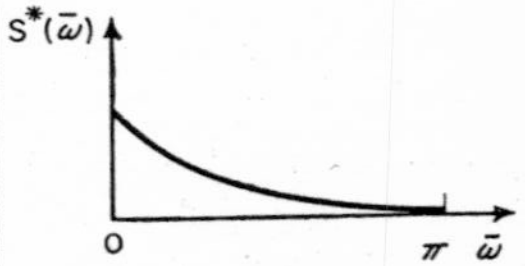
7	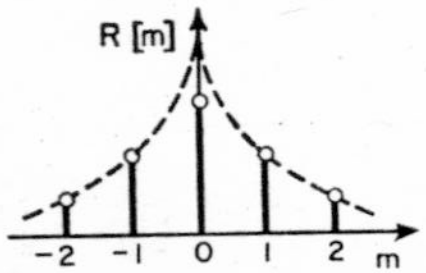	$\frac{1}{m^2}, \quad m \neq 0$ $a, \quad m = 0$	$a+\frac{\pi^2}{3}-\pi\|\bar{\omega}\|+\frac{\bar{\omega}^2}{2}$	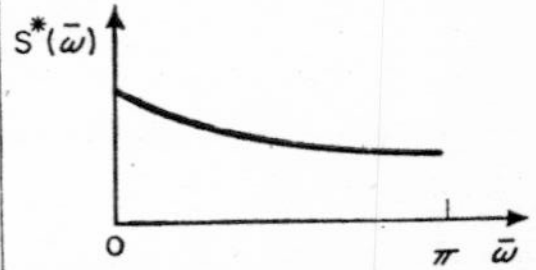

TABLE 2.2. CONTD.

No.	R [m]		S*($\bar{\omega}$)	
8	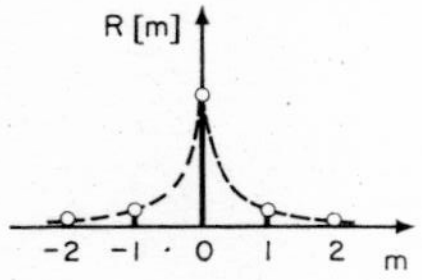	$\frac{1}{m^4}$, $m \neq 0$ a, $m = 0$	$a + \frac{\pi^4}{45} - \frac{\pi^2\overline{\omega^2}}{6} + \frac{\pi\overline{\lvert\omega\rvert^3}}{6} - \frac{\overline{\omega^4}}{24}$	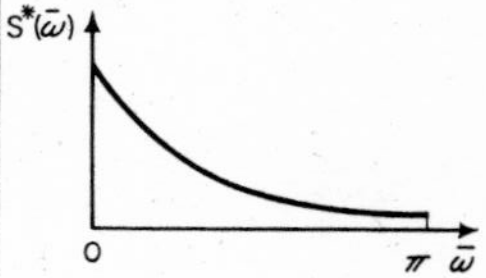
9	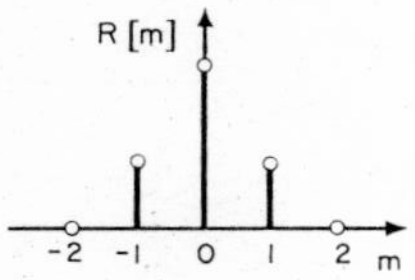	$1 + b^3$, $m = 0$ b, $m = \pm 1$ 0, $\lvert m \rvert > 1$	$\lvert e^{j\bar{\omega}} - b \rvert^2$	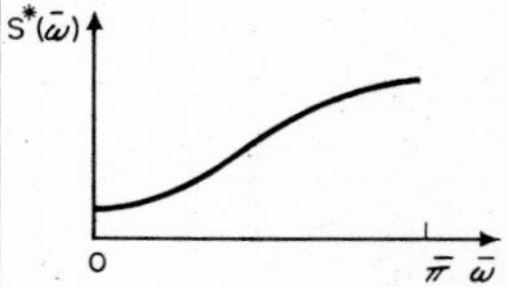
10	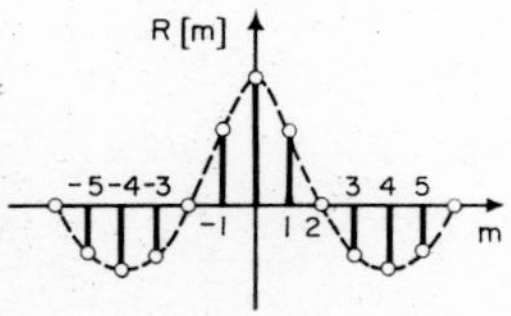	$e^{-\alpha \lvert m \rvert} \cos m\bar{\omega}_0$	$\frac{1 - e^{-\alpha}\cos(\bar{\omega} + \bar{\omega}_0)}{\lvert e^{j(\bar{\omega} + \bar{\omega}_0)} - e^{-\alpha} \rvert^2} + \frac{1 - e^{-\alpha}\cos(\bar{\omega} - \bar{\omega}_0)}{\lvert e^{j(\bar{\omega} - \bar{\omega}_0)} - e^{-\alpha} \rvert^2} - 1$	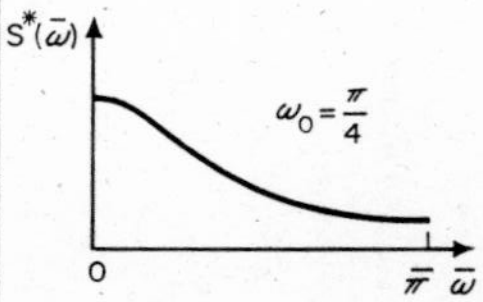

expression for the mean value of the square of the random lattice quantity in terms of the spectral density

$$\overline{f^2[n]} = R_{ff}[0] = \frac{1}{\pi}\int_0^{\pi} S_{ff}^*(\bar{\omega})\,d\bar{\omega}, \tag{2.272}$$

i.e. *the mean value of the squares of the discreta of a random lattice function is proportional to the area of the corresponding spectral density.* Thus if the graph of the spectral density $S_{ff}^*(\bar{\omega})$ is given, (Fig. 2.38) the value of $\overline{f^2[n]}$ can be found graphically as it equals the area underneath $S_{ff}^*(\bar{\omega})$ multiplied by $1/\pi$. If $S_{ff}^*(\bar{\omega})$ is a rational function, $\overline{f^2[n]}$ can be obtained in analytical form.

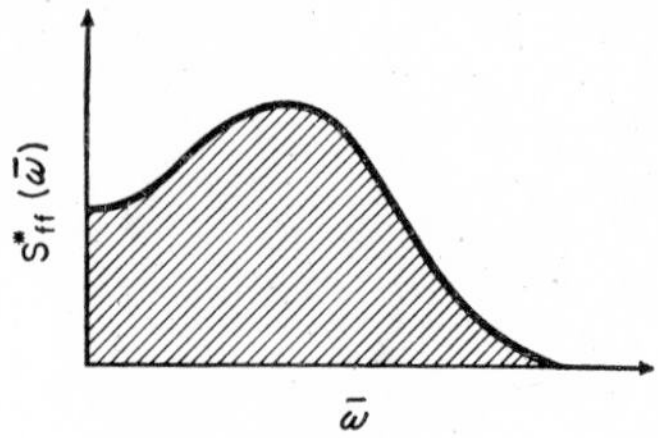

FIG. 2.38. Area under spectral density curve.

Since $S_{ff}^*(\bar{\omega})$ is an even function of $\bar{\omega}$, i.e. a function of $\bar{\omega}^2$, it can be written in the form

$$S_{ff}^*(\bar{\omega}) = \left|\frac{N^*(\bar{\omega})}{D^*(\bar{\omega})}\right|^2 = \frac{N^*(j\,\bar{\omega})\,N^*(-j\,\bar{\omega})}{D^*(j\,\bar{\omega})\,D^*(-j\,\bar{\omega})}, \tag{2.273}$$

where $D^*(q)$ and $N^*(q)$ are polynominals in e^q of degrees l_1 and l_1' respectively, for $q = j\bar{\omega}$. Hence

$$\overline{f^2[n]} = \frac{1}{\pi}\int_0^{\pi} \left|\frac{N^*(j\,\bar{\omega})}{D^*(j\,\bar{\omega})}\right|^2 d\bar{\omega}. \tag{2.274}$$

However this expression is analogous to (2.215). Using (2.199) we can see that $\overline{f^2[n]}$ equals the sum of the squares of the discreta of a lattice function $\psi[n]$ whose image is

$$\Psi^*(q) = \frac{N^*(q)}{D^*(q)}. \tag{2.275}$$

If we know the image $\Psi^*(q)$, we can express the required quantity $\overline{f^2[n]}$ in terms of the coefficients of this image by means of the formulae of § 2.6.

The properties considered in this section of random lattice functions will be used later, when we come to study the behaviour of pulse systems subjected to random excitations.

CHAPTER III

FUNDAMENTALS OF THE THEORY OF OPEN-LOOP PULSE SYSTEMS

3.1. Reduction of a pulse system to the simplest form

It was shown in Chapter I that an open-loop pulse system consists of several continuous systems and a pulse element connected in series (Fig. 3.1). An external excitation $f_T(t)$ applied to the input of the continuous system preceding the pulse element gives rise to an output

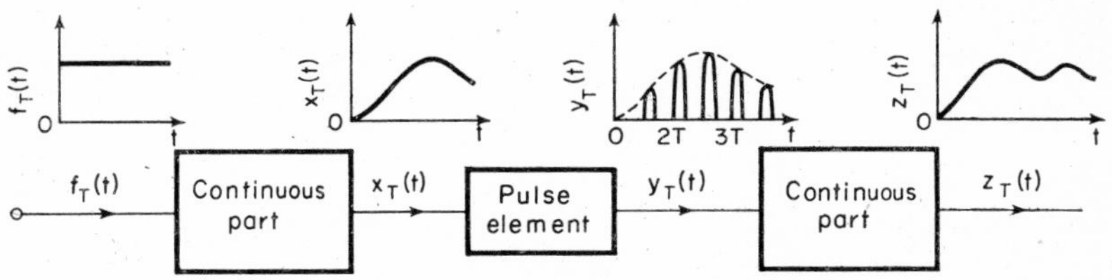

FIG. 3.1. Schematic diagram of a general pulse system.

response $x_T(t)$. This response, the input to the pulse element, is converted by the pulse element into a modulated pulse-train $y_T(t)$ which is fed to the input of the continuous system following the pulse element. The operation of the open-loop pulse system is characterised by the output of this continuous system $z_T(t)$.⁺

Pulse systems can be divided into three types, depending on the kind of pulse modulation carried out by the pulse element, i.e. depending on the type of pulse element.

In a pulse system *type one* the pulse element carries out *pulse-amplitude modulation* (PAM).

In a pulse system *type two* the pulse element carries out *pulse-width modulation* (PWM).

⁺ The suffix T denotes that the functions are associated with a pulse system in which the pulse repetition period equals T.

In a pulse system *type three* the pulse element carries out *pulse-time modulation* (PTM).

Unless there is a remark to the contrary, the continuous systems appearing in the composition of a pulse system will always be assumed linear.

The properties and operating conditions of an open-loop system remain unchanged if the continuous system preceding the pulse element is removed and an external disturbance $x_T(t)$, which equals the response of the removed continuous system to the previous excitation $f_T(t)$, is fed to the input of the pulse element. Consequently, without affecting the generality, an open-loop pulse system can be reduced to the form shown in Fig. 3.2. The reduction of the pulse system of

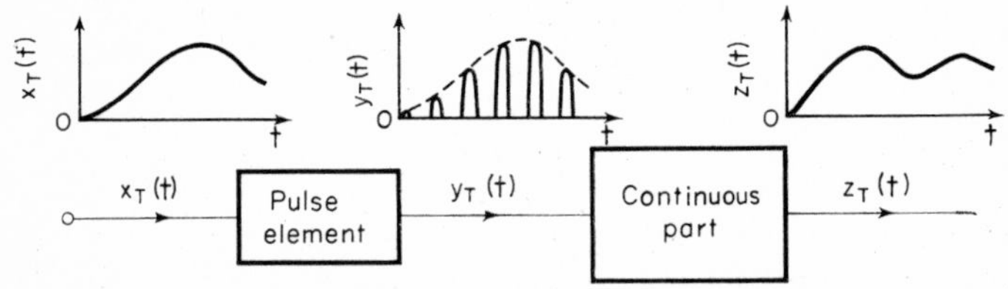

FIG. 3.2. Schematic diagram of a pulse system without the continuous part that precedes the pulse element.

Fig. 3.1 to that of Fig. 3.2 can be considered as the result of transforming the external excitation $f_T(t)$ to the input of the pulse element.

In addition to the type of modulation, a pulse element is characterised by the repetition period T or angular frequency $\omega_0 = 2\pi/T$, the slope of the characteristic k_P or $\varkappa$, and finally by the shape of the output modulated pulses $s_T(t)$ (see § 1.1). The latter will be given when characterising a particular pulse element.

By a *simple pulse element* we mean a pulse element whose output pulses are of very short duration.+ Such pulses can be represented by the delta-function $\delta(t)$. We recall that the delta-function $\delta(t)$ is zero for $t \neq 0$ and for $t = 0$ it is infinite in such a manner that $\int_{-\infty}^{+\infty} \delta(t)\mathrm{d}t = 1$. For brevity such pulses will be called *instantaneous pulses*. Thus a simple pulse element modulates instantaneous pulses so that their areas are proportional to the values of the input quantity at discrete moments of time.

+ The meaning of 'short duration' is made more precise on p. 199.

Of the three types of pulse system only type one, as follows from § 1.1, is linear with constant parameters. A type-two pulse system reduces to this only for small variations in the input quantity. It will be shown later that under the latter condition the effect of the pulses does not depend on their shape but on their area. Consequently, for small variations of the output quantity, a type-two pulse system can be reduced to a pulse system with a simple pulse element.

In an open-loop type-one pulse system in which the pulse element produces modulated pulses of arbitrary shape (Fig. 3.3*a*), the pulse element can be replaced by a simple pulse element in series with a specially chosen continuous system called the *shaping element* (Fig. 3.3*b*). The shaping element is such that its response to an instantaneous

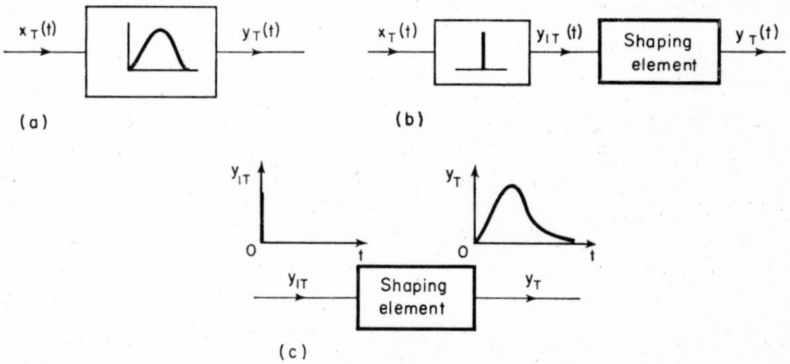

FIG. 3.3. Replacement of a pulse element (*a*) by a simple pulse element and a shaping element connected in series (*b*), where the function of the shaping element is shown in (*c*).

pulse, i.e. to an excitation in the form of a delta-function, is identical to the shape of the original pulse, i.e. it creates a pulse of the required shape from an instantaneous pulse (Fig. 3.3*c*). Thus any linear pulse system can be reduced to a pulse system consisting of a simple pulse element, a shaping element and a continuous system, connected in series (Fig. 3.4). The series combination of shaping element and continuous system is called the *reduced continuous part*. The reduced continuous part is always subjected to the action of a train of instantaneous pulses with a pulse repetition period T.

The processes in the reduced continuous part are described by linear total differential equations (if it contains only lumped parameters) or by linear partial differential equations (if it also contains distributed parameters). If $Y_{1T}(p)$ and $Z_T(p)$ denote the images of the input and output quantities of the reduced continuous part in the sense of the usual Laplace transformation, i.e.

$$Y_{1T}(p) = \int_0^\infty e^{-pt}\, y_{1T}(t)\, dt, \quad Z_T(p) = \int_0^\infty e^{-pt} z_T(t)\, dt\,, \tag{3.1}$$

then the equation of the reduced continuous part can be written in terms of these images as

$$Z_T(p) = K_T(p)\, Y_{1T}(p)\,. \tag{3.2}$$

Here it is assumed that no initial energy is stored before an input is applied to the reduced continuous part. The transfer function $K_T(p)$ is defined as the ratio of the image of the output quantity to the

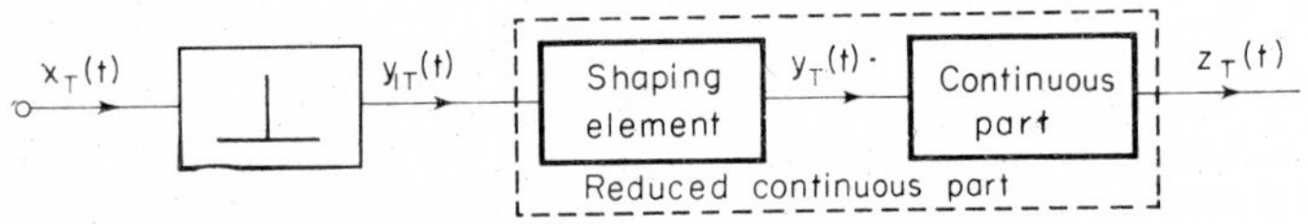

FIG. 3.4. Pulse system with a simple pulse element.

image of the input quantity. If the reduced continuous part contains only lumped parameters, the transfer function takes the form of a proper rational function, i.e.

$$K_T(q) = \frac{P_T(p)}{Q_T(p)}, \tag{3.3}$$

where $P_T(p)$ and $Q_T(p)$ are polynominals in p of degrees l_1 and l respectively ($l_1 \leqslant l$). If the reduced continuous part contains only distributed parameters, then $P_T(p)$ and $Q_T(p)$ become transcendental functions of p.

The transfer function $K_T(p)$ is an abbreviated form of writing the differential equations of the linear system and consequently it describes implicitly the dynamic properties of the system.

The properties of the reduced continuous part can also be described by characteristics which prescribe its behaviour to a given excitation. Two characteristics will play an important role in future work; they are the frequency characteristic and the pulse characteristic.

The frequency characteristic of the reduced continuous part is defined as the variation with frequency of the output, under steady-state conditions, for sinusoidal excitation. It is well-known+ that the frequency characteristic can be obtained from the transfer function $K_T(p)$ by replacing p by $j\omega$ in the latter, where ω denotes angular frequency, i.e.

$$K_T(p)_{p=j\omega} = K_T(j\omega)\,. \tag{3.4}$$

Separating the real and imaginary parts of (3.4) gives

$$K_T(j\omega) = B_T(\omega) + jM_T(\omega)\,. \tag{3.5}$$

The frequency characteristic can also be written in the exponential form

$$K_T(j\omega) = |\,K_T(\omega)\,|\,\mathrm{e}^{j\theta_T(\omega)}\,. \tag{3.6}$$

Here the modulus $|\,K_T(\omega)\,|$ defines the amplitude-frequency characteristic, and the phase $\theta_T(\omega)$ defines the phase-frequency characteristic. These characteristics are related to the real $B_T(\omega)$ and imaginary $M_T(\omega)$ parts of the frequency characteristic by the obvious relationships

$$|\,K_T(\omega)\,| = \sqrt{\{B_T^2(\omega) + M_T^2(\omega)\}}\,, \qquad \theta_T(\omega) = \arctan\frac{M_T(\omega)}{B_T(\omega)}$$

and inversely

$$B_T(\omega) = |\,K_T(\omega)\,|\cos\theta_T(\omega), \qquad M_T(\omega) = |\,K_T(\omega)\,|\sin\theta_T(\omega).$$

For a sinusoidal excitation $y_{1m}\,\mathrm{e}^{j\omega t}$, the steady-state output is given by the expression

$$\mathbf{z}_T(t) = |\,K_T(\omega)\,|\,y_{1m}\,\mathrm{e}^{j(\omega t + \theta_T(\omega))}. \tag{3.7}$$

From this we see that the frequency characteristic shows how the amplitude $|\,K_T(\omega)\,|\,y_{1m}$ and phase $\theta_T(\omega)$ of the steady-state output quantity vary with the angular frequency ω.

The pulse characteristic of the reduced continuous part is defined as its response to an input instantaneous pulse, i.e. to an excitation of the form of a delta-function. The pulse characteristic defines the behaviour of the reduced continuous part in the transient, non-steady state. Putting $y_{1T}(t) = \delta(t)$, and remembering that the image of an instantaneous pulse, i.e. the delta function, equals

$$L\{\delta(t)\} = \int_0^\infty \mathrm{e}^{-pt}\,\delta(t)\,\mathrm{d}t = 1\,, \tag{3.8}$$

+ See, for example, M. I. Kontorovich (2; 1955).

we find that the image of the pulse characteristic, which we denote by $k_T(t)$, equals the transfer function of the reduced continuous part

$$K_T(p) = L\{k_T(t)\} = \int_0^\infty e^{-pt} k_T(t) dt. \tag{3.9}$$

The pulse characteristic can be found from the well-known expansion formula+

$$k_T(t) = \sum_{\nu=1}^{l} c'_{\nu 0} e^{p_\nu t}, \tag{3.10}$$

where

$$c'_{\nu 0} = \lim_{p \to p_\nu} [K_T(p)(p - p_\nu)] = \frac{P_T(p_\nu)}{Q'_T(p_\nu)}, \tag{3.11}$$

and p_ν $(\nu = 1, 2, \ldots, l)$ are the poles of $K_T(p)$ or, what is the same thing, the roots of the equation

$$Q_T(p) = 0, \tag{3.12}$$

which are assumed simple and not equal to zero.

If (3.12) has repeated roots and roots equal to zero, for example:

$p_0 = 0$ of order r_0, $\quad p_2$ of order r_2,

p_1 of order r_1, $\quad \ldots\ldots\ldots\ldots$

$\quad p_s$ of order r_s,

so that $r_0 + r_1 + \ldots + r_s = l$ where l is the degree of the equation $Q_T(p) = 0$, then the pulse characteristic is given by the formula

$$k_T(t) = \sum_{\nu=0}^{s} \sum_{\mu=0}^{r_\nu - 1} c'_{\nu\mu} \frac{t^\mu}{\mu!} e^{p_\nu t}, \tag{3.13}$$

where

$$c'_{\nu\mu} = \frac{1}{(r_\nu - \mu - 1)!} \frac{d^{r_\nu - \mu - 1}}{dp^{r_\nu - \mu - 1}} [K_T(p)(p - p_\nu)^{r_\nu}]_{p = p_\nu}. \tag{3.14}$$

For those cases when $K_T(p)$ is a ratio of transcendental functions, we find that under certain restrictions the above formulae for $k_T(t)$ retain their form, but the number of poles becomes infinite. The expressions (3.10) or (3.13) for the pulse characteristic $k_T(t)$ may of course be used practically when the poles of the transfer function $K_T(p)$ are known and finite in number.

+ For the expansion formulae see the books by M. F. Gardner, D. L. Barnes (2; 1949); M. I. Kantorovich (2; 1955).

The pulse and frequency characteristics of a reduced continuous part are closely associated with each other. This relationship follows from well-known properties of the Fourier transformation.†

We denote the transfer function, frequency characteristic and pulse characteristic of a continuous system by $K_{T_c}(p)$, $K_{T_c}(j\omega)$ and $k_{T_c}(t)$ respectively. The pulse characteristic of the shaping element is determined by the shape of the pulse, i.e. it equals $s_T(t)$. Consequently, the transfer function and the frequency characteristic of the shaping element will be respectively the image $S_T(p)$ and the spectral function $S_T(j\omega)$ of the pulse shape. Remembering that the shaping element and the continuous system are connected in series, and assuming that when so connected there is no change in the properties of either, we can write the transfer function of the reduced continuous part $K_T(p)$ in the form

$$K_T(p) = S_T(p)\, K_{Tc}(p). \tag{3.15}$$

The frequency characteristic of the reduced continuous part is obtained by putting $p = j\omega$ in this expression:

$$K_T(j\omega) = S_T(j\omega)\, K_{Tc}(j\omega). \tag{3.16}$$

The original of (3.15) gives the pulse characteristic; using the convolution theorem,‡ it equals

$$k_T(t) = \int_0^t s_T(\lambda)\, k_{Tc}(t-\lambda)\, \mathrm{d}\lambda = s_T(t)\, b\, k_{Tc}(t), \tag{3.17}$$

where the symbol b denotes briefly the operation of convoluting.

We assume that $s_T(t)$ is a short-duration pulse which is constant in sign, and which exists in the interval 0 to t_0 and is zero for $t > t_0$. By a short-duration pulse we mean a pulse whose duration is sufficiently small that the pulse characteristic of the continuous system $k_{Tc}(t)$ can be considered to remain constant during the time of existence of the pulse $0 \leqslant t \leqslant t_0$. For a short-duration pulse we have from (3.17) for $t > t_0$

$$k_T(t) = \int_0^t s_T(\lambda)\, k_{Tc}(t-\lambda)\, \mathrm{d}\lambda \approx k_{Tc}(t) \int_0^t s_T(\lambda)\, \mathrm{d}\lambda .$$

We see from this relationship that under the above conditions the pulse characteristic $k_T(t)$ equals the pulse characteristic of the con-

† See L. A. Meyerovich, L. G. Zelichenko (1; 1956).

‡ See M. I. Kontorovich (2; 1955).

tinuous system $k_{T_c}(t)$ multiplied by the area of the pulse $s_T(t)$ acting on it. In other words, the excitation of a constant-sign short-duration pulse, irrespective of its shape, reduces to the excitation of an instantaneous pulse. This property, as was noted earlier, enables a type-two PWM system to be reduced to a type-one PAM system for small depths of modulation.

Relationships of the same form as (3.15-(3.17) exist between the output and input quantities of the reduced continuous part. Relationship (3.2) corresponds to (3.15). Putting $p = j\omega$ in (3.2) gives the relationship, analogous to (3.16), between the spectral functions of the input and output quantities of the reduced continuous part:

$$Z_T(j\omega) = K_T(j\omega)\, Y_{1T}(j\omega)\,. \tag{3.18}$$

Finally, applying the convolution theorem to (3.2), we obtain an expression analogous to (3.17)

$$z_T(t) = \int_0^t k_T(\lambda)\, y_{1T}(t-\lambda)\, \mathrm{d}\lambda = k_T(t) \mathrel{b} y_{1T}(t)\,. \tag{3.19}$$

Expressions (3.2), (3.18) and (3.19) can also be used to transform the external excitation $f_T(t)$ into the pulse-element input $x_T(t)$. For this we need only replace in these expressions $Z_T(p)$, $Z_T(j\omega)$, $z_T(t)$ by $X_T(p)$, $X_T(j\omega)$, $x_T(t)$; $Y_{1T}(p)$, $Y_{1T}(j\omega)$, $y_{1T}(t)$ by $F_T(p)$, $F_T(j\omega)$, $f_T(t)$ and $K_T(p)$, $K_T(j\omega)$, $k_T(t)$ by the transfer function, frequency characteristic and pulse characteristic of the continuous system preceding the pulse element.

The amplification factor of a pulse element k_p or $\varkappa$ will in future be referred to the shaping element, and its repetition period T will be reduced to unity. This is done by changing the time scale, i.e. by introducing the dimensionless time

$$\bar{t} = \frac{t}{T} \quad \text{or } t = T\bar{t}\,.$$

The discrete moments of time $t = 0, T, 2T, \ldots$ will now correspond to the integral values $\bar{t} = n = 0, 1, 2, \ldots$ Let us find how this affects the characteristics of the reduced continuous part.

The pulse characteristic of the reduced continuous part is obtained in this case by making the simple change of variable $t = T\bar{t}$. We denote the pulse characteristic $k_T(T\bar{t})$ by $k(\bar{t})$. Thus

$$k(\bar{t}) = k_T(t)_{t=T\bar{t}} = k_T(T\bar{t}). \tag{3.20}$$

The transfer function of the reduced continuous part corresponding to this pulse characteristic is obtained from (3.9) by putting $t = T\bar{t}$:

$$K_T(p) = \int_0^\infty e^{-pt} k_T(t) dt = T \int_0^\infty e^{-pT\bar{t}} k_T(T\bar{t})\, d\bar{t}\,.$$

Putting $p = q/T$ in this expression and using the notation of (3.20), we obtain

$$L\{k(\bar{t})\} = \int_0^\infty e^{-q\bar{t}} k(\bar{t})\, d\bar{t} = \frac{1}{T} K_T\left(\frac{q}{T}\right) = K(q). \qquad (3.21)$$

Hence the transfer function $K(q)$ of the reduced continuous part of a pulse system equals

$$K(q) = \frac{1}{T} K_T(p)_{p=\frac{q}{T}} = \frac{1}{T} K_T\left(\frac{q}{T}\right). \qquad (3.22)$$

From (3.15), $K(q)$ can be written in the form

$$K(q) = \frac{1}{T} S_T\left(\frac{q}{T}\right) K_{Tc}\left(\frac{q}{T}\right).$$

The expression

$$K_{sh.}(q) = \frac{1}{T} S_T\left(\frac{q}{T}\right) \qquad (3.23)$$

can be considered as the *transfer function of the shaping element.* This transfer function takes into account the slope of the characteristic k_p or $\varkappa$ and the repetition period T of the pulse element.

The pulse characteristic of the shaping element $k_{sh}(\bar{t})$ will equal

$$k_{sh.}(\bar{t}) = s(\bar{t}) = s_T(T\bar{t})\,. \qquad (3.24)$$

It is obtained by making a simple change in the time scale.

The expression

$$K_c(q) = K_{Tc}\left(\frac{q}{T}\right) \qquad (3.25)$$

can be considered as the *transfer function of the continuous part.*

The pulse characteristic of the continuous part will now equal+

$$k_c(\bar{t}) = T k_{T_c}(T\bar{t})\,. \qquad (3.26)$$

It is obtained by changing by a factor of T the ordinate and abscissa scales of the pulse characteristic $k_{T_c}(t)$.

+ See footnote on p. 168

If we know the transfer functions and pulse characteristics of the shaping element and the continuous part, we can easily find the transfer function, frequency characteristic and pulse characteristic of the reduced continuous part.

The transfer function $K(q)$ will now be given by the expression

$$K(q) = K_{sh.}(q)\, K_c(q) = \frac{P(q)}{Q(q)}, \qquad (3.27)$$

where $q = pT$, which is analogous to (3.15).

The frequency characteristic results on putting $q = j\bar{\omega}$ in the transfer function, where $\bar{\omega} = \omega T$ is the relative or dimensionless frequency. Thus

$$K(j\,\bar{\omega}) = K(q)_{q=j\bar{\omega}} = K_{sh.}(j\,\bar{\omega})\, K_c(j\,\bar{\omega})\,, \qquad (3.28)$$

or

$$K(j\,\bar{\omega}) = |K(\bar{\omega})|\, e^{j\theta(\bar{\omega})} = B(\bar{\omega}) + jM(\bar{\omega})\,. \qquad (3.29)$$

The pulse characteristic of the reduced continuous part $k(t)$ can be found from its transfer functions in a form similar to (3.10) and (3.13)

$$k(\bar{t}) = \sum_{\nu=1}^{l} c'_{\nu 0}\, e^{q_\nu \bar{t}}\,, \qquad (3.30)$$

where

$$c'_{\nu 0} = \frac{P(q_\nu)}{Q'(q_\nu)}, \qquad (3.31)$$

and q_ν are the poles of $K(q)$, which are assumed simple and not equal to zero; in other words q_ν are the roots of the equation

$$Q(q) = 0\,. \qquad (3.32)$$

In general, when this equation has repeated roots and roots which equal zero, we have

$$k(\bar{t}) = \sum_{\nu=0}^{s} \sum_{\mu=0}^{r_\nu - 1} c'_{\nu\mu} \frac{\bar{t}^\mu}{\mu!}\, e^{q_\nu \bar{t}}, \qquad (3.33)$$

where

$$c'_{\nu\mu} = \frac{1}{(r_\nu - \mu - 1)!} \frac{d^{r_\nu - \mu - 1}}{dq^{r_\nu - \mu - 1}} [K(q)\,(q - q_\nu)^{r_\nu}]_{q=q_\nu}\,. \qquad (3.34)$$

Obviously, the pulse characteristic $k(\bar{t})$ can also be obtained from (3.10) or (3.13) by putting $t = T\bar{t}$, writing $q_\nu = p_\nu T$, and multiplying by T.

The pulse characteristic of the reduced continuous part $k(\bar{t})$ can also be found in terms of the pulse characteristics of the shaping element and the continuous part. This is done by putting $t = T\bar{t}$ in (3.17) and using (3.26)

$$k(\bar{t}) = k_T(T\bar{t}) = \int_0^{T\bar{t}} s_T(\lambda)\, k_{Tc}(T\bar{t} - \lambda)\, d\lambda \,. \qquad (3.35)$$

Introducing a new variable $\bar{\lambda} = \lambda/T$ and using (3.24) and (3.26), we obtain

$$k(\bar{t}) = \int_0^{\bar{t}} k_{sh}(\bar{\lambda})\, k_c(\bar{t} - \bar{\lambda})\, d\bar{\lambda} \,. \qquad (3.36)$$

If the shaping element is an amplifier with gain k_p, then

$$s_T(\lambda) = k_p\, \delta(\lambda)\,,$$

and we obtain from (3.36), on account of the property of the δ-function,

$$k(\bar{t}) = k_p\, k_{Tc}(T\bar{t}) = \frac{k_p}{T}\, k_c(\bar{t}) \,. \qquad (3.37)$$

In this case the pulse characteristic of the reduced continuous part differs from that of the continuous system only in scale.

3.2. Equations and transfer functions of open-loop pulse systems

It was established in § 3.1 that, without affecting the generality, a pulse system can be reduced to the simplest form shown in Fig. 3.5.

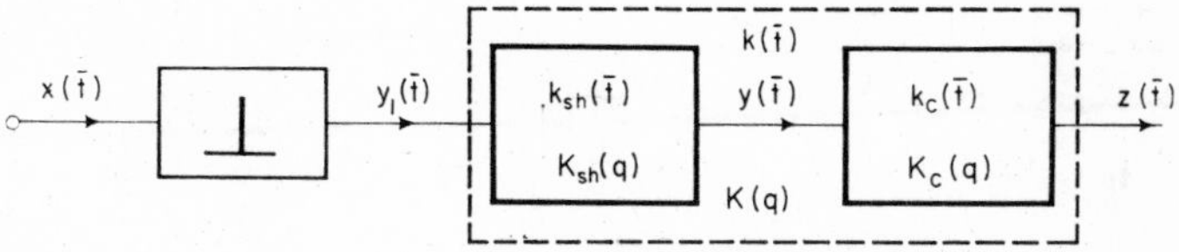

FIG. 3.5. Simplest form of a pulse system.

Hence in future we shall consider the reduced continuous part without stating this explicitly every time.

We shall assume that the external excitation is applied to the input of the pulse element. The output of the pulse element is a train of instantaneous pulses, of relative repetition period equal to unity, which have been modulated by the external excitation. The areas or intensities of the pulses equal the values of the external excitation at the discrete, equally-spaced moments of time $\bar{t} = n$. This modulated pulse train acts on the reduced continuous part of the pulse system. In this manner, an open-loop pulse system responds only to discrete values of the external excitation. This characteristic property of pulse systems permits the application of lattice functions and the associated discrete Laplace transformation described in Chapter II. We note that different external excitations (continuous functions) will give rise to the same response of the pulse system if their values coincide at the (discrete) moments when pulses appear (Fig. 3.6).

If an excitation $x(\bar{t})$ (Fig. 3.7a), where $\bar{t} = t/T$, is applied to the input of an open-loop pulse system, a train of modulated instantaneous pulses $y_1(\bar{t})$ (Fig. 3.7b) will appear at the output of the pulse element; the relative repetition period of the pulses equals unity and the 'areas' of the pulses vary according to the law $x(n)$ $(n = 0, 1, 2, \ldots)$. This pulse train acts on the reduced continuous part. The output of the reduced continuous part equals the sum of the responses to each individual instantaneous pulse (Fig. 3.7c).

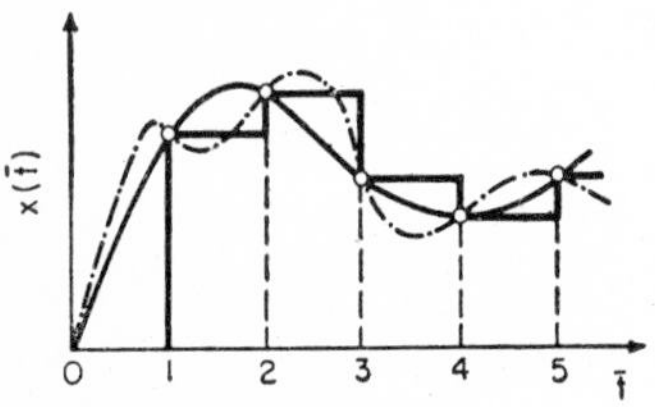

FIG. 3.6. Excitations that induce the same response in a pulse system.

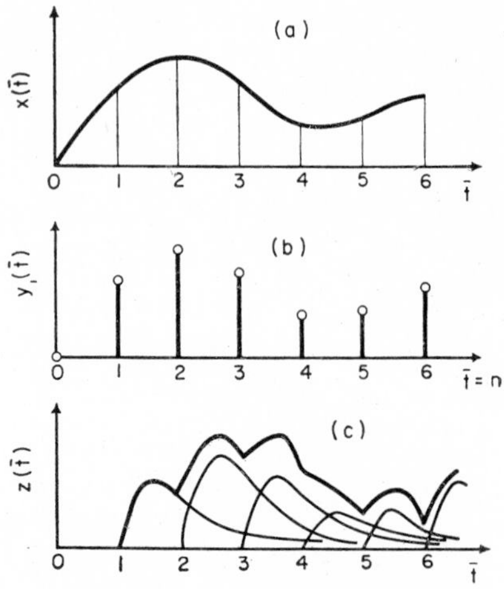

FIG. 3.7. Concerning the response of a pulse system: (a) the input and its corresponding lattice function, (b) modulated instantaneous pulses, (c) formation of the output.

The pulse characteristic of the reduced continuous part $k(\bar{t})$ is its response to an instantaneous pulse. If the instantaneous pulse is applied at the instant $\bar{t} = m$, where m is an integer, the response of the reduced continuous part will equal

$$k(\bar{t} - m) \qquad \text{for} \quad \bar{t} \geqslant m,$$

$$k(\bar{t} - m) \equiv 0 \ \text{for} \ \ \bar{t} \leqslant m.$$

Thus the expression for the response of the reduced continuous part $z(\bar{t})$ to a train of instantaneous pulses $y_1(\bar{t})$, as can be seen from Fig.

3.7*c*, can be formed in the following manner. In the time interval $0 \leqslant \bar{t} \leqslant 1$

$$z(\bar{t}) = x(0)\, k(\bar{t}),$$

in the time interval $1 \leqslant \bar{t} \leqslant 2$

$$z(\bar{t}) = x(0)\, k(\bar{t}) + x(1)\, k(\bar{t} - 1),$$

in the time interval $2 \leqslant \bar{t} \leqslant 3$

$$z(\bar{t}) = x(0)\, k(\bar{t}) + x(1)\, k(\bar{t} - 1) + x(2)\, k(\bar{t} - 2)$$

and in general in the time interval $n \leqslant \bar{t} \leqslant n + 1$

$$z(\bar{t}) = \sum_{m=0}^{n} x(m)\, k(\bar{t} - m). \tag{3.38}$$

Put $\bar{t} = n + \varepsilon$ in (3.38), where n is an integer; $\varepsilon = \Delta t/T$ is the relative time, which lies in the interval 0 to 1; T is the repetition period; Δt is the time measured from the beginning of each pulse.

On introducing the lattice function notation

$$x(m) = x[m], \quad z(n + \varepsilon) = z[n, \varepsilon], \quad k(n + \varepsilon) = k[n, \varepsilon],$$

we can write (3.38) in the form

$$z[n, \varepsilon] = \sum_{m=0}^{n} x[m]\, k[n - m, \varepsilon], \quad 0 \leqslant \varepsilon \leqslant 1. \tag{3.39}$$

This expression sets up the relationship between the input and output quantities, which take the form of lattice functions, of an open-loop pulse system. In contrast to the input quantity $x[m]$, the output quantity of the open-loop pulse system $z[n, \varepsilon]$ is a displaced lattice function and depends on the parameter ε.

If for a given value of n we let ε vary from 0 to 1, then formula (3.39) gives the value of the output variable of the pulse system at any moment of time $\bar{t} = n + \varepsilon$ ($n = 0, 1, 2, \ldots$ and $0 \leqslant \varepsilon < 1$). In order to make a more complete and detailed investigation of pulse systems it is convenient to transform from equations in the lattice functions themselves to equations in their images. We thus apply a D-transformation to both sides of (3.39)

$$D\{z[n, \varepsilon]\} = D\left\{\sum_{m=0}^{n} x[m]\, k[n - m, \varepsilon]\right\}.$$

Using the theorem on the multiplication of images (Theorem 11), the left side of this expression can be written in the form

$$D\left\{\sum_{m=0}^{n} x[m]\, k[n - m, \varepsilon]\right\} = D\{x[n]\}\, D\{k[n, \varepsilon]\}.$$

Denoting the images of the input and output quantities by

$$D\{x[n]\} = X^*(q), \quad D\{z[n, \varepsilon]\} = Z^*(q, \varepsilon)$$

the equation of an open-loop pulse system in terms of the images becomes

$$Z^*(q, \varepsilon) = K^*(q, \varepsilon)\, X^*(q) \tag{3.40}$$

where

$$K^*(q, \varepsilon) = D\{k[n, \varepsilon]\}\,. \tag{3.41}$$

These equations describe the processes in type-one (PAM) pulse systems. For small depths of modulation, as has been mentioned previously, they also hold for type-two (PWM) open-loop pulse systems. The equations for type-three (PTM) pulse systems, even for small depths of modulation, have a form different from that of the above equations. Type-three pulse systems will be examined in § 3.4.

In the above manner, the equation of an open-loop pulse system can be written in two forms — in terms of the originals (lattice functions) (3.39), or in terms of the images (3.40). The latter form enables the *transfer function of an open-loop pulse system* to be introduced; this is an important concept and is defined as the ratio of the image of the output of the open-loop pulse system to the image of the input:

$$K^*(y, \varepsilon) = \frac{Z^*(q, \varepsilon)}{X^*(q)}\,.$$

In conformity with the definition of the D-transformation (2.20), the transfer function of an open-loop pulse system (3.41) can be written as

$$K^*(q, \varepsilon) = \sum_{n=0}^{\infty} \mathrm{e}^{-qn}\, k[n, \varepsilon]\,. \tag{3.42}$$

Since

$$k[n, \varepsilon] = k(n + \varepsilon) = k(\bar{t})$$

is the pulse characteristic of the reduced continuous part, it follows from (3.42) that the *transfer function of an open-loop pulse system equals the discrete Laplace transformation (D-transformation) of the pulse characteristic of the reduced continuous part* $k(\bar{t})$.

It will sometimes prove convenient to express the transfer function of an open-loop pulse system in terms of the differences of the pulse characteristic of the reduced continuous part $\Delta^\nu k[n, \varepsilon]$. Such an expression for $K^*(q, \varepsilon)$ is obtained on writing in formula (2.55)

$$f[n] = k[n, \varepsilon]\,, \quad \Delta^r f[n] = \Delta^r k[n, \varepsilon]$$

and therefore

$$F^*(q) = K^*(q, \varepsilon).$$

(2.55) then gives

$$K^*(q, \varepsilon) = \frac{1}{(e^q - 1)^r} D\{\Delta^r k[n, \varepsilon]\} + \sum_{\nu=0}^{r-1} \frac{e^q}{(e^q - 1)^{\nu-1}} \Delta^\nu k[0, \varepsilon],$$

or more explicitly

$$K^*(q, \varepsilon) = \frac{1}{(e^q - 1)^r} \sum_{n=0}^{\infty} e^{-qn} \Delta^r k[n, \varepsilon] + \sum_{\nu=0}^{r-1} \frac{e^q}{(e^q - 1)^{\nu+1}} \Delta^\nu k[0, \varepsilon]. \quad (3.43)$$

For $r = 0$ we obtain expression (3.41), which defines the D-transformation of the function $k[n, \varepsilon]$.

The transfer function of an open-loop pulse system $K^*(q, \varepsilon)$ can also be expressed in terms of the transfer function of the reduced continuous part $K(q)$. This is done using the $\mathfrak{D}$-transformation, i.e. by the relationship derived in § 2.8, which relates the image $F^*(q, \varepsilon)$ of a lattice function to the image $F(q)$ of the corresponding continuous function

$$F^*(q, \varepsilon) = D\{f[n, \varepsilon]\} = \mathfrak{D}\{F(q)\},$$

or explicitly

$$F^*(q, \varepsilon) = \sum_{n=0}^{\infty} e^{-qn} f[n, \varepsilon] = \sum_{r=-\infty}^{\infty} e^{(q+2\pi jr)\varepsilon} F(q + 2\pi jr).$$

As the image of the pulse characteristic of the reduced continuous part $k(\bar{t})$ equals the transfer function of the reduced continuous part, then by putting

$$f[n, \varepsilon] = k[n, \varepsilon]$$

and therefore

$$F(q) = K(q), \quad F^*(q, \varepsilon) = K^*(q, \varepsilon)$$

in the previous relationship, we obtain

$$K^*(q, \varepsilon) = \mathfrak{D}\{K(q)\},$$

or explicitly

$$K^*(q, \varepsilon) = \sum_{r=-\infty}^{\infty} e^{(q+2\pi jr)\varepsilon} K(q + 2\pi jr), \quad (3.44)$$

i.e. the transfer function of an open-loop pulse system equals the discrete Laplace transformation ($\mathfrak{D}$-transformation) of the transfer function of the reduced continuous part $K(q)$.

Expressions (3.42), (3.43) and (3.44) give, in the form of series, the transfer function of an open-loop pulse system $K^*(q, \varepsilon)$ in terms of the pulse characteristic $k(\bar{t}) = k[n, \varepsilon]$ or transfer function $K(q)$ of the reduced continuous part. These expressions are valid for any linear reduced continuous part with lumped or distributed parameters.

For the case when the reduced continuous part contains lumped parameters and possibly delay units, and if the poles of its transfer function are known (or, what is the same thing, if an analytic expression for the pulse characteristic is known), then the series (3.42), (3.43) and (3.44) can be summed to give the transfer function of the open-loop pulse system $K^*(q, \varepsilon)$ in closed form.

We now consider the most important particular cases.

Pulse systems with instantaneous pulses. We shall assume initially that the shaping element is an amplifier of gain k_P. In this case the transfer function of the reduced continuous part will be given by

$$K(q) = \frac{k_p}{T} K_c(q) = \frac{k_p}{T} \frac{P_c(q)}{Q_c(q)}. \tag{3.45}$$

Consequently, the expression for the pulse characteristic (3.30) can be written

$$k(\bar{t}) = \frac{k_p}{T} k_c(\bar{t}) = \sum_{\nu=1}^{l} c'_{\nu_0} e^{q_\nu \bar{t}}, \tag{3.46}$$

where, from (3.31),

$$c'_{\nu_0} = \frac{P(q_\nu)}{Q'(q_\nu)} = \frac{k_p P_c(q_\nu)}{T Q'_c(q)}. \tag{3.47}$$

Here, for the meantime, it is assumed that the poles of $K(q)$ are simple. From the pulse characteristic $k(\bar{t})$ we obtain the corresponding displaced lattice function

$$k[n, \varepsilon] = k(n + \varepsilon) = \sum_{\nu=1}^{l} c'_{\nu_0} e^{q_\nu n} e^{q_\nu \varepsilon}. \tag{3.48}$$

Substituting $k[n, \varepsilon]$ in (3.41) and using the linearity theorem (Theorem 1), we obtain

$$K^*(q, \varepsilon) = \sum_{\nu=1}^{l} c'_{\nu_0} e^{q_\nu \varepsilon} D\{e^{q_\nu n}\}.$$

However

$$D\{e^{q_\nu n}\} = \frac{e^q}{e^q - e^{q_\nu}},$$

and so we finally obtain

$$K^*(q, \varepsilon) = \sum_{\nu=1}^{l} c'_{\nu_0} \frac{e^q}{e^q - e^{q_\nu}} e^{q_\nu \varepsilon}, \quad 0 \leqslant \varepsilon \leqslant 1. \tag{3.49}$$

This same result can be obtained by applying the $\mathfrak{D}$-transformation to the transfer function of the reduced continuous part $K(q)$, $K(q)$ being expanded as a sum of simple fractions:

$$K(q) = \sum_{\nu=1}^{l} \frac{c'_{\nu_0}}{q - q_\nu}.$$

In fact, in conformity with (2.233), we have.

$$K^*(q, \varepsilon) = \mathfrak{D}\{K(q)\}.$$

We obtain on substituting for $K(q)$ and changing the order of summation [of (2.236)]

$$K^*(q, \varepsilon) = \sum_{\nu=1}^{l} c'_{\nu_0} \mathfrak{D}\left\{\frac{1}{q - q_\nu}\right\}.$$

However [see (2.235)] it was shown earlier that

$$\mathfrak{D}\left\{\frac{1}{q - q_\nu}\right\} = \frac{e^q}{e^q - e^{q_\nu}} e^{q_\nu \varepsilon},$$

and the resulting expression for $K^*(q, \varepsilon)$ reduces to (3.49).

We always assume that $\varepsilon > 0$. Sometimes, for example when investigating systems with several pulse elements, it becomes necessary to consider $K^*(q, \varepsilon)$ for $\varepsilon < 0$, i.e. $K^*(q, -\varepsilon)$ for $\varepsilon > 0$. In this case

$$k[n, -\varepsilon] = k[n-1, 1-\varepsilon].$$

For $n = 0$

$$k[0, -\varepsilon] = 0,$$

since for negative values of the argument the pulse characteristic is identically equal to zero. Applying the discrete Laplace transformation to $k[n, -\varepsilon]$, we have

$$K^*(q, -\varepsilon) = D\{k[n, -\varepsilon]\} = D\{k[n-1, 1-\varepsilon]\}.$$

However, from the original-translation theorem (Theorem 2),

$$D\{k[n-1, 1-\varepsilon]\} = e^{-q} D\{k[n, 1-\varepsilon]\} = e^{-q} K^*(q, 1-\varepsilon).$$

Consequently,

$$K^*(q, -\varepsilon) = e^{-q} K^*(q, 1-\varepsilon).$$

In this manner

$$K^*(q, \varepsilon) = \begin{cases} K^*(q, \varepsilon) & \text{for } \varepsilon \geqslant 0 \\ e^{-q} K^*(q, 1+\varepsilon) & \text{for } \varepsilon \leqslant 0 \end{cases}. \tag{3.50}$$

In particular, we obtain from (3.50) for $\varepsilon = 0$

$$K^*(q, \pm 0) = \begin{cases} K^*(q, +0), & \varepsilon = +0 \\ e^{-q} K^*(q, 1), & \varepsilon = -0 \end{cases}. \tag{3.51}$$

$K^*(q, \pm 0)$ denotes the values of the transfer function to the right and the left of $\varepsilon = 0$. For those cases when the pulse characteristic of the reduced continuous part $k(\bar{t})$ equals zero for $\bar{t} = 0$, the left and right values of $K^*(q, \pm 0)$ become equal, i.e.

$$K^*(q, -0) = K^*(q, +0) = e^{-q} K^*(q, 1)\,. \tag{3.52}$$

For those cases when

$$k(0) \neq 0\,,$$

the left and right values of $K^*(q, \pm 0)$ differ by the value of the step $k(0)$. With open-loop pulse systems the presence or absence of a step in $k(\bar{t})$ for $\bar{t} = 0$ does not play an important role. Thus, we are restricted

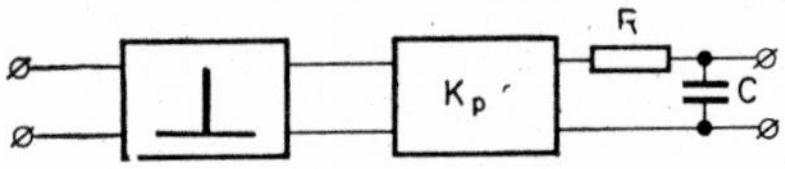

FIG. 3.8. A simple pulse system.

here only by the remarks relating to formula (3.50). This question will be examined in more detail in § 5.4, in connection with the stability of closed-loop pulse systems.

EXAMPLE. Consider the elementary pulse system shown schematically in Fig. 3.8. The reduced continuous part consists of a shaping element — an amplifier of gain k_p, and a four terminal RC network. The output quantity is the voltage on capacitor C. The transfer function of the continuous part equals

$$K_{Tc}(p) = \frac{1/Cp}{R + 1/Cp} = \frac{1}{T_1 p + 1}\,,$$

where $T_1 = RC$ is the time constant. Putting $p = q/T$ in $K_{Tc}(p)$ and writing $T/T_1 = \beta$, where T is the repetition period, we have from (3.25)

$$K_c(q) = K_{Tc}\left(\frac{q}{T}\right) = \frac{P_c(q)}{Q_c(q)} = \frac{\beta}{q + \beta}\,.$$

The transfer function $K_c(q)$ has one pole at $q_1 = -\beta$, for which

$$c'_{10} = \frac{k_p}{T}\frac{P_c(-\beta)}{Q'_c(-\beta)} = \frac{k_p \beta}{T} = \frac{k_p}{T_1} = k_0\,.$$

Consequently, we obtain from formula (3.49)

$$K^*(q, \varepsilon) = k_0 \frac{e^q}{e^q - e^{-\beta}} e^{-\beta\varepsilon}, \qquad 0 \leqslant \varepsilon \leqslant 1\,. \tag{3.53}$$

$K^*(q, \varepsilon)$ can also be found in a different manner. The transfer function of the reduced continuous part equals

$$K(q) = K_{sh}(q)\, K_c(q) = \frac{k_p}{T} \frac{\beta}{q+\beta} = \frac{k_0}{q+\beta}.$$

Thus

$$K^*(q, \varepsilon) = \mathfrak{D}\{K(q)\} = k_0\, \mathfrak{D}\left\{\frac{1}{q+\beta}\right\}.$$

However

$$\mathfrak{D}\left\{\frac{1}{q-\beta}\right\} = \frac{e^q}{e^q - e^{-\beta}}\, e^{-\beta\varepsilon},$$

and we arrive at the same formula. Equation (3.53) gives for $\varepsilon = 0$

$$K^*(q, 0) = k_0 \frac{e^q}{e^q - e^{-\beta}}.$$

From (3.51) we have

$$K^*(q, -0) = e^{-q} K^*(q, 1) = k_0 \frac{e^{-\beta}}{e^q - e^{-\beta}}.$$

Thus in this case the right and left values of the transfer function $K^*(q, 0)$ are different.

Pulse systems with instantaneous pulses and a delay element. Let us now assume that the shaping element takes the form of a delay element, i.e. an element whose output is an undistorted reproduction of its input but delayed by a constant amount τ, called the time-delay.+ The transfer function of this element equals $e^{-p\tau}$ or $e^{-q\bar{\tau}}$, where $\bar{\tau} = \tau/T$ is the relative time-delay. In this case the transfer function of the reduced continuous part equals

$$K(q) = \frac{k_p}{T} e^{-q\bar{\tau}} K_c(q). \tag{3.54}$$

The pulse characteristic (the original) corresponding to this image equals

$$k(\bar{t}) = \frac{k_p}{T} k_c(\bar{t} - \bar{\tau}) = \sum_{\nu=0}^{l} c'_\nu\, e^{q_\nu(\bar{t}-\bar{\tau})}, \tag{3.55}$$

and for negative values of the argument, i.e. $\bar{t} < \bar{\tau}$

$$k(\bar{t}) = \frac{k_p}{T} k_c(\bar{t} - \bar{\tau}) \equiv 0.$$

The relative delay $\bar{\tau}$ can always be written in the form

$$\bar{\tau} = m_1 + \bar{\tau}_1,$$

where m_1 is an integer and $0 \leqslant \bar{\tau} \leqslant 1$.

+ The case when the delay element is contained in the continuous part can be reduced to the case considered here.

Putting $\bar{t} = n + \varepsilon$ in (3.55) gives the displaced lattice function

$$k[n, \varepsilon] = \frac{k_p}{T} k_c(n - m_1 + \varepsilon - \bar{\tau}_1) = \sum_{\nu=1}^{l} c'_{\nu 0}\, e^{q_\nu(n-m_1)}\, e^{q_\nu(\varepsilon-\bar{\tau}_1)}.$$

Remembering that $k[n, \varepsilon]$ is identically equal to zero for negative values of the argument $(n - m_1 + \varepsilon - \bar{\tau}_1)$, i.e. for $n < m_1 + 1$ and $0 \leqslant \varepsilon \leqslant \bar{\tau}_1$, the latter expression can be rewritten in the form

$$\left.\begin{aligned} &k[n, \varepsilon] = \sum_{\nu=1}^{l} c'_{\nu_0} e^{q_\nu(n-m_1-1)} e^{q_\nu(1+\varepsilon-\bar{\tau}_1)} \\ &\quad \text{for } 0 \leqslant \varepsilon \leqslant \bar{\tau}_1 \text{ and } n \geqslant m_1 + 1, \\ &k[n, \varepsilon] = \sum_{\nu=1}^{l} c'_{\nu_0} e^{q_\nu(n-m_1)} e^{q_\nu(\varepsilon-\bar{\tau}_1)} \\ &\quad \text{for } \bar{\tau}_1 \leqslant \varepsilon \leqslant 1 \text{ and } n \geqslant m_1. \end{aligned}\right\} \tag{3.56}$$

This shows that $k[n, \varepsilon]$ has different analytical forms in the intervals $0 \leqslant \varepsilon \leqslant \bar{\tau}_1$ and $\bar{\tau}_1 \leqslant \varepsilon \leqslant 1$.

Since $k[n, \varepsilon]$ is known, the determination of $K^*[q, \varepsilon]$ in accordance with (3.41) reduces to applying the discrete Laplace transformation to $k[n, \varepsilon]$. Substituting in (3.41) the value of $k[n, \varepsilon]$ from (3.56), we have, using the linearity theorem (Theorem 1), that

$$\left.\begin{aligned} K^*(q, \varepsilon) &= \sum_{\nu=1}^{l} c'_{\nu_0} e^{q_\nu(1+\varepsilon-\bar{\tau}_1)} D\{e^{q_\nu(n-m_1-1)}\}, \\ &\qquad 0 \leqslant \varepsilon \leqslant \bar{\tau}_1, \\ K^*(q, \varepsilon) &= \sum_{\nu=1}^{l} c'_{\nu_0} e^{q_\nu(\varepsilon-\bar{\tau}_1)} D\{e^{q_\nu(n-m_1)}\}, \\ &\qquad \bar{\tau}_1 \leqslant \varepsilon \leqslant 1. \end{aligned}\right\} \tag{3.57}$$

However, from the original-translation theorem (Theorem 2),

$$D\{e^{q_\nu(n+k)}\} = \frac{e^q}{e^q - e^{q_\nu}}\, e^{-kq} = \frac{1}{e^{(k-1)q}(e^q - e^{q_\nu})}\,.$$

Putting $k = m_1 + 1$ and $k = m_1$ in this expression and substituting the resulting image in (3.57), we obtain the expression for the transfer function in closed form:

$$\left.\begin{aligned} K^*(q, \varepsilon) &= \sum_{\nu=1}^{l} c'_{\nu 0} \frac{e^{q_\nu}}{e^{qm_1}(e^q - e^{q_\nu})}\, e^{q_\nu(\varepsilon-\bar{\tau}_1)}, \\ &\qquad 0 \leqslant \varepsilon \leqslant \bar{\tau}_1, \\ K^*(q, \varepsilon) &= \sum_{\nu=1}^{l} c'_{\nu 0} \frac{e^q}{e^{qm_1}(e^q - e^{p_\nu})}\, e^{q_\nu(\varepsilon-\bar{\tau}_1)}, \\ &\qquad \tau_1 \leqslant \varepsilon \leqslant 1. \end{aligned}\right\} \tag{3.58}$$

When a delay element is present the pulse-system transfer function $K^*(q, \varepsilon)$ has different analytical forms in the intervals $0 \leqslant \varepsilon \leqslant \bar{\tau}_1$ and $\bar{\tau}_1 \leqslant \varepsilon \leqslant 1$. This result can be obtained by a slightly different method which uses the $\mathfrak{D}$-transformation. In this case we write (3.54) in the form

$$K_\tau(q) = e^{-qm_1} e^{-q\bar{\tau}_1} K(q)\,, \tag{3.59}$$

where m_1 is an integer, $\bar{\tau}_1 < 1$ and

$$K(q) = \frac{k_p}{T} K_c(q)$$

is the transfer function of the reduced continuous part in the absence of the delay element.

Applying the $\mathfrak{D}$-transformation to (3.59) gives

$$K^*(q, \varepsilon) = \mathfrak{D}\{K_\tau(q)\} = \mathfrak{D}\{e^{-qm_1} e^{-q\bar{\tau}_1} K(q)\}\,.$$

Using the theorem on multiplication by e^{-kq} (k an integer) (Theorem 18), we obtain

$$K^*(q, \varepsilon) = e^{-qm_1} \mathfrak{D}\{e^{-q\bar{\tau}_1} K(q)\}\,.$$

Denoting for the meantime the transfer function of the pulse system with no delay element (3.49) by

$$\mathfrak{D}\{K(q)\} = K^*(q, \varepsilon)_{\tau=0}\,,$$

and using the theorem on multiplication by $e^{-\gamma q}$ $(\gamma < 1)$ (Theorem 19), we find

$$K^*(q, \varepsilon) = \begin{cases} e^{-q(m_1+1)} K^*(q, 1 + \varepsilon - \bar{\tau}_1)_{\tau=0}\,, & 0 \leqslant \varepsilon \leqslant \bar{\tau}_1\,, \\ e^{-qm_1} K^*(q, \varepsilon - \bar{\tau}_1)_{\tau=0}\,, & \bar{\tau}_1 \leqslant \varepsilon \leqslant 1\,. \end{cases} \tag{3.60}$$

Equations (3.58) result on substituting in (3.60) the value of $K^*(q, \varepsilon)_{\tau=0}$ from (3.49). Formula (3.60) shows how the transfer function of a pulse system with delay can be obtained from that of the system without delay (3.49).

If the relative time-delay equals an integer, i.e. $\tau = m_1$ and $\bar{\tau}_1 = 0$, then (3.60) gives

$$K^*(q, \varepsilon) = e^{-qm_1} K^*(q, \varepsilon)_{\tau=0}\,. \tag{3.61}$$

In this case the transfer function of the system with delay is formed from the transfer function of the system without delay (3.49) by multiplying by e^{-qm_1}. This also follows from the original-translation theorem (Theorem 2).

If the relative delay is less than unity, i.e.

$$m_1 = 0 \quad \text{and} \quad \bar{\tau} = \bar{\tau}_1 < 1,$$

then it follows from (3.60) that

$$K^*(q, \varepsilon) = \begin{cases} e^{-q} K^*(q, 1 + \varepsilon - \bar{\tau}_1)_{\tau=0}, & 0 \leqslant \varepsilon \leqslant \bar{\tau}_1, \\ K^*(q, \varepsilon - \bar{\tau}_1)_{\tau=0}, & \bar{\tau}_1 \leqslant \varepsilon \leqslant 1. \end{cases} \tag{3.62}$$

On replacing $\varepsilon - \bar{\tau}_1$ by $\mp \varepsilon$ in the right side of these expressions, they become identical to the previously obtained expressions for $K^*(q, \varepsilon)$ (3.50) for negative and positive ε.

If the transfer function of the reduced continuous part $K(q)$ has multiple poles, the expression for the pulse characteristic takes the form

$$k(\bar{t}) = \frac{k_p}{T} k_c(\bar{t}) = \sum_{\nu=0}^{s} \sum_{\mu=0}^{r_\nu - 1} c'_{\nu\mu} \frac{\bar{t}^\mu}{\mu!} e^{q_\nu \bar{t}}, \tag{3.63}$$

where, from (3.34) and (3.45),

$$c'_{\nu\mu} = \frac{1}{(r_\nu - \mu - 1)!} \frac{d^{r_\nu - \mu - 1}}{dq^{r_\nu - \mu - 1}} \left[\frac{k_p P_c(q)}{T Q_c(q)} (q - q_\nu)^{r_\nu} \right]_{q = q_\nu}. \tag{3.64}$$

Noting that

$$\bar{t}^\mu e^{q_\nu \bar{t}} = \frac{d^\mu}{dq_\nu^\mu} [e^{q_\nu \bar{t}}],$$

the pulse characteristic $k(\bar{t})$ can be written in the form

$$k(\bar{t}) = \frac{k_p}{T} k_c(\bar{t}) = \sum_{\nu=0}^{s} \sum_{\mu=0}^{r_\nu - 1} \frac{c'_{\nu\mu}}{\mu!} \frac{d^\mu}{dq_\nu^\mu} [e^{q_\nu \bar{t}}]$$

in the absence of delay ($\bar{\tau} = 0$), and in the form

$$k(\bar{t}) = 0, \quad \bar{t} < \tau,$$

$$k(\bar{t}) = \frac{k_p}{T} k_c(\bar{t} - \bar{\tau}) = \sum_{\nu=0}^{s} \sum_{\mu=0}^{r_\nu - 1} \frac{c'_{\nu\mu}}{\mu!} \frac{d^\mu}{dq_\nu^\mu} [e^{q_\nu (\bar{t} - \bar{\tau})}], \quad \bar{t} \geqslant \tau, \tag{3.65}$$

in the presence of delay.

On introducing the lattice functions, and remembering that from the theorem on differentiation with respect to a parameter (Theorem 9)

$$D\left\{\frac{d^\mu}{dq_\nu^\mu} e^{q_\nu (n-k)}\right\} = \frac{d^\mu}{dq_\nu^\mu} D\{e^{q_\nu (n-k)}\},$$

we can show in precisely the same manner as above that

$$\left.\begin{aligned} K^*(q,\varepsilon) &= \sum_{\nu=0}^{s}\sum_{\mu=0}^{r_\nu-1} \frac{c'_{\nu\mu}}{\mu!}\frac{\mathrm{d}^\mu}{\mathrm{d}q_\nu^\mu}\left[\frac{\mathrm{e}^{q_\nu}}{\mathrm{e}^{qm_1}(\mathrm{e}^q-\mathrm{e}^{q_\nu})}\,\mathrm{e}^{q_\nu(\varepsilon-\bar{\tau}_1)}\right], \quad 0\leqslant\varepsilon\leqslant\bar{\tau}_1, \\ K^*(q,\varepsilon) &= \sum_{\nu=0}^{s}\sum_{\mu=0}^{r_\nu-1} \frac{c'_{\nu\mu}}{\mu!}\frac{\mathrm{d}^\mu}{\mathrm{d}q_\nu^\mu}\left[\frac{\mathrm{e}^{q}}{\mathrm{e}^{qm_1}(\mathrm{e}^q-\mathrm{e}^{q_\nu})}\,\mathrm{e}^{q_\nu(\varepsilon-\bar{\tau}_1)}\right], \quad \bar{\tau}\leqslant\varepsilon\leqslant 1. \end{aligned}\right\} \quad (3.66)$$

If $r_0 = 0$ (i.e. $K(q)$ has no poles at $q = 0$), $r_\nu = 1$ ($\nu = 1, 2, \ldots, s = l$), then (3.66) gives (3.58).

If $r_0 = 1$ (i.e. $K(q)$ has one pole at $q = 0$), $r_\nu = 1$ ($\nu = 1, 2, \ldots, s = l - 1$), then we obtain from (3.66)

$$\left.\begin{aligned} K^*(q,\varepsilon) &= c'_{00}\frac{1}{\mathrm{e}^{qm_1}(\mathrm{e}^q-1)} + \sum_{\nu=1}^{l-1} c'_{\nu 0}\frac{\mathrm{e}^{q_\nu}}{\mathrm{e}^{qm_1}(\mathrm{e}^q-\mathrm{e}^{q_\nu})}\,\mathrm{e}^{q_\nu(\varepsilon-\bar{\tau}_1)}, \\ &\qquad 0\leqslant\varepsilon\leqslant\bar{\tau}_1, \\ K^*(q,\varepsilon) &= c'_{00}\frac{1}{\mathrm{e}^{q(m_1-1)}(\mathrm{e}^q-1)} + \sum_{\nu=1}^{l-1} c'_{\nu 0}\frac{1}{\mathrm{e}^{q(m_1-1)}(\mathrm{e}^q-\mathrm{e}^{q_\nu})}\,\mathrm{e}^{q_\nu(\varepsilon-\bar{\tau}_1)}, \\ &\qquad \bar{\tau}_1\leqslant\varepsilon\leqslant 1, \end{aligned}\right\} \quad (3.67)$$

where

$$c'_{00} = \frac{k_p P_C(0)}{T Q_{C1}(0)}, \qquad Q_C(q) = Q_{C1}(q)\,q\,. \quad (3.68)$$

If $r_0 = 2$ (i.e. $K(q)$ has a double pole at $q = 0$), $r_\nu = 1$ ($\nu = 1, 2, \ldots, s = l - 2$), then (3.66) gives, after some manipulation

$$\left.\begin{aligned} K^*(q,\varepsilon) &= c'_{00}\frac{1}{\mathrm{e}^{qm_1}(\mathrm{e}^q-1)} + c'_{01}\frac{(1+\varepsilon-\bar{\tau}_1)\,\mathrm{e}^q-\varepsilon+\bar{\tau}_1}{\mathrm{e}^{qm_1}(\mathrm{e}^q-1)^2} + \\ &\quad + \sum_{\nu=1}^{l-2} c'_{\nu 0}\frac{\mathrm{e}^{q_\nu}}{\mathrm{e}^{qm_1}(\mathrm{e}^q-\mathrm{e}^{q_\nu})}\,\mathrm{e}^{q_\nu(\varepsilon-\bar{\tau}_1)}, \qquad 0\leqslant\varepsilon\leqslant\bar{\tau}_1, \\ K^*(q,\varepsilon) &= c'_{00}\frac{1}{\mathrm{e}^{q(m_1-1)}(\mathrm{e}^q-1)} + c'_{01}\frac{(\varepsilon-\bar{\tau}_1)\,\mathrm{e}^q+1-\varepsilon+\tau_1}{\mathrm{e}^{qm_1}(\mathrm{e}^q-1)^2} + \\ &\quad + \sum_{\nu=0}^{l-2} c'_{\nu 0}\frac{1}{\mathrm{e}^{q(m_1-1)}(\mathrm{e}^q-\mathrm{e}^{q_\nu})}\,\mathrm{e}^{q_\nu(\varepsilon-\bar{\tau}_1)}, \quad \bar{\tau}_1\leqslant\varepsilon\leqslant 1, \end{aligned}\right\} \quad (3.69)$$

where

$$\left.\begin{aligned} c'_{00} &= \frac{\mathrm{d}}{\mathrm{d}q}\left[\frac{k_p P_C(q)}{T Q_{C2}(q)}\right]_{q=0}, \qquad c'_{01} = \frac{k_p P(0)}{T Q_{C2}(0)}, \\ Q_C(q) &= Q_{C2}(q)\,q^2\,. \end{aligned}\right\} \quad (3.70)$$

These results can also be obtained from (3.58) by a limiting process.

EXAMPLE. Consider a simple pulse system similar to that shown in Fig. 3.8 but having a shaping element with a relative delay, where m is an integer and $\bar{\tau}_1 < 1$. Remembering that the transfer function of the continuous part is

$$\bar{\tau} = m_1 + \bar{\tau}_1 ,$$

$$K_C(q) = \frac{P_C(q)}{Q_C(q)} = \frac{\beta}{q+\beta}$$

and, as was shown in the example on page 210

$$c'_{10} = \frac{k_p\, P(-\beta)}{TQ'(-\beta)} = \frac{k_p}{T_1} = k_0 ,$$

we obtain from formula (3.58).

$$\left.\begin{aligned} K^*(q,\varepsilon) &= k_0 \frac{e^{-\beta}}{e^{qm_1}(e^q - e^{-\beta})} e^{-\beta(\varepsilon - \bar{\tau})}, \quad & 0 \leqslant \varepsilon \leqslant \bar{\tau}_1, \\ K^*(q,\varepsilon) &= k_0 \frac{1}{e^{q(m_1-1)}(e^q - e^{-\beta})} e^{-\beta(\varepsilon - \bar{\tau}_1)}, \quad & \bar{\tau}_1 \leqslant \varepsilon \leqslant 1. \end{aligned}\right\} \tag{3.71}$$

We find in particular for $m_1 = 0$ and $\bar{\tau} = \bar{\tau}_1 < 1$:

$$\left.\begin{aligned} K^*(q,\varepsilon) &= k_0 \frac{e^{-\beta}}{e^q - e^{-\beta}} e^{-\beta(\varepsilon - \bar{\tau}_1)}, \quad & 0 \leqslant \varepsilon \leqslant \bar{\tau}_1, \\ K^*(q,\varepsilon) &= k_0 \frac{e^q}{e^q - e^{-\beta}} e^{-\beta(\varepsilon - \bar{\tau}_1)}, \quad & \bar{\tau}_1 \leqslant \varepsilon \leqslant 1. \end{aligned}\right\} \tag{3.72}$$

Finally, if $\bar{\tau}_1 = 0$ and thus $\bar{\tau} = m_1$, we obtain from the second formula of (3.71)

$$K^*(q,\varepsilon) = k_0 \frac{1}{e^{q(m_1-1)}(e^q - e^{-\beta})} e^{-\beta\varepsilon}, \quad 0 \leqslant \varepsilon \leqslant 1. \tag{3.73}$$

Pulse systems with rectangular pulses. We now assume that the shaping element produces rectangular pulses of relative duration γ. In such a pulse system a train of amplitude-modulated rectangular pulses acts on the continuous part. In order to find the transfer function of the open-loop pulse system $K^*(q, \varepsilon)$, we first find the pulse characteristic and transfer function of the reduced continuous part.

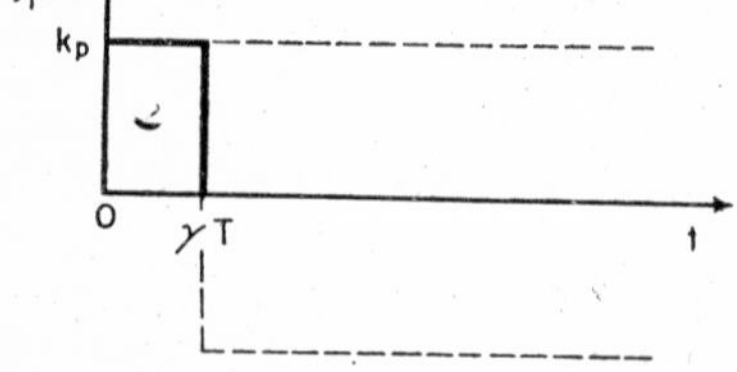

FIG. 3.9. Formation of a rectangular pulse.

A rectangular pulse of amplitude k_p and relative duration γ can be considered as the sum of the step $k_p \cdot 1(t)$ at the moment $t=0$ and the step

$k_p \cdot 1(t - \gamma T)$ of opposite sign at the moment $t = \gamma T$ (Fig. 3.9), i.e.

$$y_T(\bar{t}T) = \begin{cases} k_p 1(t), & 0 \leqslant t < \gamma T, \\ k_p [1(t) - 1(t - T\gamma)], & \gamma T \leqslant t. \end{cases}$$

The transient function or time characteristic of the continuous part

$$h(\bar{t}) = \int_0^{\bar{t}} k_C(\bar{t})\, d\bar{t} \tag{3.74}$$

is the response of the continuous part to a unit step excitation. Inserting the value of $k_C(\bar{t})$ from (3.46) and using (3.47), $h(\bar{t})$ can be written explicitly in the form

$$h(\bar{t}) = \frac{P_C(0)}{Q_C(0)} + \sum_{\nu=1}^{l} \frac{P_C(q_\nu)}{q_\nu Q'_C(q_\nu)} e^{q_\nu \bar{t}}. \tag{3.75}$$

By the principle of superposition the pulse characteristic of the reduced continuous part can now be written in the form

$$k(\bar{t}) = \begin{cases} k_p h(\bar{t}), & 0 \leqslant \bar{t} \leqslant \gamma, \\ k_p [h(\bar{t}) - h(\bar{t} - \gamma)], & \gamma \leqslant \bar{t}. \end{cases} \tag{3.76}$$

The transfer function of the shaping element (3.23), given by the image of the rectangular pulse, equals

$$K_{sh.}(q) = \frac{k_p}{T} \left(\frac{1 - e^{-pT\gamma}}{p} \right)_{p = \frac{q}{T}} = k_p \frac{1 - e^{q\gamma}}{q}.$$

Consequently, the transfer function of the reduced continuous part is

$$K(q) = K_{sh.}(q)\, K_C(q) = k_p \frac{1 - e^{-q\gamma}}{q} K_c(q). \tag{3.77}$$

On substituting the above expression for $k(\bar{t})$ in (3.42) with $\bar{t} = n + \varepsilon$, or $K(q)$ in (3.44), expressions for $K^*(q, \varepsilon)$ in the present example are obtained in the form of series.

$K^*(q, \varepsilon)$ is found in a closed form by summing these series. A quicker method uses the previously obtained results and the following considerations. The reduced continuous part can be considered as two systems connected in parallel (Fig. 3.10), the transfer functions of which equal

$$k_p \frac{K_C(q)}{q}$$

and

$$k_p \frac{K_C(q)}{q} e^{-q\gamma}.$$

We shall assume for generality that these transfer functions have repeated poles, and we use the formulae (3.66) for the transfer function of the open-loop pulse system. Putting in these formulae $m_1 = 0$, $\bar{\tau}_1 = 0$ and $\bar{\tau}_1 = \gamma$, and remembering that the transfer

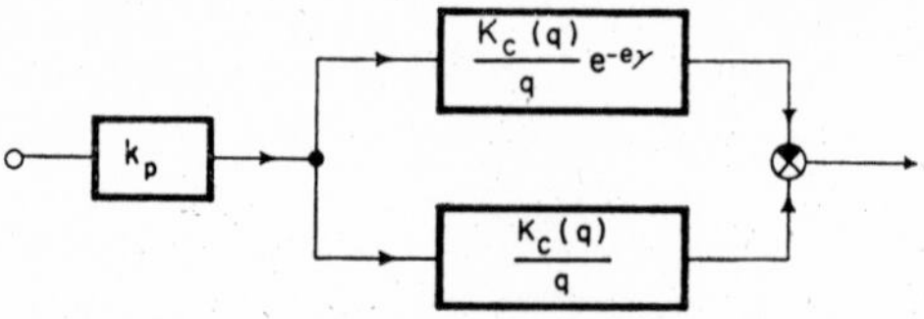

FIG. 3.10. The reduced continuous part is presented here as a parallel combination.

function of systems in parallel equals the sum of the individual transfer functions, we obtain

$$\left.\begin{aligned} K^*(q,\varepsilon) &= \sum_{\nu=0}^{s}\sum_{\mu=0}^{r_\nu-1}\frac{c_{\nu\mu}}{\mu!}\frac{\mathrm{d}^\mu}{\mathrm{d}q_\nu^\mu}\left\{\frac{\mathrm{e}^q}{\mathrm{e}^y-\mathrm{e}^{q_\nu}}\,\mathrm{e}^{q_\nu\varepsilon}-\frac{\mathrm{e}^{q_\nu}}{\mathrm{e}^q-\mathrm{e}^{q_\nu}}\,\mathrm{e}^{q_\nu(\varepsilon-\gamma)}\right\},\\ &\qquad 0\leqslant\varepsilon\leqslant\gamma,\\ K^*(q,\varepsilon) &= \sum_{\nu=0}^{s}\sum_{\mu=0}^{r_\nu-1}\frac{c_{\nu\mu}}{\mu!}\frac{\mathrm{d}^\mu}{\mathrm{d}q_\nu^\mu}\left\{\frac{\mathrm{e}^q}{\mathrm{e}^q-\mathrm{e}^{q_\nu}}\,\mathrm{e}^{q_\nu\varepsilon}-\frac{\mathrm{e}^{q}}{\mathrm{e}^q-\mathrm{e}^{q_\nu}}\,\mathrm{e}^{q_\nu(\varepsilon-\gamma)}\right\},\\ &\qquad \gamma\leqslant\varepsilon\leqslant 1.\end{aligned}\right\}\quad(3.78)$$

Here

$$c_{\nu\mu} = \frac{1}{(r_\nu-\mu-1)!}\frac{\mathrm{d}^{r_\nu-\mu-1}}{\mathrm{d}q^{r_\nu-\mu-1}}\left[\frac{k_p P_C(q)}{qQ_C(q)}(q-q_\nu)^{r_\nu}\right]_{q=q_\nu}, \qquad (3.79)$$

the number of poles at $q = 0$, equal to r_0, being increased by one due to the pole at $q = 0$ of the shaping element.

In formulae (3.78) we have replaced the difference of the derivatives by the derivative of the difference. We obtain finally, on adding the terms in the curly brackets of (3.78),

$$\left.\begin{aligned} K^*(q,\varepsilon) &= \sum_{\nu=0}^{s}\sum_{\mu=0}^{r_\nu=1}\frac{c_{\nu\mu}}{\mu!}\frac{\mathrm{d}^\mu}{\mathrm{d}q_\nu^\mu}\left[\frac{\mathrm{e}^q-\mathrm{e}^{q_\nu(1-\gamma)}}{\mathrm{e}^q-\mathrm{e}^{q_\nu}}\,\mathrm{e}^{q_\nu\varepsilon}\right], \qquad 0\leqslant\varepsilon\leqslant\gamma,\\ K^*(q,\varepsilon) &= \sum_{\nu=0}^{s}\sum_{\mu=0}^{r_\nu-1}\frac{c_{\nu\mu}}{\mu!}\frac{\mathrm{d}^\mu}{\mathrm{d}q_\nu^\mu}\left[\frac{\mathrm{e}^q(\mathrm{e}^{q_\nu\gamma}-1)}{\mathrm{e}^q-\mathrm{e}^{q_\nu}}\,\mathrm{e}^{q_\nu(\varepsilon-\gamma)}\right], \qquad \gamma\leqslant\varepsilon\leqslant 1.\end{aligned}\right\}\quad(3.80)$$

The first expression gives $K^*(q, \varepsilon)$ for values of ε lying within the pulse, and the second for values of ε lying outside the pulse.

We now consider particular cases of these formulae.

If $K_C(q)$ has only simple poles which are, moreover, not equal to zero, then $r_0 = 1$, $r_\nu = 1$ ($\nu = 1, 2, \ldots, s = l$) and we obtain from (3.80) for $\mu = 0$

$$\left.\begin{aligned} K^*(q, \varepsilon) &= \sum_{\nu=0}^{l} c_{\nu 0} \frac{e^q - e^{q_\nu(1-\gamma)}}{e^q - e^{q_\nu}} e^{q_\nu \varepsilon} = \\ &= c_{00} + \sum_{\nu=1}^{l} c_{\nu 0} \frac{e^q - e^{q_\nu(1-\gamma)}}{e^q - e^{q_\nu}} e^{q_\nu \varepsilon}, \quad 0 \leqslant \varepsilon \leqslant \gamma, \\ K^*(q, \varepsilon) &= \sum_{\nu=0}^{l} c_{\nu 0} \frac{e^q (e^{q_\nu \gamma} - 1)}{e^q - e^{q_\nu}} e^{q_\nu(\varepsilon-\gamma)} = \\ &= \sum_{\nu=1}^{l} c_{\nu 0} \frac{e^q (e^{q_\nu \gamma} - 1)}{e^q - e^{q_\nu}} e^{q_\nu(\varepsilon-\gamma)}, \qquad \gamma \leqslant \varepsilon \leqslant 1. \end{aligned}\right\} \tag{3.81}$$

For $\mu = 0$ expression (3.79) gives the values of the coefficients $C_{\nu 0}$ as

$$c_{00} = \frac{k_p P_C(0)}{Q_C(0)}, \qquad c_{\nu 0} = \frac{k_p P_C(q_\nu)}{Q'_C(q_\nu)\, q_\nu} = \frac{T c'_{\nu 0}}{q_\nu}. \tag{3.82}$$

If $K_C(q)$ has a single pole at $q = 0$ and if all the remaining poles are simple, i.e. $r_0 = 2$, $r_\nu = 1$ ($\nu = 1, 2, \ldots, s = l - 1$), then we find on evaluating the derivatives in (3.80) and (3.79)

$$\left.\begin{aligned} K^*(q, \varepsilon) &= c_{00} + c_{01}\left(\varepsilon + \frac{\gamma}{e^q - 1}\right) + \sum_{\nu=1}^{l-1} c_{\nu 0} \frac{e^q - e^{q_\nu(1-\gamma)}}{e^q - e^{q_\nu}} e^{q_\nu \varepsilon}, \\ &\qquad\qquad 0 \leqslant \varepsilon \leqslant \gamma, \\ K^*(q, \varepsilon) &= c_{01} \frac{\gamma e^q}{e^q - 1} + \sum_{\nu=1}^{l-1} c_{\nu 0} \frac{(e^{q_\nu \gamma} - 1)\, e^q}{e^q - e^{q_\nu}} e^{q_\nu(\varepsilon-\lambda)}, \\ &\qquad\qquad \gamma \leqslant \varepsilon \leqslant 1. \end{aligned}\right\} \tag{3.83}$$

In these expressions

$$c_{00} = \frac{d}{dq}\left[\frac{k_p P_C(q)}{Q_{C1}(q)}\right]_{q=0}, \quad c_{01} = \frac{k_p P_C(0)}{Q_{C1}(0)}, \quad c_{\nu 0} = \frac{k_p P_C(q_\nu)}{Q'_{C1}(q_\nu)\, q_\nu^2} = \frac{T c'_{\nu 0}}{q_\nu}, \tag{3.84}$$

where

$$Q_C(q) = Q_{C1}(q)\, q.$$

Finally, if $K_C(q)$ has a pole of order two at $q = 0$ and if the remaining poles are simple, i.e. $r_0 = 3$ and $r_\nu = 1$ ($\nu = 1, 2, \ldots, s = l - 2$), then on evaluating the derivatives in (3.80) and (3.79) we obtain

$$K^*(q,\varepsilon) = c_{00} + c_{01}\left(\varepsilon + \frac{\gamma}{e^q - 1}\right) + \frac{c_{02}}{2\,!}\left[\varepsilon^2 + \frac{2\,\gamma(\varepsilon+1) - \gamma}{e^q - 1} + \frac{2\,\gamma}{(e^q - q)^2}\right] +$$

$$+ \sum_{\nu=1}^{l-2} c_{\nu 0}\, \frac{e^q - e^{q_\nu (1-\gamma)}}{e^q - e^{q_\nu}}\, e^{q_\nu \varepsilon}, \quad 0 \leqslant \varepsilon \leqslant \gamma, \tag{3.85}$$

$$K^*(q,\varepsilon) = c_{01}\,\frac{\gamma\, e^q}{e^q - 1} + \frac{c_{02}}{2\,!}\left[\frac{(2\,\varepsilon - \gamma)\,\gamma\, e^q}{e^q - 1} + \frac{2\,\gamma\, e^q}{(e^q - 1)^2}\right] +$$

$$+ \sum_{\nu=1}^{l-2} c_{\nu 0}\, \frac{(e^{q_\nu \gamma} - 1)\, e^q}{e^q - e^{q_\nu}}\, e^{q_\nu (\varepsilon - \gamma)}, \qquad \gamma \leqslant \varepsilon \leqslant 1.$$

In these expressions

$$\left.\begin{aligned} c_{00} &= \frac{1}{2\,!}\frac{d^2}{dq^2}\left[\frac{k_p P_C(q)}{Q_{C2}(q)}\right]_{q=0}, & c_{01} &= \frac{d}{dq}\left[\frac{k_p P_C(q)}{Q_{C2}(q)}\right]_{q=0}, \\ c_{02} &= \frac{k_p P_C(0)}{Q_{C2}(0)}, & c_{\nu 0} &= \frac{k_p P_C(0)}{Q'_{\nu 2}(q_\nu)\, q_\nu^3} = \frac{T c'_{\nu 0}}{q_\nu}, \end{aligned}\right\} \tag{3.86}$$

$$Q_p(q) = Q_{C2}(q)\, q^2.$$

If the reduced continuous part has a delay $\bar{\tau} = m_1$, where m_1 is an integer, the right sides of $K^*(q, \varepsilon)$ must be multiplied by $e^{-q m_1}$. The derivation of the analogous formulae for the transfer function when $\bar{\tau} = m_1 + \bar{\tau}_1$ $(\bar{\tau}_1 < 1)$ is left to the reader.

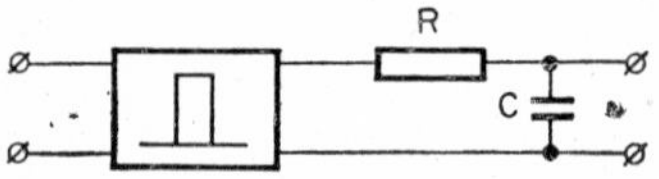

FIG. 3.11. A simple pulse system in which the pulse element produces rectangular pulses.

We note that by making γ tend to zero and putting $k_p \gamma = \mathrm{const}/T$, the above expressions for the transfer function reduce to the transfer function of a pulse system with instantaneous pulses; for $\varepsilon = 0$ we always obtain the left value of the transfer function, i.e., $K^*(q, -0)$.

EXAMPLE. We consider a simple pulse system similar to that shown in Fig. 3.8 but differing in that the pulse element generates rectangular pulses Fig. (3.11). Since the transfer function of the continuous part equals

$$K_C(q) = \frac{P_C(q)}{Q_C(q)} = \frac{\beta}{q + \beta},$$

we find from (3.82)

$$c_{00} = \frac{k_p P_C(0)}{Q_C(0)} = k_p, \qquad c_{10} = \frac{k_p P_C(q_1)}{Q'_C(q_1)\, q_1} = \frac{k_p\, \beta}{-\beta} = -k_p$$

and thus formulae (3.81) give

$$\left.\begin{aligned} K^*(q,\varepsilon) &= k_p\left[1-\frac{e^q-e^{-\beta(1-\gamma)}}{e^q-e^{-\beta}}\,e^{-\beta\varepsilon}\right], \quad 0\leqslant\varepsilon\leqslant\gamma,\\ K^*(q,\varepsilon) &= k_p\frac{(1-e^{-\beta\gamma})\,e^q}{e^q-e^{-\beta}}\,e^{-\beta(\varepsilon-\gamma)}, \quad \gamma\leqslant\varepsilon\leqslant 1. \end{aligned}\right\} \tag{3.87}$$

For $\gamma = 1$ the first expression of (3.87) gives

$$K^*(q,\varepsilon) = k_p\left[1-\frac{e^q-1}{e^q-e^{-\beta}}\,e^{-\beta\varepsilon}\right]. \tag{3.88}$$

For $\gamma \to 0$ and $k_p\,\gamma = \text{const}/T$ we obtain, from the second expression of (3.87), the previously obtained expression for the transfer function (3.53).

It has been shown that the transfer function of an open-loop pulse system can be expressed in the form of series in terms of the pulse characteristic $k(\bar{t})$ or transfer function $K(q)$ of the reduced continuous part. It can also be written in closed form if the poles of the transfer function $K(q)$ are known or if the pulse characteristic $k(\bar{t})$ is known analytically.

We now establish a few properties of the transfer function of an open-loop pulse system.

The transfer function of a pulse system $K^*(q, \varepsilon)$ is a periodic function of q on varying q parallel to the imaginary axis, i.e.

$$K^*(q + 2\pi jr, \varepsilon) = K^*(q, \varepsilon), \tag{3.89}$$

where r is an integer, $\varepsilon = \text{const}$. This follows, for example, on replacing q by $q + 2\pi jr$ in the expressions for the transfer function $K^*(q, \varepsilon)$ (3.42) or (3.44), or (3.66), remembering that

$$e^{q+2\pi jr} = e^q.$$

In this manner, the transfer function of a pulse system is completely defined by its values in the strip of the complex q-plane $-\pi < \operatorname{Im} q \leqslant \pi$ (Fig. 3.12). In the strips of width 2π lying above and below this strip (called in future the *principal* strip) the values of $K^*(q, \varepsilon)$ repeat periodically for $\varepsilon = \text{const}$.

We see from the expressions giving $K^*(q, \varepsilon)$ in closed form that *the transfer function of a pulse system is an analytic function in the fundamental strip, except at the finite number of points — the poles q_ν.* These poles are independent of ε and τ (if $\tau < 1$) and coincide with the poles of the transfer function of the reduced continuous part $K_{sh.}(q)\,K_C(q) = K(q)$, or differ from them by $\pm 2r\pi j$ $(r = 1, 2, \ldots)$.

If two poles of $K(q)$ differ only in their imaginary parts and moreover by an amount $\pm 2r\pi j$, where r is an integer, then these poles will correspond to the same pole of $K^*(q, \varepsilon)$. Thus in this case $K^*(q, \varepsilon)$ *may have a smaller number of poles than* $K(q)$. This property is a consequence of the periodicity of $K^*(q, \varepsilon)$ along the imaginary axis.

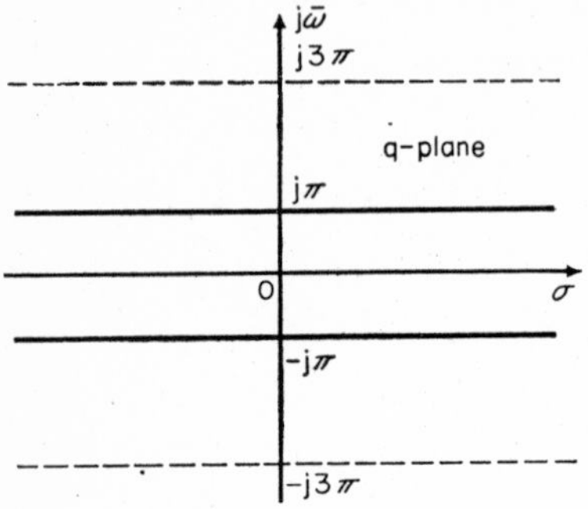

FIG. 3.12. The complex q-plane.

To each complex pole q_ν of the transfer function of a pulse system $K^*(q, \varepsilon)$ there corresponds a complex-conjugate pole $q_{\nu+1}$, except for the particular case when the imaginary part of the pole equals $\pm j\pi$, i.e. when the poles lie on the boundaries of the strip $-\pi < \operatorname{Im} q \leqslant \pi$. In this case we select the pole lying on the upper boundary of the strip, i.e. $+j\pi$. Complex-conjugate coefficients $c'_{\nu\mu}$ and $c'_{\nu+1,\mu}$ (or $c_{\nu\mu}$ and $c_{\nu+1,\mu}$) correspond to the complex-conjugate poles. For $q = 0$ and $q = j\pi$ we have from (3.42)

$$K^*(0, \varepsilon) = \sum_{n=0}^{\infty} k[n, \varepsilon],$$
$$K^*(j\pi, \varepsilon) = \sum_{n=0}^{\infty} (-1)^n k[n, \varepsilon]. \tag{3.90}$$

Thus for $q = 0$ and $q = j\pi$ the *transfer function* $K^*(q, \varepsilon)$ *takes real values*. This can be shown using the closed representation of $K^*(q, \varepsilon)$.

The degree of the denominator of $K^*(q, \varepsilon)$ with respect to e^q is the same as that of the denominator of $K(q)$ with respect to q if the delay $\bar{\tau}$ in the linear system does not exceed unity, and is increased by m if the delay $\bar{\tau}$ is greater than m but less than $m + 1$.+

If the transfer function $K(q)$ of the reduced continuous part is written as a sum of transfer functions $K_r(q)$, *then the transfer function* $K^*(q, \varepsilon)$ *equals the sum of* $K_r^*(q, \varepsilon)$, where the lattice functions $K_r^*(q, \varepsilon)$ correspond to $K_r(q)$. This obvious property follows directly from the definition of $K^*(q, \varepsilon)$. It was used, in fact, when representing $K^*(q, \varepsilon)$ in closed form, for the representation of $k_C(t)$ or $K_C(q)$ as sums of components corresponds physically to representing the continuous

+ It is assumed here that the difference between the imaginary parts of any two poles is not a multiple of 2π.

part (if it contains only lumped parameters: Fig. 3.13*a*) as a parallel set of elementary continuous parts with pulse characteristics equal to $c'_{\nu 0}\, e^{q_\nu \bar{t}}$ ($\nu = 1, 2, \ldots, l$), and transfer functions equal to $c'_{\nu 0}/(q - q_\nu)$ ($\nu = 1, 2, \ldots, l$) (Fig. 3.13*b*).

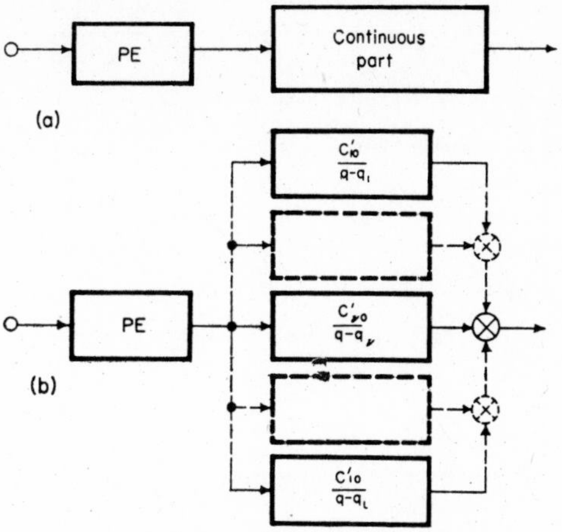

FIG. 3.13. Replacement of an arbitrary continuous part (*a*) by a number of simpler continuous parts connected in parallel (*b*).

Using the $\mathfrak{D}$-transformation theorems, which were established in § 2.8 and which are given in Appendix A 4, a number of properties result which we give in tabular form for convenience. These properties facilitate the computation of $K^*(q, \varepsilon)$ from $K(q)$.

TABLE 3.1.

Relationship between the Transfer Function of a Pulse System and that of its Reduced Continuous Part

$K(q)$	$K^*(q, \varepsilon)$
$e^{-m_1 q} K(q)$, m — integer	$e^{-m_1 q} K^*(q, \varepsilon)$
$e^{-\bar{\tau}_1 q} K(q)$, $\bar{\tau} < 1$	$e^{-q} K^*(q, 1 - \bar{\tau}_1 + \varepsilon)$, $0 < \varepsilon < \bar{\tau}_1$ $K(q, \varepsilon - \bar{\tau}_1)$, $\bar{\tau} < \varepsilon < 1$
$qK(q)$	$\dfrac{dK^*(q, \varepsilon)}{d\varepsilon}$
$\dfrac{1}{q} K(q)$	$\displaystyle\int_0^\varepsilon K^*(q, \varepsilon)\, d\varepsilon + \frac{1}{e^q - 1} \int_0^1 K^*(q, \varepsilon)\, d\varepsilon$

In those cases when $K(q)$ and $K^*(q, \varepsilon)$ have different numbers of poles, an estimation of the properties of a pulse system using its transfer function for $\varepsilon = 0$, i.e. using $K^*(q, 0)$, may lead to erroneous conclusions. This is illustrated by the following example.

Example. Let

$$K(q) = \frac{1}{q + a} + \frac{\pi}{(q + \beta)^2 + \pi^2}.$$

From the table of Appendix A 4 we find from the linearity theorem that

$$K^*(q, \varepsilon) = \frac{e^q}{e^q - e^{-a}} + e^{-\beta\varepsilon} \frac{\sin \pi\varepsilon}{e^q - e^{-\beta}}.$$

$K^*(q, \varepsilon)$ has one pole less than $K(q)$. For $\varepsilon = 0$ we have

$$K^*(q, 0) = \frac{e^{-q}}{e^q - e^{-a}}.$$

From this we see that $K^*(q, 0)$ does not take into account the second term of $K(q)$. This is because the lattice function corresponding to the second term is identically equal to zero for $\varepsilon = 0$+

We note in conclusion that digital computing devices and pulse or discrete filters consisting of delay elements (an example is shown in Fig. 3.14*a*) have transfer functions $K^*(q, \varepsilon)$ even for $\varepsilon = 0$. In fact, since that transfer function of a delay element is $e^{-p\tau}$ or e^{-q} for $\bar{\tau} = \tau/T = 1$, the transfer function of the pulse filter can be written in the form

$$K^*(q, 0) = \sum_{\nu=0}^{l} b_{l-\nu} e^{-q\nu} = \frac{b_l e^{ql} + b_{l-1} e^{q(l-1)} + \dots + b_0}{e^{ql}}. \quad (3.91)$$

A digital computing device, as was mentioned in § 1.3, can be described by a difference equation corresponding to the computing program. For example

$$u_2[n] = \sum_{\nu=0}^{l} b_{l-\nu} u_1[n - \nu].$$

Applying the D-transformation to this equation and using the original-translation theorem (Theorem 2), we obtain an equation in terms of the images:

$$U_2^*(q) = \left\{ \sum_{\nu=0}^{l} b_{l-\nu} e^{-q\nu} \right\} U_1^*(q),$$

+ This is considered in more detail in the works by Barker [4; 1952] and Jury [4, 1957].

from which we find the transfer function, which is identical in form to that obtained above. With a pulse filter with feedback paths (Fig. 3.14*b*), or with a program in which the result of the computations depends not only on the input quantity but also on the output quantity:

$$\sum_{\nu=0}^{l} a_{l-\nu} u_2 [n - \nu] = \sum_{\nu=0}^{l} b_{l-\nu} u_1 [n - \nu] ,$$

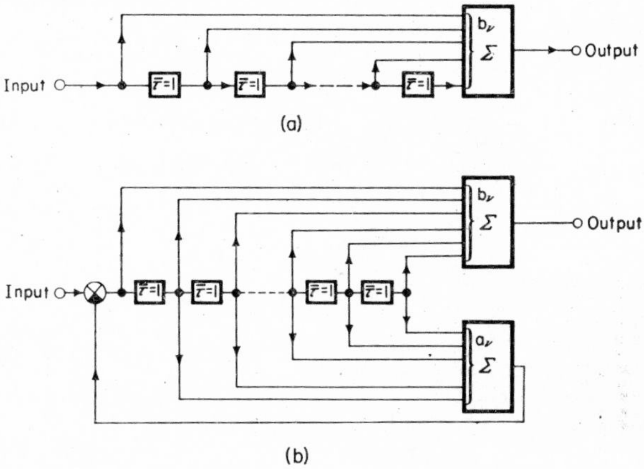

FIG. 3.14. A pulse filter (*a*), and a pulse filter with feedback (*b*).

the equation in the images takes the form

$$\left\{ \sum_{\nu=0}^{l} a_{l-\nu} e^{-q\nu} \right\} U_2^*(q) = \left\{ \sum_{\nu=0}^{l} b_{l-\nu} e^{-q\nu} \right\} U_1^*(q) .$$

The transfer function now has the more general form

$$K^*(q, 0) = \frac{U_2^*(q)}{U_1^*(q)} = \frac{\sum\limits_{\nu=0}^{l} b_{l-\nu} e^{-q\nu}}{\sum\limits_{\nu=0}^{l} a_{l-\nu} e^{-q\nu}} , \tag{3.92}$$

or, multiplying the numerator and denominator by e^{ql}

$$K^*(q, 0) = \frac{\sum\limits_{\nu=0}^{l} b_\nu e^{q\nu}}{\sum\limits_{\nu=0}^{l} a_\nu e^{q\nu}} . \tag{3.93}$$

Some of the coefficients b_l, b_{l-1}, . . . may equal zero. These transfer functions coincide in external form with the transfer function $K^*(q, \varepsilon)$ for $\varepsilon = 0$.

In this manner pulse or discrete filters and digital computing devices can be classed as: open-loop pulse systems, if there is no feedback; closed-loop pulse systems, if there is feedback.

Sometimes, as with pulse systems, it is convenient to consider a pulse filter or digital computing device as a complex pulse element which varies the modulation law of the input pulses.

3.3. Equation and transfer functions of open-loop pulse systems with several pulse elements

Systems with several pulse elements are formed by interconnecting pulse systems, each of which contains a single pulse element.

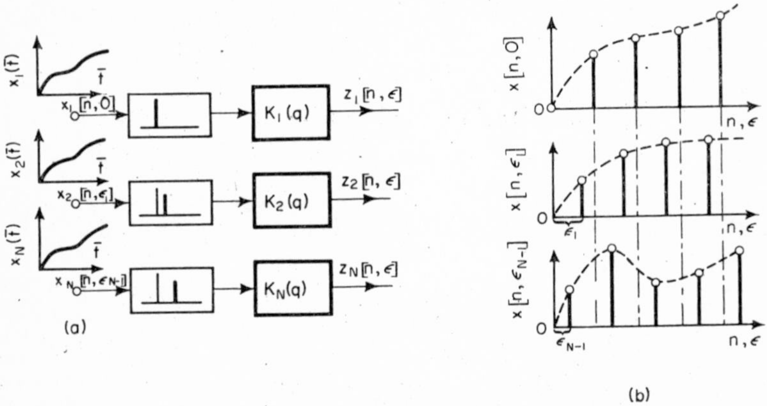

FIG. 3.15. Synchronously operating but unconnected pulse systems (a), and the corresponding input lattice functions (b).

Consider N such pulse systems (Fig. 3.15a) which, for the moment, are not interconnected. We assume that the repetition period T characterising the operation of these pulse elements is the same for all, and that in general pulses do not appear at the same moment. Physically, this means that the pulse elements are working in synchronism but are not in phase. For such out-of-phase operation, the rth pulse element responds to the value of the input quantity at the moments $\bar{t} = n + \varepsilon_{r-1}$ ($r = 1, 2, 3, \ldots, N$); the moments when pulses appear are displaced with respect to those of one of the systems (the first) by amounts $\varepsilon_1, \varepsilon_2, \ldots \varepsilon_{N-1}$ (Fig. 3.15b).

For the first system ($r = 1$) we assume $\varepsilon_0 = 0$. The displaced lattice functions representing the input quantities of the pulse systems are

$$x_1[n, 0],\ x_2[n, \varepsilon_1],\ x_3[n, \varepsilon_2],\ \ldots,\ x_N[n, \varepsilon_{N-1}],$$

where $X_r^*(q, \varepsilon_{r-1})$ denotes the image of the corresponding displaced lattice function $x_r[n, \varepsilon_{r-1}]$ $(r = 1, 2, \ldots, N)$.

If the pulse elements operate in phase, i.e. $\varepsilon_{r-1} = 0$ for $r = 1, 2, \ldots, N$, then their transfer functions will equal $K_r^*(q, \varepsilon)$. For out-of-phase operation, the transfer function of the rth pulse system equals

$$K_r^*(q, \varepsilon - \varepsilon_{r-1})$$

or, as was shown in § 3.2, more explicitly

$$K_r^*(q, \varepsilon - \varepsilon_{r-1}) = \begin{cases} K_r^*(q, \varepsilon - \varepsilon_{r-1}) & \text{for } \varepsilon \geqslant \varepsilon_{r-1}, \\ e^{-q} K_r^*(q, 1 + \varepsilon - \varepsilon_{r-1}) & \text{for } \varepsilon \leqslant \varepsilon_{r-1}. \end{cases} \quad (3.94)$$

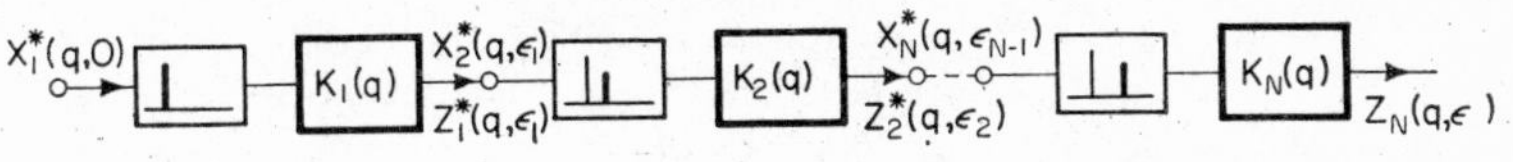

FIG. 3.16. Pulse systems connected in series.

Consequently, in this latter case, the equations of the pulse systems in terms of the images can be written in the form

$$\left.\begin{aligned} Z_1^*(q, \varepsilon) &= K_1^*(q, \varepsilon)\, X_1^*(q, 0), \\ Z_2^*(q, \varepsilon) &= K_2^*(q, \varepsilon - \varepsilon_1)\, X_2^*(q, \varepsilon_1), \\ &\cdots\cdots\cdots\cdots\cdots\cdots \\ Z_N^*(q, \varepsilon) &= K_N^*(q, \varepsilon - \varepsilon_{N-1})\, X^*{}_N(q, \varepsilon_{N-1}). \end{aligned}\right\} \quad (3.95)$$

We further assume that when one pulse system is attached to any other, the operating conditions of the former are unaffected.

When the pulse systems are connected in series (Fig. 3.16) the output quantity of one pulse system forms the input quantity of the next. In this case, for out-of-phase operation, we have

$$\left.\begin{aligned} X_2^*(q, \varepsilon_1) &= Z_1^*(q, \varepsilon_1), \\ X_3(q, \varepsilon_2) &= Z_2^*(q, \varepsilon_2), \\ &\cdots\cdots\cdots\cdots \\ X_N^*(q, \varepsilon_{N-1}) &= Z_{N-1}^*(q, \varepsilon_{N-1}). \end{aligned}\right\} \quad (3.96)$$

Substituting in these equations the values of $Z_r^*(q, \varepsilon_r)$ from (3.95), we have

$$X_2^*(q, \varepsilon_1) = K_1^*(q, \varepsilon_1)\, X_1^*(q, 0),$$

$$X_3^*(q, \varepsilon_2) = K_2^*(q, \varepsilon_2 - \varepsilon_1)\, X_2^*(q, \varepsilon_1),$$

$$\cdots\cdots\cdots\cdots\cdots\cdots\cdots\cdots$$

$$X_N^*(q, \varepsilon_{N-1}) = K_{N-1}^*(q, \varepsilon_{N-1} - \varepsilon_{N-2})\, X_{N-1}^*(q, \varepsilon_{N-2}),$$
$$Z_N^*(q, \varepsilon) = K_N^*(q, \varepsilon - \varepsilon_{N-1})\, X_N^*(q, \varepsilon_{N-1}).$$

Multiplying these equations together gives the equation of the series-connected pulse systems in terms of the images:

$$Z_N^*(q, \varepsilon) = K_1^*(q, \varepsilon_1)\, K_2^*(q, \varepsilon_2 - \varepsilon_1) \ldots$$
$$\ldots K_{N-1}^*(q, \varepsilon_{N-1} - \varepsilon_{N-2})\, K_N^*(q, \varepsilon - \varepsilon_{N-1})\, X_1^*(q, 0). \qquad (3.97)$$

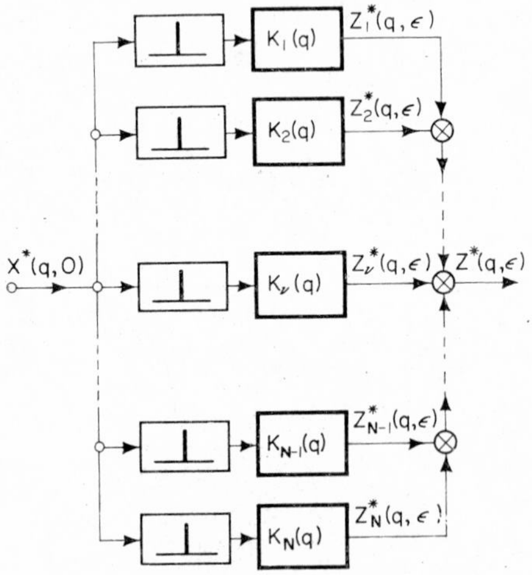

FIG. 3.17. Pulse systems connected in parallel.

Thus the transfer function of series-connected pulse systems is given by

$$K^*(q, \varepsilon) = \left[\prod_{r=1}^{N-1} K_r^*(q, \varepsilon_r - \varepsilon_{r-1})\right] K_N^*(q, \varepsilon - \varepsilon_{N-1}). \qquad (3.98)$$

Hence, *the transfer function of series-connected pulse systems equals the product of the individual transfer functions, of which the first N—1 are taken for values of* ε *given by* $\varepsilon = \varepsilon_r - \varepsilon_{r-1}$ ($r = 1, 2, \ldots, N-1$). This is due to the fact that each pulse system responds only to discrete values of its input quantity, when $\varepsilon = \varepsilon_{r-1}$ and $\bar{t} = n$.

If all the pulse elements operate in phase, i.e. $\varepsilon_{r-1} = 0$ ($r = 1, 2, \ldots, N$), then the transfer function of the series-connected pulse systems is

$$K^*(q, \varepsilon) = \left[\prod_{r=1}^{N-1} K_r^*(q, 0)\right] K_N^*(q, \varepsilon). \qquad (3.99)$$

For parallel-connection of the pulse systems (Fig. 3.17) and in-phase operation of the pulse elements, the input quantity is the same for all the pulse systems and the output is the sum of the individual outputs. In this case we have

$$X_1^*(q, 0) = X_2^*(q, 0) = \ldots = X_N^*(q, 0) = X^*(q, 0)$$

and

$$Z^*(q, \varepsilon) = Z_1^*(q, \varepsilon) + Z_2^*(q, \varepsilon) + \ldots + Z_N(q, \varepsilon)\,. \qquad (3.100)$$

Inserting here the values of $Z_r^*(q, \varepsilon)$ from equations (3.95) for $\varepsilon_r = 0$, and remembering that the images of the input quantities are the same, we find the equation of parallel-connected pulse systems in terms of the images:

$$Z^*(q, \varepsilon) = [K_1^*(q, \varepsilon) + K_2^*(q, \varepsilon) + \ldots + K_N^*(q, \varepsilon)]\, X^*(q, 0)\,. \quad (3.101)$$

This gives the transfer function of parallel-connected pulse systems as

$$K^*(q, \varepsilon) = \sum_{r=1}^{N} K_r^*(q, \varepsilon)\,. \qquad (3.102)$$

Hence, *for in-phase operation of the pulse elements, the transfer function of parallel-connected pulse systems equals the sum of the individual transfer functions.* We note that in this case the parallel-connected pulse systems can be replaced by a single pulse system in which the pulse element acts on the parallel-connected continuous parts (Fig. 3.18). This follows from the properties of the transfer function of a pulse system established in § 3.2.

We now consider parallel-connected pulse systems with out-of-phase pulse elements. The lattice functions representing the input quantities of the pulse elements are in this case different (Fig. 3.19). These lattice functions can be obtained from a single displaced lattice function $x[n, \varepsilon]$ by assigning the parameter ε different values, i.e.

$$x[n, \varepsilon_0],\ x[n, \varepsilon_1],\ \ldots,\ x[n, \varepsilon_{N-1}],$$

where $\varepsilon_0 = 0$.

Inserting in (3.100) the values of $Z_r^*(q, \varepsilon)$ from (3.95), with $X_r^*(q, \varepsilon_{r-1}) = X^*(q, \varepsilon_{r-1})$, we obtain

$$Z^*(q, \varepsilon) = K_1^*(q, \varepsilon)\, X^*(q, 0) + K_2^*(q, \varepsilon - \varepsilon_1)\, X^*(q, \varepsilon_1) + \ldots$$
$$\ldots + K_N^*(q, \varepsilon - \varepsilon_{N-1})\, X^*(q, \varepsilon_{N-1}),$$

or briefly

$$Z^*(q, \varepsilon) = \sum_{r=1}^{N} K_r^*(q, \varepsilon - \varepsilon_{r-1})\, X^*(q, \varepsilon_{r-1})\,. \qquad (3.103)$$

Equation (3.103) corresponds to parallel-connected pulse systems when the pulse elements are working out-of-phase. In general this pulse system cannot be characterised by a single transfer function. If however $X^*(q, \varepsilon_{r-1}) = X^*(q, 0)$ $(r = 1, 2, \ldots, N)$ does not depend on ε, for example in the case of a step excitation, then

$$Z^*(q, \varepsilon) = \left[\sum_{r=1}^{N} K_r^*(q, \varepsilon - \varepsilon_{r-1})\right] X^*(q, 0)$$

and the expression in the square brackets may be considered as the transfer function.

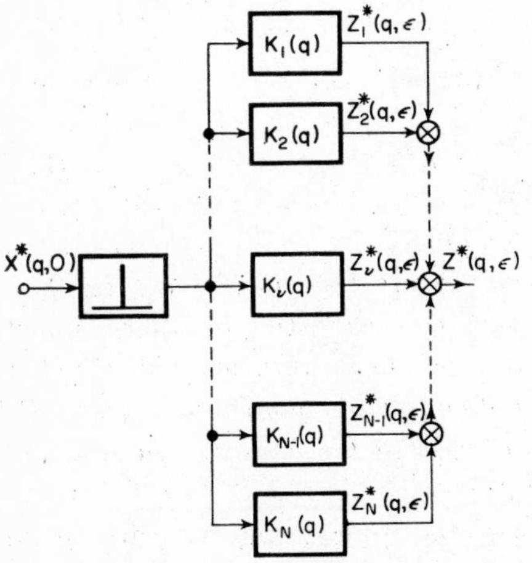

FIG. 3.18. A pulse system equivalent to parallel-connected pulse systems whose pulse elements are in synchronism and in phase.

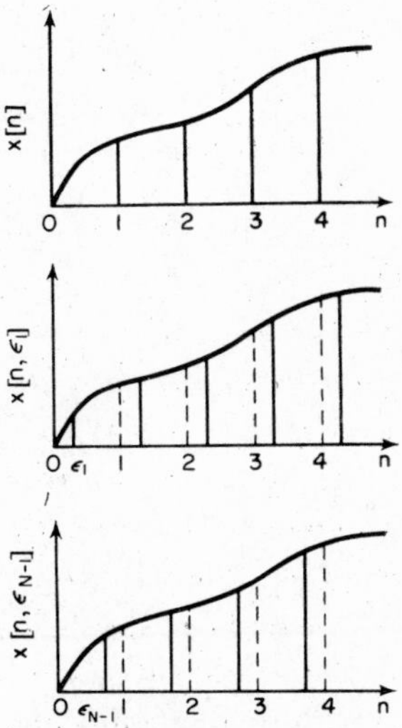

FIG. 3.19. Input lattice functions where the pulse elements are out of phase.

If the reduced continuous parts of the pulse system are the same, we have

$$K_r^*(q, \varepsilon) = K_1^*(q, \varepsilon) \text{ for } r = 2, 3, \ldots, N$$

and thus from (3.103) we have

$$Z^*(q, \varepsilon) = \sum_{r=1}^{N} K_1^*(q, \varepsilon - \varepsilon_{r-1}) X^*(q, \varepsilon_{r-1}). \tag{3.104}$$

This equation corresponds to a pulse system consisting of a single reduced continuous part and N pulse elements working out-of-phase (Fig. 3.20). However, N pulse elements can be replaced by a single

complex pulse element whose output pulse train equals the sum of the output pulse trains shown in Fig. 3.19, i.e. it is modulated in phase by a periodic function. A pulse system with this type of pulse element can be considered as a pulse system with a periodically

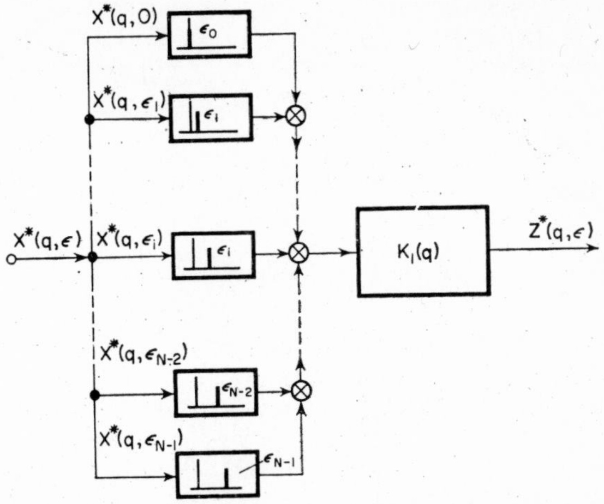

FIG. 3.20. A pulse system consisting of N out-of-phase pulse elements and a single continuous part.

varying repetition period (Fig. 3.21).+ For the particular case when

$$\varepsilon_r - \varepsilon_{r-1} = \frac{1}{N} = \text{const} \quad (r = 1, 2, 3, \ldots, N),$$

i.e. $\varepsilon_r = r/N$, we can consider the pulse system as a pulse system with a relative repetition period of $1/N$ (Fig. 3.22).

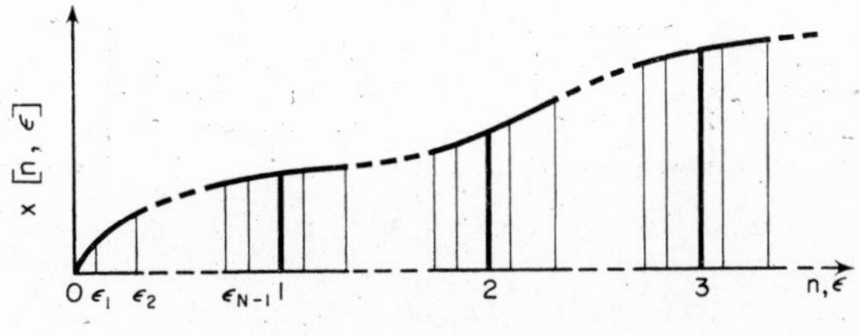

FIG. 3.21. Output train of a complex pulse element.

Consequently, *a pulse system with a relative repetition period of* $1/N$ *can be formed from a reduced continuous part whose input is attached to N pulse elements having a relative repetition period of unity.* This

+ See the authors own book [4; 1955].

can be used to determine the equation of interconnected pulse systems having unequal repetition periods. For example two series-connected pulse systems, the repetition period of one being a multiple of the other (Fig. 3.23*a*), can be reduced to an equivalent pulse system containing

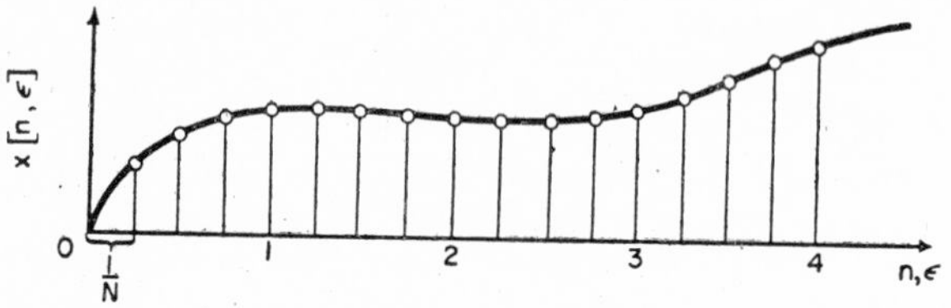

Fig. 3.22. Output train of a complex pulse element whose repetition period is $1/N$.

pulse elements of the same repetition period (Fig. 3.23*b*). On the basis of this equivalent system, and using equations (3.95), (3.104), we find the system equation to be

$$X_1^*(q, \varepsilon) = K_1^*(q, \varepsilon)\, X^*(q, 0),$$

$$Z^*(q, \varepsilon) = \sum_{r=1}^{N} K_2^*\left(q, \varepsilon - \frac{r-1}{N}\right) X_1^*\left(q, \frac{r-1}{N}\right).$$

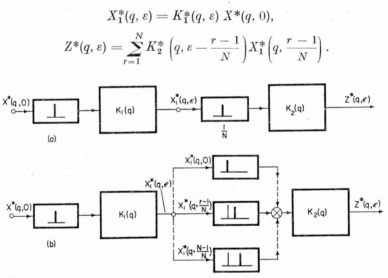

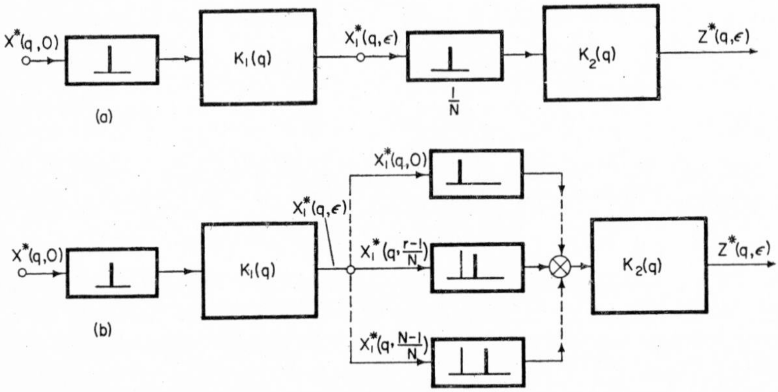

Fig. 3.23. Series-connected pulse systems with multiple repetition periods (*a*) and the equivalent pulse system (*b*).

Putting $\varepsilon = (r-1)/N$ $(r = 1, 2, \ldots, N)$ and substituting the value of $X_1^*(q, (r-1)/N)$ in the second equation, we find

$$Z^*(q, \varepsilon) = \left[\sum_{r=1}^{N} K_1^*\left(q, \frac{r-1}{N}\right) K_2^*\left(q, \varepsilon - \frac{r-1}{N}\right)\right] X(q, 0). \quad (3.105)$$

This gives the transfer function of two series-connected pulse systems with multiple repetition periods:

$$K^*(q, \varepsilon) = \sum_{r=1}^{N} K_1^*\left(q, \frac{r-1}{N}\right) K_2^*\left(q, \varepsilon - \frac{r-1}{N}\right), \quad (3.106)$$

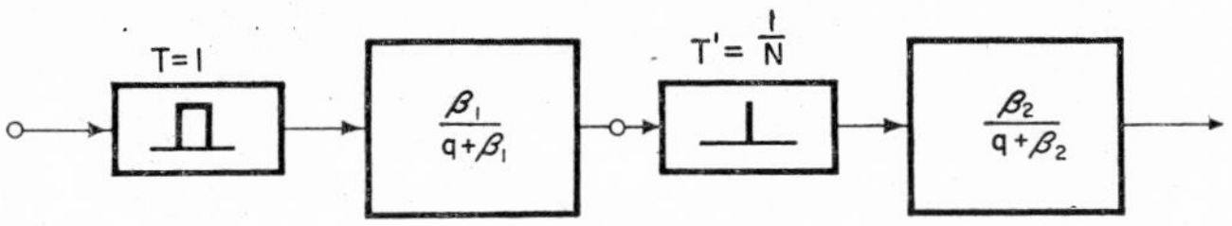

FIG. 3.24. Series-connected simple pulse systems with multiple repetition periods.

or, in more detail using (3.94),

$$K^*(q, \varepsilon) = \sum_{r=1}^{i} K_1^*\left(q, \frac{r-1}{N}\right) K_2^*\left(q, \varepsilon - \frac{r-1}{N}\right) + e^{-q} \sum_{r=i+1}^{N} K_1^*\left(q, \frac{r-1}{N}\right) \times$$

$$\times K_2^*\left(q, 1 + \varepsilon - \frac{r-1}{N}\right), \quad \frac{i-1}{N} \leqslant \varepsilon < \frac{i}{N} \quad (i = 1, 2, \ldots, N). \quad (3.107)$$

In particular for $\varepsilon = 0$, $i = 1$, we obtain+

$$K^*(q, 0) = K_1^*(q, 0)\, K_2^*(q, 0) + e^{-q} \sum_{r=2}^{N} K_1^*\left(q, \frac{r-1}{N}\right) K_2^*\left(q, 1 - \frac{r-1}{N}\right). \quad (3.108)$$

EXAMPLE. Consider two series-connected pulse systems (Fig. 3.24) with multiple repetition periods.

In the first pulse system rectangular pulses ($\gamma = 1$) are formed, and in the second — instantaneous pulses with a repetition period N times smaller than that of the first. It was shown in § 3.2 that for identical repetition periods, the transfer functions of these pulse systems equal

$$K_1^*(q, \varepsilon) = k_{1p}\left[1 - \frac{e^q - 1}{e^q - e^{-\beta_1}} e^{-\beta_1 \varepsilon}\right], \qquad 0 \leqslant \varepsilon \leqslant 1, \quad (3.109)$$

and

$$K_2^*(q, \varepsilon) = k_0 \frac{e^q}{e^q - e^{-\beta_2}} e^{-\beta_2 \varepsilon}, \qquad 0 \leqslant \varepsilon \leqslant 1, \quad (3.110)$$

where $k_0 = k_p/T$.

Replacing ε by $(r-1)/N$ in (3.109) and ε by $\varepsilon - (r-1)/N$ in (3.110), we obtain

$$K_1^*\left(q, \frac{r-1}{N}\right) = k_{1p}\left[1 - \frac{e^q - 1}{e^q - e^{-\beta_1}} e^{-\beta_1 \frac{r-1}{N}}\right] \qquad (r = 1, 2, \ldots, N)$$

+ Another method of finding $K^*(q, 0)$ has been given by Krans [4;1951a].

and using (3.94)

$$K_2^*\left(q, \varepsilon - \frac{r-1}{N}\right) = \begin{cases} k_0 \dfrac{e^q}{e^q - e^{-\beta_2}} e^{-\beta_2\left(\varepsilon - \frac{r-1}{N}\right)}, & \dfrac{r-1}{N} \leqslant \varepsilon \leqslant 1, \\ k_0 \dfrac{1}{e^q - e^{-\beta_2}} e^{-\beta_2\left(1+\varepsilon - \frac{r-1}{N}\right)}, & 0 \leqslant \varepsilon \leqslant \dfrac{r-1}{N}. \end{cases}$$

The transfer function of this open-loop pulse system is found using formula (3.107)

$$K^*(q, \varepsilon) = \sum_{r=1}^{i} k_{1p} k_0 \left[1 - \frac{e^q - 1}{e^q - e^{-\beta_1}} e^{-\beta_1 \frac{r-1}{N}}\right] \frac{e^q}{e - e^{-\beta_2}} e^{-\beta_2\left(\varepsilon - \frac{r-1}{N}\right)} +$$
$$+ \sum_{r=i+1}^{N} k_{1p} k_0 \left[1 - \frac{e^q - 1}{e^q - e^{-\beta_1}} e^{-\beta_1 \frac{r-1}{N}}\right] \frac{1}{e^q - e^{-\beta_2}} e^{-\beta_2\left(1+\varepsilon - \frac{r-1}{N}\right)}, \qquad (3.111)$$
$$\frac{i-1}{N} \leqslant \varepsilon \leqslant \frac{i}{N}.$$

In particular, for $\varepsilon = 0$ we have $i = 1$, and thus from (3.111)

$$K^*(q, 0) = k_{1p} k_0 \left\{\left[1 - \frac{e^q - 1}{e^q - e^{-\beta_1}}\right] \frac{e^q}{e^q - e^{-\beta_2}} + \right.$$
$$\left. + \sum_{r=2}^{N} \left[1 - \frac{e^q - 1}{e^q - e^{-\beta_1}} e^{-\beta_1 \frac{r-1}{N}}\right] \frac{e^{-\beta_2\left(1 - \frac{r-1}{N}\right)}}{e^q - e^{-\beta_2}}\right\}$$

or

$$K^*(q, 0) = k_{1p} k_0 \left\{\frac{1}{e^q - e^{-\beta_2}} \left(e^q + \sum_{r=1}^{N} e^{-\beta_2\left(1 - \frac{r-1}{N}\right)}\right) - \right.$$
$$\left. - \frac{e^q - 1}{(e^q - e^{-\beta_1})(e^q - e^{-\beta_2})} \left(e^q + \sum_{r=1}^{N} e^{-\beta_2\left(1 - \frac{r-1}{N}\right) - \beta_1 \frac{r-1}{N}}\right)\right\}.$$

Since

$$\sum_{r=1}^{N} e^{-\beta_2\left(1 - \frac{r-1}{N}\right) - \beta_1 \frac{r-1}{N}} = \frac{e^{-\left(\beta_1 + \frac{\beta_2}{N}\right)} - e^{-\left(\frac{\beta_1}{N} + \beta_2\right)}}{e^{-\frac{\beta_1}{N}} - e^{-\frac{\beta_2}{N}}} = b_0(\beta_1, \beta_2, N), \qquad (3.112)$$

we obtain finally, on substituting this value for $\beta_1 = 0$ and $\beta_1 \neq 0$ in the previous expression

$$K^*(q, 0) = k_{1p} k_0 \left\{\frac{e^q + b_0(0, \beta_2, N)}{e^q - e^{-\beta_2}} - \frac{(e^q - 1)\left(e^q + b_0(\beta_1, \beta_2, N)\right)}{(e^q - e^{-\beta_1})(e^q - e^{-\beta_2})}\right\}. \qquad (3.113)$$

Let us now assume that the ratio of the repetition periods of two series-connected pulse systems is a rational number, i.e. it takes the form N_1/N, where N_1 and N are whole numbers. Such series-connected pulse systems can be represented by their equivalent forms, which contain pulse elements of relative repetition period equal to unity (Fig. 3.25). In this case, from (3.104), the system equation takes the form:

$$X_1^*(q, \varepsilon) = \sum_{s=1}^{N_1} K_1^* \left(q, \varepsilon - \frac{s-1}{N_1}\right) X^* \left(q, \frac{s-1}{N_1}\right),$$

$$Z^*(q, \varepsilon) = \sum_{r=1}^{N} K_2^* \left(q, \varepsilon - \frac{r-1}{N}\right) X_1^* \left(q, \frac{r-1}{N}\right).$$

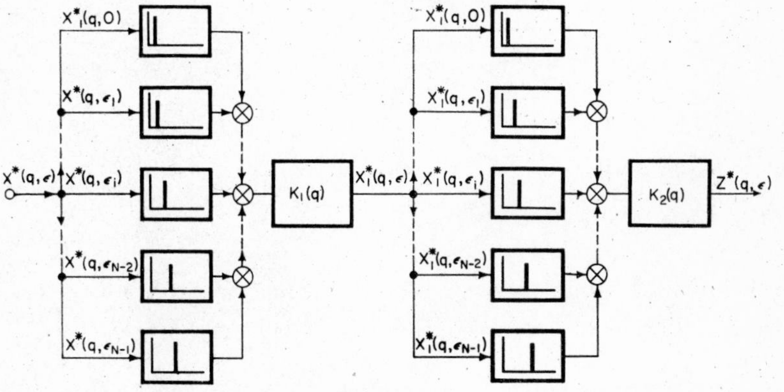

Fig. 3.25. Series-connected pulse systems with non-multiple repetition periods.

Putting $\varepsilon=(r-1)/N$ in the first equation and substituting $X_1^*(q, (r-1)/N$ in the second, we obtain:

$$Z^*(q, \varepsilon) = \sum_{r=1}^{N} K_2^* \left(q, \varepsilon - \frac{r-1}{N}\right) \sum_{s=1}^{N_1} K_1^* \left(q, \frac{r-1}{N} - \frac{s-1}{N_1}\right) X^* \left(q, \frac{s-1}{N_1}\right). \tag{3.114}$$

In this case, as in (3.103), the pulse system cannot be characterised by a single transfer function.

We shall conclude by giving the equation of a multiple-connected pulse system, i.e. a pulse system with N pulse elements working out-of-phase, one reduced continuous part, N external excitations and N output quantities (Fig. 3.26). We denote by $K_{sr}(q)$ the transfer function relating the input y_r to the output Z_s of the continuous part.

The equation of the reduced continuous part in terms of the images can then be written

$$Z_s(q) = \sum_{r=1}^{N} K_{sr}(q)\, Y_r(q)\,, \quad s = 1, 2, \ldots, N\,.$$

Applying the same reasoning as before we conclude that the equation

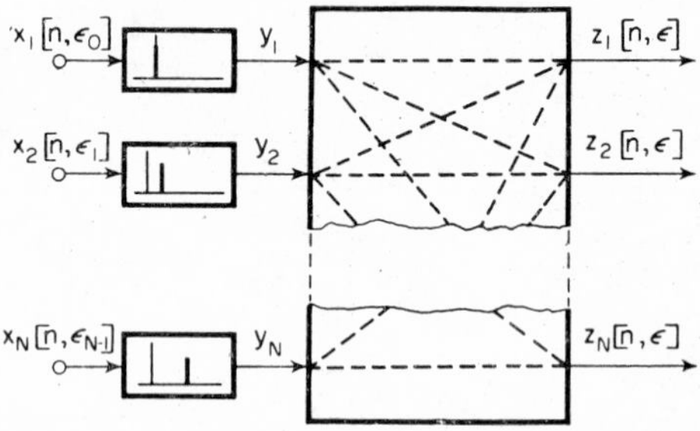

FIG. 3.26. Diagram of a multiple-connected pulse system.

of the pulse system in terms of the displaced lattice functions will have the form

$$Z_s^*(q, \varepsilon) = \sum_{r=1}^{N} K_{sr}^*(q, \varepsilon - \varepsilon_{r-1})\, X_r^*(q, \varepsilon_{r-1})\,, \quad s = 1, 2, \ldots, N\,. \qquad (3.115)$$

The equations in terms of the originals result on transforming from images to originals. We leave this to the reader.

The above rules for determining the transfer functions and equations for interconnected pulse systems remain valid in those cases when the pulse systems take the form of pulse filters or digital computing devices.

3.4. Equations and transfer functions of open-loop pulse systems with variable parameters

In the open-loop pulse systems considered above it has been assumed that the parameters of both the pulse element and the continuous part are constant. In a number of cases, however, these parameters are functions of the external excitation, i.e. in the long run they are functions of time. Thus, for example in pulse-width modulation (PWM) the duration of the pulses γ is varied, while in pulse-time modulation (PTM) the phase (PPM) or repetition frequency (period) (PFM) is varied. Often the parameters of the pulse element are constant and it is the parameters of the continuous part that vary, for example the time constants. Such pulse systems come under *pulse systems with variable parameters.*

If the parameters of the pulse element are variable, the pulse system is depicted as in Fig. 3.27*a*; if the parameters of the continuous part are variable, the pulse system is depicted as in Fig. 3.27*b*. The response of a pulse system with constant parameters to a pulse applied at the moment $\bar{t} = m$ equals the pulse characteristic displaced by a time $\bar{t} = m$, i.e. $k[n-m, \varepsilon]$. For a system with variable parameters the pulse characteristic does not depend on the difference $(n-m)$ but on the individual values of n and m, where n is the current moment of time, the reference moment, and m is the moment the pulse is applied. Thus for a pulse system with variable parameters the pulse characteristic will have the form

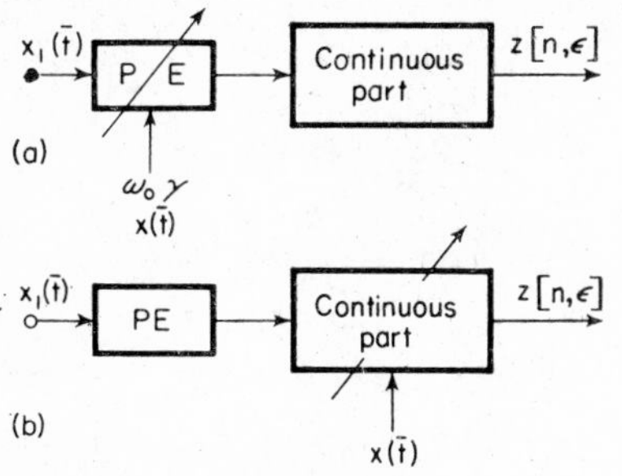

FIG. 3.27. Pulse system with variable parameters.

$$k[n, m, \varepsilon].$$

Since the pulse system with variable parameters is assumed linear, we may apply the principle of superposition and, in particular, the argument used when deducing the equation of a pulse system with constant parameters (§ 3.2). This gives us the equation of a pulse system with variable parameters in terms of the originals:

$$z[n, \varepsilon] = \sum_{m=0}^{n} x[m]\, k[n, m, \varepsilon]. \qquad (3.116)$$

It is analogous to the equation of a pulse system with constant parameters (3.39). Since

$$k[n, m, \varepsilon] \equiv 0 \quad \text{for} \quad n < m, \qquad (3.117)$$

as the pulse response cannot appear before the excitation is applied and $x[m] \equiv 0$ for $m < 0$, then (3.116) can also be written in the form

$$z[n, \varepsilon] = \sum_{m=-\infty}^{\infty} x[m]\, k[n, m, \varepsilon]. \qquad (3.118)$$

According to the inversion formula (2.175)

$$x[m] = \frac{1}{2\pi j} \int_{c-j\pi}^{c+j\pi} X^*(q)\, e^{qm}\, dq\,.$$

Inserting this value of $x[m]$ in (3.118) and changing the order of summation and integration, we obtain

$$z[n,\varepsilon] = \frac{1}{2\pi j} \int_{c-j\pi}^{c+j\pi} X^*(q) \left[\sum_{m=-\infty}^{\infty} k[n, m, \varepsilon]\, e^{-q(n-m)} \right] e^{qn}\, dq\,.$$

Putting

$$K^*(q, n, \varepsilon) = \sum_{m=-\infty}^{\infty} e^{-q(n-m)}\, k[n, m, \varepsilon]\,; \tag{3.119}$$

then

$$z[n,\varepsilon] = \frac{1}{2\pi j} \int_{c-j\pi}^{c+j\pi} X^*(q)\, K^*(q, n, \varepsilon)\, e^{qn}\, dq\,,$$

or briefly

$$z[n, \varepsilon] = D^{-1}\{K^*(q, n, \varepsilon)\, X^*(q)\}\,.$$

We have on applying the D-transformation to $z[n, \varepsilon]$:

$$Z^*(q, \varepsilon) = D\big\{D^{-1}\{K^*(q, n, \varepsilon)\, X^*(q)\}\big\}\,. \tag{3.120}$$

This is the equation of an open-loop pulse system, with variable parameters, in terms of the images; it is analogous to the equation of a pulse system with constant parameters. The pulse characteristic $k[n, m, \varepsilon]$ now depends not only on the variables n and ε, but also on the variable m — the discrete time, which defines the instant the pulse is applied. Correspondingly, the transfer function $K^*(q, n, \varepsilon)$ now depends not only on the variables q and ε, but also on the current discrete moments of time n.

Using (3.117) the transfer function (3.119) can be written in the form

$$K^*(q, n, \varepsilon) = \sum_{m=-\infty}^{\infty} e^{-q(n-m)}\, k[n, m, \varepsilon]\,,$$

or, making the change of variable $n - m = r$,

$$K^*(q, n, \varepsilon) = \sum_{r=0}^{\infty} e^{-qr}\, k[n, n - r, \varepsilon]\,, \tag{3.121}$$

where r is the difference between the reference moment and the moment the pulse is applied.

To find the transfer function we must first find the pulse characteristic of the reduced continuous part, i.e. the response of the reduced continuous part to an excitation of the form of an instantaneous pulse. Mathematically this problem reduces to solving a linear differential equation with variable coefficients

$$a_l'(t)\, z_T^{(l)}(t) + \dots + a_1'(t)\, z_T'(t) + a_0'(t)\, z_T(t) =$$
$$= b_{l_1}'(t)\, y_T^{(l_1)}(t) + \dots + b_1'(t)\, y_T'(t) + b_0'(t)\, y_T(t)\,,$$

where $y_T(t) = \delta(t - \lambda)$ is the delta-function. In the general case this equation is insoluble. However, an approximate solution can be obtained without difficulty.[+] In fact, if the parameters vary slowly we may assume that

$$K_{TC}(p, t) \approx \frac{b_{l_1}'(t)\, p^{l_1} + \dots + b_1'(t)\, p + b_0'(t)}{a_l'(t)\, p^l + \dots + a_1'(t)\, p + a_0'(t)}\,.$$

Transforming to the dimensionless parameters $q = pT$ and $\bar{t} = t/T$, we obtain the transfer function of the reduced continuous part:

$$K(q,\bar{t}) = \frac{k_p}{T} K_{TC}\left(\frac{q}{T}, T\bar{t}\right) \approx$$
$$\approx \frac{k_p\, P_C(q, \bar{t})}{TQ_C(q, \bar{t})} = \frac{k_p}{T}\, \frac{b_{l_1}'(\bar{t})\, q^{1} + \dots + b_1'(\bar{t})\, p + b_0'(\bar{t})}{a_l'(\bar{t})\, p^l + \dots + a_1'(\bar{t})\, p + a_0'(\bar{t})}\,. \tag{3.122}$$

The pulse characteristic, which gives the response of the continuous part at the moment $\bar{t}$ to an instantaneous pulse applied at $\bar{\lambda}$, is found by using the expansion formula and is

$$k(\bar{t}, \bar{t} - \bar{\lambda}) = \sum_{\nu=1}^{l} c_{\nu 0}'(\bar{t}) e^{q_\nu(\bar{t}), (\bar{t} - \bar{\lambda})}, \tag{3.123}$$

where $q_\nu(\bar{t})$ are the poles of $K(q, \bar{t})$ and

$$c_{\nu 0}'(\bar{t}) = \frac{kp\, P_C(q_\nu(\bar{t}), \bar{t})}{TQ_C'(q_\nu(\bar{t}), \bar{t})}\,.$$

If we take $t - \bar{\lambda} = n - r + \varepsilon$ and $\bar{t} = n$ as parameters, the formulae deduced in the previous sections are applicable to expressions (3.122) and (3.123). Consequently, the transfer function of the pulse system can be written approximately as

$$K^*(q, n, \varepsilon) \approx \sum_{r=-\infty}^{\infty} e^{(q + 2\pi jr)\varepsilon} K(q + 2\pi\, jr, n)\,. \tag{3.124}$$

[+] See Zadeh [3; 1950].

Alternatively, putting $\bar{t} = n$ and $\bar{\lambda} = r - \varepsilon$ in (3.123), we obtain the lattice function

$$k[n, n - r, \varepsilon] = \sum_{\nu=1}^{l} c'_{\nu 0}[n] e^{q_\nu[n]\varepsilon} e^{q_\nu[n](n-r)}. \tag{3.125}$$

Substituting $k(n, n - r, \varepsilon)$ in expression (3.121) and considering n and ε as parameters, we obtain in the same manner as for open-loop pulse systems with constant parameters:

$$K^*(q, n, \varepsilon) = \sum_{\nu=1}^{l} c'_{\nu 0}[n] \frac{e^q}{e^q - e^{q_\nu(n)}} e^{q_\nu[n]\varepsilon}. \tag{3.126}$$

If the shaping element produces rectangular pulses, then we have

$$\left. \begin{aligned} K^*(q, n, \varepsilon) &= c_{00}[n] + \sum_{\nu=1}^{l} c_{\nu 0}[n] \frac{e^q - e^{q_\nu(n)(1-\gamma)}}{e^q - e^{q_\nu(n)}} e^{q_\nu[n]\varepsilon}, \\ & \qquad\qquad 0 \leqslant \varepsilon \leqslant \gamma, \\ K^*(q, n, \varepsilon) &= \sum_{\nu=1}^{l} c_{\nu 0}[n] \frac{(e^{q_\nu(n)\gamma} - 1) e^q}{e^q - e^{q_\nu(n)}} e^{q_\nu[n](\varepsilon - \gamma)}, \quad \gamma \leqslant \varepsilon \leqslant 1, \end{aligned} \right\} \tag{3.127}$$

where

$$c_{00}[n] = \frac{k_p P_C(0, n)}{Q_C(0, n)} \quad \text{and} \quad c_{\nu 0}[n] = \frac{k_C P_C(q_\nu[n], n)}{Q'_C(q_\nu[n], n) q_\nu[n]}.$$

Comparing (3.126) with (3.49) and (3.127) with (3.81) we see that provided the changes in the variable parameters are small, the transfer function $K^*(q, n, \varepsilon)$ can be obtained in closed form by replacing q_ν by $q_\nu[n]$ and $C_{\nu 0}$ by $C_{\nu 0}[n]$ in the transfer function of the open-loop pulse system with constant parameters.

EXAMPLE. Suppose the equation of the continuous part is

$$T_1 (1 + at) \frac{dz_T(t)}{dt} + z_T(t) = k_p y_T(t).$$

Put $\bar{t} = t / T$ and write

$$\frac{T}{T_1} = \beta, \qquad a T = \bar{a};$$

then

$$(1 + \bar{a}\bar{t}) \frac{dz(\bar{t})}{d\bar{t}} + \beta z(\bar{t}) = k_p \beta y(\bar{t}).$$

If $\bar{a}$ is small, then from (3.122) the transfer function of the continuous part is

$$K(q, \bar{t}) = \frac{k_0}{(1 + \bar{a}\bar{t})q + \beta}, \tag{3.128}$$

where $k_0 = k_p/T_1$. The transfer function has a pole at

$$q_1(\bar{t}) = -\frac{\beta}{1 + \bar{a}\bar{t}},$$

and thus, from formulae (3.125) and (3.126), the pulse characteristic is given by

$$k[n, m, \varepsilon] = \frac{k_0}{1 + \bar{a}n} e^{-\frac{\beta(m+\varepsilon)}{1+\bar{a}n}} \tag{3.129}$$

while the transfer function is

$$K^*(q, n, \varepsilon) = \frac{k_0}{1 + \bar{a}n} \frac{e^q \cdot e^{-\frac{\beta\varepsilon}{1+\bar{a}n}}}{e^q - e^{-\beta/(1+\bar{a}n)}}. \tag{3.130}$$

For $\bar{a} = 0$ we obtain the result for a pulse system with constant parameters.†

If the parameters of the continuous part vary step-wise and periodically, taking one value during a pulse $0 \leqslant \varepsilon \leqslant \gamma$ and another between pulses $\gamma \leqslant \varepsilon \leqslant 1$, the pulse characteristic and transfer function can in fact be obtained accurately, and not just approximately.

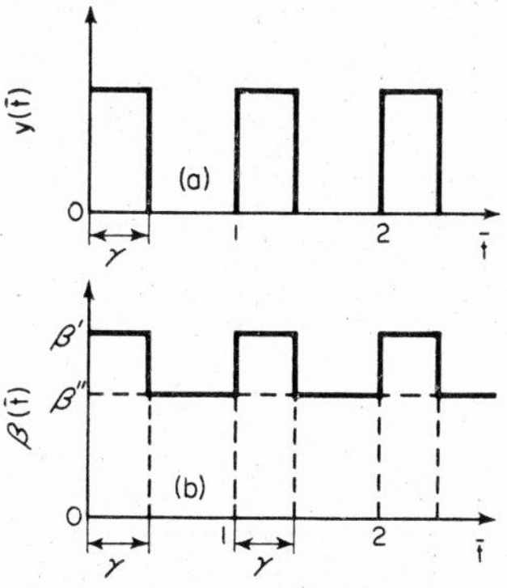

FIG. 3.28. Periodic, step-wise variation of a parameter of the continuous part; input quantity (*a*), variation of parameter (*b*).

The determination of the pulse characteristic, and thereafter the transfer function, reduces to solving and fitting two linear equations with coefficients which are constant but which take different values in the two intervals $0 \leqslant \varepsilon \leqslant \gamma$ and $\gamma \leqslant \varepsilon \leqslant 1$. In the general case, for an arbitrary continuous system, the solution of this problem is difficult and the final result is very unwieldy.‡

We restrict ourselves to the case of a *simple pulse system with step-wise changing parameters*, where the transfer function is easily obtainable from that of a simple pulse system with constant parameters.

We assume that the shaping network of the simple pulse system produces rectangular pulses of duration γ (Fig. 3.28*a*) and that in the interval $0 \leqslant \varepsilon \leqslant \gamma$ (i.e. during pulses) the parameter of the continuous part takes one value, and in the interval $\gamma \leqslant \varepsilon \leqslant 1$ (i.e.

† Open-loop pulse systems with variable parameters are considered by G. P. Tartakovskii [3; 1956a], [3; 1956b], [3; 1957] and Freeman [4.1], [4.2].

‡ See for example, F. M. Kilin (4; 1957), E. A. Rozenman (3; 1957).

outside pulses) it takes another value (Fig. 3.28*b*). The continuous part is thus described by two equations, or equivalently by two transfer functions:

$$K_C(q) = \frac{k\beta'}{q+\beta'}, \quad 0 \leqslant \varepsilon \leqslant \gamma; \qquad K_C(q) = \frac{k\beta''}{q+\beta''}, \quad \gamma \leqslant \varepsilon \leqslant 1.$$

We denote the ratio of β'' to β' by a, so that

$$\beta'' = a\beta'.$$

The transfer functions can then be written

$$\frac{k\beta'}{q+\beta'}, \quad 0 \leqslant \varepsilon \leqslant \gamma; \qquad \frac{k\beta'}{q/a+\beta'}, \quad \gamma \leqslant \varepsilon \leqslant 1.$$

The replacement in the second transfer function of q by q/a corresponds to changing the time scale by a factor a. Thus to find the transfer function of a simple pulse system with a step-wise changing parameter, we must take into account the time scale in the respective intervals, and consequently the time intervals $1-\gamma$ between pulses must be multiplied by a.+ Since the relative repetition period equals unity, or $\gamma + (1-\gamma)$, the transfer function of the simple pulse system (3.87) can be rewritten in the form

$$K^*(q, \varepsilon) = k_0 \left[1 - \frac{e^q - e^{-\beta(1-\gamma)}}{e^q - e^{-\beta\gamma-\beta(1-\gamma)}} e^{-\beta\varepsilon}\right], \quad 0 \leqslant \varepsilon \leqslant \gamma,$$

$$K^*(q, \varepsilon) = k_0 \frac{(1-e^{-\beta\gamma})\, e^q}{e^q - e^{-\beta\gamma-\beta(1-\gamma)}} e^{-\beta(\varepsilon-\gamma)}, \quad \gamma \leqslant \varepsilon \leqslant 1,$$

where $k_0 = k_p k$.

Replacing in this expression

$$\begin{aligned} \beta\gamma \quad &\text{by} \quad \beta'\gamma, \\ \beta(1-\gamma) \quad &\text{by} \quad \beta''(1-\gamma), \\ \beta = \beta\gamma + \beta(1-\gamma) \quad &\text{by} \quad \beta'\gamma + \beta''(1-\gamma), \\ \beta\varepsilon \quad &\text{by} \quad \beta'\varepsilon, \\ \beta(\varepsilon-\gamma) \quad &\text{by} \quad \beta''(\varepsilon-\gamma), \end{aligned}$$

which corresponds to changing the time scale in the intervals between pulses, we finally obtain the expression for the transfer function of

+ The idea of changing the time scale is due to O. M. Kryzhanovskii.

a simple pulse system with step-wise changing parameters.

$$\left.\begin{aligned} K^*(q,\varepsilon) &= k_0\left[1-\frac{e^q - e^{-\beta''(1-\gamma)}}{e^q - e^{-\beta'\gamma-\beta''(1-\gamma)}}\,e^{-\beta'\varepsilon}\right], \qquad (0\leqslant\varepsilon\leqslant\gamma,\\ K^*(q,\varepsilon) &= k_0\,\frac{(1-e^{-\beta'\gamma})\,e^q}{e^q - e^{-\beta'\gamma-\beta''(1-\gamma)}}\,e^{-\beta''(\varepsilon-\gamma)}, \qquad \gamma\leqslant\varepsilon\leqslant 1. \end{aligned}\right\} \tag{3.131}$$

For $\varepsilon = 0$ the first formula gives

$$K^*(q,\varepsilon) = k_0\,\frac{1-e^{-\beta'\gamma}}{e^q - e^{-\beta'\gamma-\beta''(1-\gamma)}}\,e^{-\beta''(1-\gamma)}. \tag{3.132}$$

This transfer function is the same as that which results from the difference equation (2.134). As is evident from (3.131) the transfer function $K^*(q, \varepsilon)$ of a simple pulse system with step-wise periodically changing parameters has a pole

$$\beta_{av} = \beta'\gamma + \beta''(1-\gamma),$$

which depends on the poles of the two transfer functions of the continuous part β' and β''. The quantity β_{av} is the mean weighted value of β' and β'', or the centroid.

In this manner the theory of a simple pulse system with a step-wise, periodically varying parameter reduce essentially to the theory of a simple pulse system with constant parameters.

We consider finally open-loop pulse systems in which the parameters of the pulse element vary. Such systems include pulse systems in which, as well as PWM or PPM, there is also PAM, i.e. double modulation is carried out. These systems have two input quantities. If PAM takes place according to the law (Fig. 3.29*a*) $x_1[n]$ and PWM takes place according to the law (Fig. 3.29*b*) $\gamma_M[n] = \varkappa\,|\,x[n]\,|$, then Fig. 3.29*c* shows the resulting pulse train acting on the continuous part of the system. The sign of $x[n]$ governs the polarity of each pulse.

The response of the continuous part to a pulse of relative duration γ_M applied at the moment $\bar{t} = m$ equals

$$\begin{aligned} &h(\bar{t}-m), && m\leqslant\bar{t}\leqslant m+\gamma_M,\\ &h(\bar{t}-m)-h(\bar{t}-m-\gamma_M[m]), && m+\gamma_M\leqslant t, \end{aligned}$$

where $h(t)$ is the response of the continuous part to a unit step, and is given by formula (3.75). The response of the continuous part to a pulse can be considered as the pulse characteristic of the reduced continuous part $k(\bar{t})$. Putting $\bar{t} = n + \varepsilon$ and $\gamma_M[m] = \varkappa \mid x[m] \mid$ in the latter, using lattice functions notation we obtain

$$k[n, m\,\varepsilon] = \begin{cases} h[n-m, \varepsilon] \operatorname{sign} x[m] & 0 \leqslant \varepsilon \leqslant \varkappa \mid x[m] \mid . \\ (h[n-m, \varepsilon] - h[n-m, \varepsilon - \varkappa \mid x[m] \mid]) \operatorname{sign} x[m], & \\ & \varkappa \mid x[m] \mid \leqslant \varepsilon \leqslant 1 . \end{cases}$$

The expression for the output quantity of the present pulse system

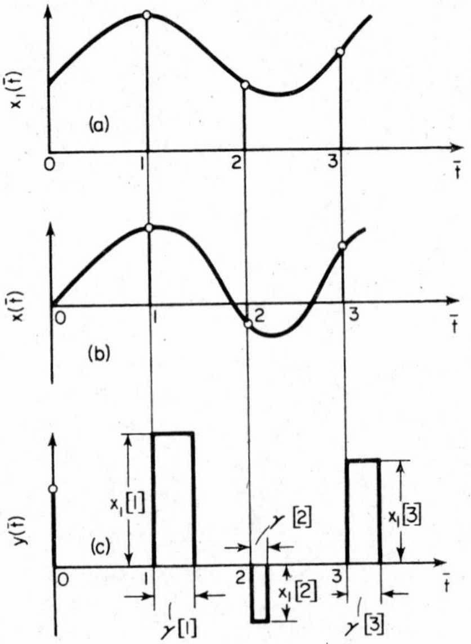

FIG. 3.29. Modulating functions (a) $x_1(\bar{t})$, (b) $x(\bar{t})$ and (c) the rectangular pulse train $y(\bar{t})$ acting on the continuous part.

is obtained by summing the responses to the individual pulses, which are of height $x_1[m]$ and duration $\varkappa \mid x[m] \mid$; using (3.39) we obtain

$$\left.\begin{aligned} z[n, \varepsilon] = & \sum_{m=0}^{n-1} x_1[m] (h[n-m, \varepsilon] - \\ & - h[n-m, \varepsilon - \varkappa \mid x[m] \mid]) \operatorname{sign} x[m] + \\ & + x_1[n] h[0, \varepsilon] \operatorname{sign} x[n], \quad 0 \leqslant \varepsilon \leqslant \varkappa \mid x[n] \mid , \\ z[n, \varepsilon] = & \sum_{m=0}^{n-1} x_1[m] (h[n-m, \varepsilon] - \\ & - h[n-m, \varepsilon - \varkappa \mid x[m] \mid] \mid \operatorname{sign} x[m] + \\ & + x_1[n] \mid h[0, \varepsilon] - h[0, \varepsilon - \varkappa \mid x[n] \mid] \operatorname{sign} x[n], \\ & \qquad \varkappa \mid x[n] \mid \leqslant \varepsilon \leqslant 1 . \end{aligned}\right\} \quad (3.133)$$

If we assume that the depth of the PWM is small, i.e. that

$$\gamma_M[m] = \varkappa \,|\, x[m] \,| \ll 1 ,$$

then we may restrict ourselves to the linear approximation

$$k[n, m, \varepsilon] \approx \dot{h}[n - m, \varepsilon] \,\varkappa\, |\, x[m] \,|\, \operatorname{sign} x[m] =$$

$$= \varkappa\, x[m]\, \dot{h}[n - m, \varepsilon], \quad \gamma_M[m] \leqslant \varepsilon \leqslant 1 .$$

Since

$$\dot{h}[n - m, \varepsilon] = k[n - m, \varepsilon],$$

where $k[n - m, \varepsilon]$ is the pulse characteristic of the reduced continuous part, we obtain finally

$$k[n, m, \varepsilon] = \varkappa\, x[m]\, k[n - m, \varepsilon].$$

Consequently, in this case the second equation of (3.133) can be written in the form

$$z[n, \varepsilon] = \sum_{m=0}^{n} x_1[m]\, \varkappa\, x[m]\, k[n - m, \varepsilon]. \tag{3.134}$$

In particular, for $x_1[m] = x_{10} =$ const., we arrive at the equation of a type-one pulse system in terms of the originals

$$z[n, \varepsilon] = \varkappa\, x_{10} \sum_{m=0}^{n} x[m]\, k[n - m, \varepsilon]. \tag{3.135}$$

The equation in terms of the images is obtained by applying a D transformation to both sides of (3.135):

$$Z^*(p, \varepsilon) = \varkappa\, x_{10}\, K^*(q, \varepsilon)\, X^*(q), \tag{3.136}$$

where $K^*(q, \varepsilon)$ is given, in the usual manner, by the formulae of § 3.2. Thus the results obtained in the preceding sections are applicable in this case.

We now assume that in the pulse system PAM takes place according to the law (Fig. 3.30*a*) $x_1[n]$ and PPM accordng to the law (Fig. 3.30*b*) $\varepsilon_M[n] = \varkappa \,|\, x[n] \,|$. Figure 3.30*c* shows the pulse train, modulated in amplitude and phase, which acts on the continuous part. The sign of $x[n]$ determines the polarity of the instantaneous pulses.

The response of the reduced continuous part to an instantaneous pulse applied at the moment $\bar{t} = m + \varepsilon_M[m]$ is $k(\bar{t} - m - \varepsilon_M[m])$, where $k(\bar{t})$ is the pulse characteristic of the reduced continuous part.

For $\bar{t} = n + \varepsilon$ and $\varepsilon_M[m] = \varkappa \mid x[m] \mid$, this response can be written as the lattice function

$$k[n, m, \varepsilon] = \begin{cases} k\left[n - m - 1, 1 + \varepsilon - \varkappa \mid x[m] \mid\right], & 0 \leqslant \varepsilon \leqslant \varkappa \mid x[m] \mid, \\ k\left[n - m, \varepsilon - \varkappa \mid x[m] \mid\right], & \varkappa \mid x[m] \mid \leqslant \varepsilon \leqslant 1. \end{cases}$$

Using formula (3.39), we obtain the expression for the output quantity as the sum of the individual responses

$$z[n, \varepsilon] = \sum_{m=0}^{n} x_1[m]\, k\left[n - m, \varepsilon - \varkappa \mid x[m] \mid\right] \operatorname{sign} x[m] \quad (3.137)$$

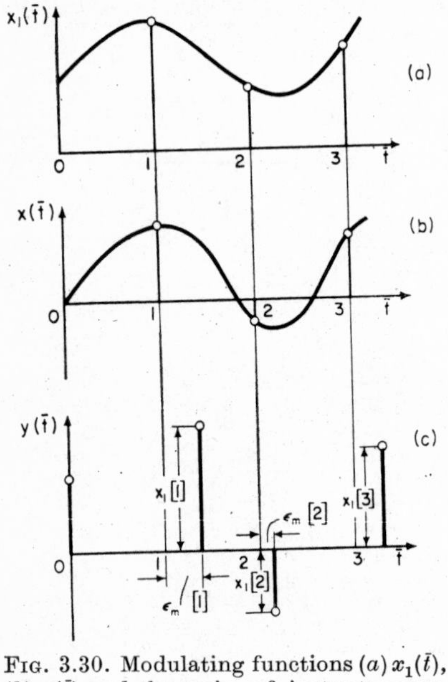

FIG. 3.30. Modulating functions (a) $x_1(\bar{t})$, (b) $x(\bar{t})$ and the train of instantaneous pulses (c) $y(\bar{t})$ acting on the continuous part.

for

$$\varepsilon_M[n] \leqslant \varepsilon \leqslant 1 + \varepsilon_M[n+1].$$

If the depth of the PWM is small, i.e.

$$\varepsilon_M[m] = \varkappa \mid x[m] \mid \ll 1,$$

we may restrict ourselves to the linear approximation

$$k(\bar{t} - m - \varepsilon_M[m]) \approx k(\bar{t} - m) - \dot{k}(\bar{t} - m)\, \varepsilon_M[m].$$

For $\bar{t} = n + \varepsilon$ we have

$$k[n - m, \varepsilon] - \varkappa \mid x[m] \mid = k[n-m, \varepsilon] - \dot{k}[n-m, \varepsilon]\, \varkappa \mid x[m] \mid.$$

Inserting this value in (3.137) and remembering that

$$\mid x[m] \mid \operatorname{sign} x[m] = x[m],$$

we obtain

$$z[n, \varepsilon] = \sum_{m=0}^{n} x_1[m]\, k[n - m, \varepsilon] \operatorname{sign} x[m] - \\ - \sum_{m=0}^{n} x_1[m]\, \varkappa\, x[m]\, \dot{k}[n - m, \varepsilon]. \quad (3.138)$$

This equation corresponds to the non-linear type-one pulse system shown in Fig. 3.31. It consists of two pulse systems, the reduced continuous parts of which equal $k(\bar{t})$ and $\dot{k}(\bar{t})$, and thus the transfer functions equal $K(q)$ and $qK(q) - k(0)$. In addition there is in the circuit a relay element, which forms sign $x[m]$, and two multipliers, which form the products $x_1[m]$ sign $x[m]$ and $x_1[m]\varkappa \mid x[m] \mid$.

A type-three pulse system results on putting $x_1[m] = x_{10} =$ const. in (3.137). We then obtain

$$z[n, \varepsilon] = x_{10} \sum_{m=0}^{n} k[n - m, \varepsilon] \operatorname{sign} x[m] - \varkappa x_{10} \sum_{m=0}^{n} x[m] \dot{k}[n - m, \varepsilon]. \quad (3.139)$$

The equation in terms of the images is obtained by applying the

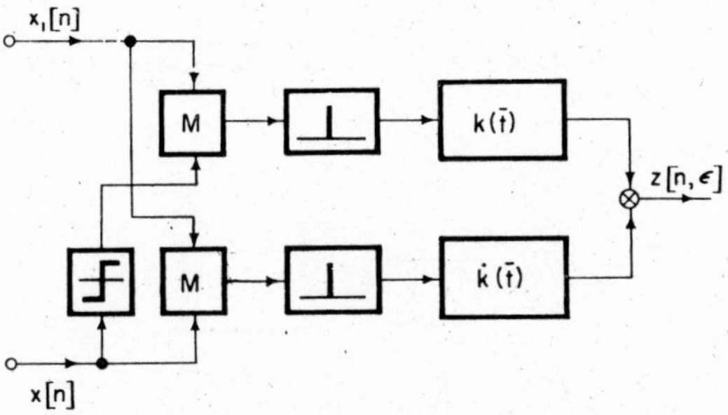

FIG. 3.31. Diagram of a pulse system with PAM and PPM for small depths of modulation.

D-transformation to (3.139) and using the convolution theorem (Theorem 11):

$$D\{z[n, \varepsilon]\} = D\{k[n, \varepsilon]\} D\{\operatorname{sign} x[n]\} - \varkappa D\{x[n]\} D\{\dot{k}[n, \varepsilon]\}. \quad (3.140)$$

However, by definition

$$D\{k[n, \varepsilon]\} = K^*(q, \varepsilon).$$

We obtain, using the theorem on differentiation with respect to a parameter (Theorem 9) or the theorem on multiplication by q (Theorem 22)

$$D\{\dot{k}[n, \varepsilon]\} = \frac{\partial}{\partial \varepsilon} K^*(q, \varepsilon).$$

With the usual notation for the images of the input and output quantities, we can finally write (3.140) in the form

$$Z^*(q, \varepsilon) = x_{10} K^*(q, \varepsilon) D\{\operatorname{sign} x[n]\} - x_{10} \varkappa \left[\frac{\partial}{\partial \varepsilon} K^*(q, \varepsilon)\right] X^*(q, 0). \quad (3.141)$$

Equations (3.139) and (3.141) correspond to the nonlinear pulse system shown in Fig. 3.32*a*. It consists of a nonlinear, or more accurately a relay pulse system, and a conventional linear type-one pulse system connected in parallel.

If it is known that $x[m]$ is everywhere positive, then sign $x[m]$ can be omitted from (3.139). This is equivalent to removing the relay

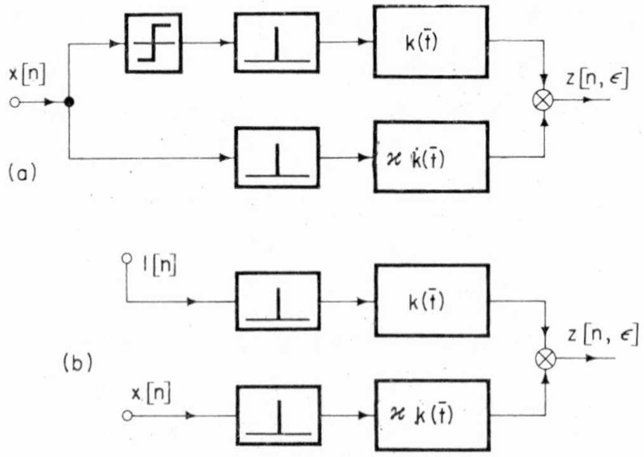

FIG. 3.32. Diagram of a nonlinear type-one pulse system (*a*), which is equivalent for small depths of modulation to a type-three pulse system (*b*).

element from the pulse system and applying a constant excitation equal to unity (Fig. 3.32*b*).

In the above manner we see that for small depths of modulation the theory of pulse systems types two and three reduces to the theory of pulse systems type one.

3.5. Response of open-loop pulse systems to typical excitations

Let us assume that some excitation is applied to the pulse system. It can be represented as a lattice function $x[n]$, since the pulse element only responds to discrete values of the excitation. This excitation gives rise to a variation in the output quantity, the response of the pulse system.

The response can be calculated using the equation of the pulse system in terms of the images

$$Z^*(q, \varepsilon) = K^*(q, \varepsilon)\, X^*(q) \tag{3.142}$$

or in terms of the originals

$$z[n, \varepsilon] = \sum_{m=0}^{n} k[n - m, \varepsilon]\, x[m]. \tag{3.143}$$

Here $Z^*(q, \varepsilon)$ and $X^*(q)$ are the images of the output and input quantities respectively, these latter quantities being written as lattice functions $z[n, \varepsilon]$ and $x[n]$, and $K^*(q, \varepsilon)$ is the pulse-system transfer function — the image of the pulse characteristic $k[n, \varepsilon]$.

For a fixed value of ε the lattice function $z[n, \varepsilon]$ gives the discrete values of the response at the moments $\bar{t} = n + \varepsilon$. The value of the response at any instant $\bar{t} = n + \varepsilon$ is obtained by varying ε from 0 to 1 in $z[n, \varepsilon]$. Consequently, $z[n, \varepsilon]$ is an analytical expression for the response of the pulse system to a given excitation.

$z[n, \varepsilon]$ can be obtained by substituting the image of the external excitation in (3.142) and then transforming to the originals using the theorems of the discrete Laplace transformation. $z(n, \varepsilon)$ can also be found from (3.143) by inserting the known lattice functions $k[n - n, \varepsilon]$ and $x[m]$ and then carrying out the summation. In a number of cases this method proves convenient. However, the first method is often preferable from the point of view of generality and similarity to the analysis of continuous systems. By using the transfer function we can avoid doing the summation, and also make use of image-original tables to simplify calculations.

In the general case (for an arbitrary excitation) $z[n, \varepsilon]$ is found by applying the inverse discrete Laplace transformation (2.173) to $Z^*(q, \varepsilon)$:

$$z[n, \varepsilon] = D^{-1}\{Z^*(q, \varepsilon)\},$$

or, more explicitly, from (2.176)

$$z[n, \varepsilon] = \frac{1}{2\pi j} \int_{c-j\pi}^{c+j\pi} K^*(q, \varepsilon)\, X^*(q)\, e^{qn}\, dq\,. \tag{3.144}$$

The expansion formulae (2.155) and (2.158) can be used in a number of cases. However, for typical excitations it is better to determine $z[n, \varepsilon]$ directly. For simplicity we shall assume at the moment that all the poles of the transfer function of the reduced continuous part are simple and not equal to zero. The case when there are multiple poles and poles equal to zero can easily be dealt with by the limiting process, or by using the expressions for $K^*(q, \varepsilon)$ given in §§ 3.2 and 3.4. We assume in addition that there is no delay τ in the continuous part. The presence of a delay corresponds, as is obvious from physical considerations, to a shift in the response $z[n, \varepsilon]$ by a time equal to the time-dealy τ.

Step-type excitation. Suppose the input excitation has the form of a step (Fig. 3.33*a*). The corresponding lattice function (Fig. 3.33*b*)

$$x[n] = x_0 1[n], \qquad n \geqslant 0,$$

has, as was shown in § 2.2 (2.28), the image

$$X^*(q) = D\{x_0 1[n]\} = x_0 \frac{e^q}{e^q - 1}.$$

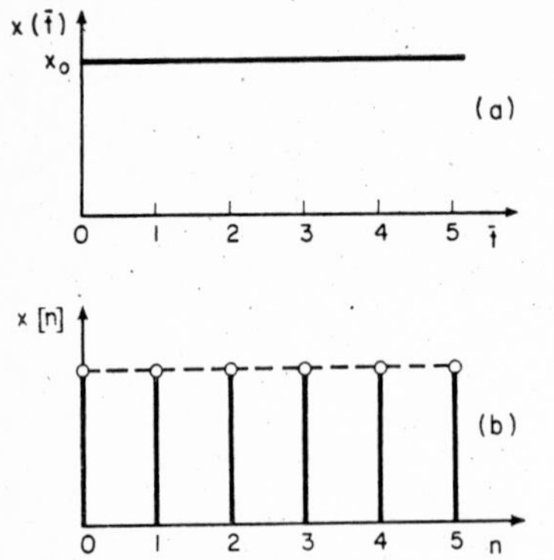

FIG. 3.33. Step excitation (*a*), and the corresponding lattice function (*b*).

From the equation of the pulse system (3.142) we obtain the image of the output:

$$Z^*(q, \varepsilon) = K^*(q, \varepsilon)\, x_0 \frac{e^q}{e^q - 1}$$

or, substituting the expression for $K^*(q, \varepsilon)$ from (3.49),

$$Z^*(q, \varepsilon) = x_0 \sum_{\nu=1}^{l} c'_{\nu 0} \frac{e^q}{e^q - e^{q_\nu}} \frac{e^q}{e^q - 1} e^{q_\nu \varepsilon},$$

$$0 \leqslant \varepsilon \leqslant 1. \tag{3.145}$$

To go from images to originals we use the transformation

$$\frac{e^q}{(e^q - e^{q_\nu})(e^q - 1)} e^q \doteqdot \frac{1}{1 - e^{q_\nu}} (1 - e^{q_\nu (n+1)}), \tag{3.146}$$

which is obtained by applying the real-translation theorem (Theorem 2) to (2.79). We then find

$$z[n, \varepsilon] = x_0 \sum_{\nu=1}^{l} \frac{c'_{\nu 0}}{1 - e^{q_\nu}} e^{q_\nu \varepsilon} - x_0 \sum_{\nu=1}^{l} \frac{c'_{\nu 0}}{1 - e^{q}} e^{q_\nu (n+1+\varepsilon)}. \tag{3.147}$$

Putting $q = 0$ in expression (3.49) for $K^*(q, \varepsilon)$ gives

$$K^*(0, \varepsilon) = \sum_{\nu=1}^{l} \frac{c'_{\nu 0}}{1 - e^{q_\nu}} e^{q_\nu \varepsilon}. \tag{3.148}$$

Substituting this expression in (3.147) enables us to write the output quantity in the form

$$z[n, \varepsilon] = x_0 K^*(0; \varepsilon) - x_0 \sum_{\nu=1}^{l} \frac{c'_{\nu 0}}{1 - e^{q_\nu}} e^{q_\nu (n+1+\varepsilon)}. \tag{3.149}$$

Formula (3.149), which gives the response of the pulse system to a step input, i.e. to a constant excitation, consists of two parts.

The first part is independent of n, and the second depends on n. This second term characterises the *transient process or response*. The nature of the transient process depends on the nature of the poles q_ν of the transfer function. Real and negative q_ν give rise in (3.149) to monotonically decreasing lattice functions. Complex conjugate values of q_ν give rise in (3.149) to decreasing oscillatory lattice functions. Finally, real and positive q_ν or complex q_ν with positive real parts give rise in (3.149) to monotonically or oscillatory increasing lattice functions.

If the continuous part is a passive system, i.e. it does not contain internal sources of energy, all the poles of its transfer function will have negative real parts and, consequently as time increase (i.e. as n increases) the transient response will tend to zero and a *steady-state* or *stationary* response, given by the first part of (3.149), will be established in the pulse system

$$z_s[n, \varepsilon] = z[\infty, \varepsilon] = x_0 K^*(0, \varepsilon). \tag{3.150}$$

Thus, to obtain the steady-state response, it is sufficient to multiply x_0 *by the pulse-system transfer function for* $q = 0$.

The steady-state response can be expressed in another form by using the series representations of the transfer function. Thus, putting $q = 0$ in (3.42) and (3.44), we obtain respectively

$$z_s[n, \varepsilon] = z[\infty, \varepsilon] = x_0 \sum_{n=0}^{\infty} k[n, \varepsilon], \tag{3.151}$$

$$z_s[n, \varepsilon] = z[\infty, \varepsilon] = x_0 \sum_{r=-\infty}^{\infty} e^{2\pi j r \varepsilon} K(2\pi jr). \tag{3.152}$$

It follows from (3.151) *that the steady-state response is given by the product of* x_0 *and the infinite sum of the values of the pulse characteristic for* $n = 0, 1, 2, \ldots$

Expression (3.152) gives the steady-state response $z_s[n, \varepsilon] = z[\infty, \varepsilon]$ in the form of a Fourier series. This result can also be obtained from physical considerations; we represent the unmodulated instantaneous pulses as a Fourier series, find the steady-state response of the linear system to the harmonics, then finally add up these responses. In the present case the steady-state response is periodic, with a relative period of unity.

Expression (3.149), which determines the response of a pulse system, is analogous to the usual Heaviside formula. This expression can be written in terms of real numbers. Let the transfer function $K^*(q, \varepsilon)$

have 2μ complex-conjugate poles $q_\nu = \sigma_\nu \pm j\bar{\omega}_\nu$ and $l - 2\mu$ real poles $q_\nu = \sigma_\nu$. Then, combining the terms in (3.149) with complex-conjugate poles, we have

$$z[n, \varepsilon] = x_0 \Big\{ K^*(0, \varepsilon) - 2 \sum_{\nu=1}^{\mu} C_\nu e^{\sigma_\nu(n+1+\varepsilon)} \cos [\bar{\omega}_\nu(n + 1 + \varepsilon) + \psi_\nu] - \\ - \sum_{\nu=2\mu+1}^{l} \frac{c'_{\nu 0}}{1 - e^{\sigma_\nu}} e^{\sigma_\nu(n+1+\varepsilon)} \Big\}. \tag{3.153}$$

Here

$$C_\nu = \left| \frac{c'_{\nu 0}}{1 - e^{\sigma_\nu + j\bar{\omega}_\nu}} \right|, \qquad \psi_\nu = \arg \frac{c'_{\nu 0}}{1 - e^{\sigma_\nu + j\bar{\omega}_\nu}}$$

and

$$K^*(0, \varepsilon) = 2 \sum_{\nu=1}^{\mu} C_\nu e^{\sigma_\nu \varepsilon} \cos (\bar{\omega}_\nu \varepsilon + \psi_\nu) + \sum_{\nu=2\mu+1}^{l} \frac{c'_{\nu 0}}{1 - e^{\sigma_\nu}} e^{\sigma_\nu \varepsilon}. \tag{3.154}$$

Obviously, from (3.150), $K^*(0, \varepsilon)$ can also be written in a form analogous to formula (3.151) or (3.152). The pulse system response to a unit step input can be calculated from (3.153) in terms of the transfer function $K(q)$ of the reduced continuous part if the poles of $K(q)$ are known.

If the pulse-system shaping element produces rectangular pulses, formulae similar to the above can be found on the basis of the equivalent circuit of Fig. 3.10, by combining the transfer functions (3.49) and (3.58), or by the above method, using in this case the transfer functions (3.81) instead of the transfer function (3.49). We shall only give the final results, leaving their verification to the reader. In this case we find

$$z[n, \varepsilon] = x_0 \Big\{ K^*(0, \varepsilon) - \sum_{\nu=1}^{l} \frac{1 - e^{-q_\nu \gamma}}{1 - e^{q_\nu}} e^{q_\nu(n+1+\varepsilon)} \Big\}, \tag{3.155}$$

where $K^*(0, \varepsilon)$ is given by the expressions

$$K^*(0, \varepsilon) = \begin{cases} c_{00} + \sum_{\nu=1}^{l} c_{\nu 0} \dfrac{1 - e^{q_\nu(1-\gamma)}}{1 - e^{q_\nu}} e^{q_\nu \varepsilon}, & 0 \leqslant \varepsilon \leqslant \gamma, \\ \sum_{\nu=1}^{l} c_{\nu 0} \dfrac{e^{q_\nu \gamma} - 1}{1 - e^{q_\nu}} e^{q_\nu(\varepsilon - \gamma)}, & \gamma \leqslant \varepsilon \leqslant 1. \end{cases} \tag{3.156}$$

The steady-state value $z_s[n, \varepsilon] = z[\infty, \varepsilon]$ is given by expression (3.150) but now $K^*(0, \varepsilon)$ is to be found from (3.156). $K^*(0, \varepsilon)$ can also be found in terms of series (3.151), (3.152), which involve the pulse characteristic or transfer function. The mean value of $z_s[n, \varepsilon]$ equals

$$\overline{z_s[n, \varepsilon]} = \int_0^1 z_s[n, \varepsilon] \, \mathrm{d}\varepsilon \tag{3.157}$$

or, using (3.150),

$$\overline{z_s[n, \varepsilon]} = x_0 \int_0^1 K^*(0, \varepsilon) \, \mathrm{d}\,\varepsilon .$$

However, according to the inverse $\mathfrak{D}$-transformation (2.229) we have

$$K(q) = \int_0^1 K^*(q, \varepsilon) \, \mathrm{e}^{-q\varepsilon} \, \mathrm{d}\,\varepsilon.$$

Putting $q = 0$ in this expression gives

$$K(0) = \int K^*(0, \varepsilon) \, \mathrm{d}\,\varepsilon$$

and consequently

$$\overline{z_s[n, \varepsilon]} = x_0 K(0). \tag{3.158}$$

Thus, *the mean value $z_s[n, \varepsilon]$ equals the initial value of the transfer function of the reduced continuous part multiplied by x_0.*

Putting $\gamma = 1$ in (3.155) gives

$$z[n, \varepsilon] = x_0 \left\{ c_{00} + \sum_{\nu=1}^{l} c_{\nu 0} \, \mathrm{e}^{q_\nu (n+\varepsilon)} \right\},$$

which, on replacing $n + \varepsilon$ by $\bar{t}$, coincides with the usual Heaviside formula. This is obvious physically: for $\gamma = 1$ the continuous part is subjected to a step excitation, and not to a train of pulses.

EXAMPLE: Calculate the response of the simple pulse system of Fig. 3.8. The transfer function of its reduced continuous part equals

$$K(q) = \frac{\beta}{q + \beta} .$$

We have from (3.147)

$$z[n, \varepsilon] = x_0 \left\{ K^*(0, \varepsilon) - \frac{k_0}{1 - \mathrm{e}^{-\beta}} \mathrm{e}^{-\beta(n+1+\varepsilon)} \right\},$$

where $k_0 = k_p/T$

$$K^*(0, \varepsilon) = \frac{k_0}{1 - \mathrm{e}^{-\beta\varepsilon}} \mathrm{e}^{-\beta\varepsilon}. \tag{3.159}$$

Substituting (3.159) in the expression for $z[n, \varepsilon]$ gives finally.

$$z[n, \varepsilon] = x_0 \frac{k_0}{1 - \mathrm{e}^{-\beta}} (1 - \mathrm{e}^{-\beta(n+1)}) \, \mathrm{e}^{-\beta\varepsilon}. \tag{3.160}$$

$z[n, \varepsilon]$ is shown qualitatively in Fig. 3.34*a*. At times $\bar{t} = n$ a step occurs in the output voltage due to the application of an instantaneous pulse to the continuous system, i.e. a pulse of infinitely small duration and infinitely large height. Physically, the step corresponds to the charging of the capacitor for a time equal to the duration of the pulse.

If the shaping element produces rectangular pulses, then

$$c_{\nu 0} = \frac{T c'_{\nu 0}}{q_\nu}$$

and therefore, from (3.155) and (3.156), we obtain

$$z[n, \varepsilon] = x_0 \left\{ K^*(0, \varepsilon) + k_p \frac{1 - e^{\beta\gamma}}{1 - e^{-\beta}} e^{-\beta(n+1+\varepsilon)} \right\}, \tag{3.161}$$

where

$$K^*(0, \varepsilon) = \begin{cases} k_p \left[1 - \dfrac{1 - e^{-\beta(1-\gamma}}{1 - e^{-\beta}} e^{-\beta\varepsilon} \right], & 0 \leqslant \varepsilon \leqslant \gamma, \\ k_p \dfrac{1 - e^{-\beta\gamma}}{1 - e^{-\beta}} e^{-\beta(\varepsilon-\gamma)}, & \gamma \leqslant \varepsilon \leqslant 1. \end{cases} \tag{3.162}$$

The form of $z[n, \varepsilon]$ in this case is shown in Fig. 3.34*b*. For $\gamma \to 0$ but $k_p\gamma = $ $= \text{const}/T$, the response reduces to that of Fig. 3.34*a*.

The response of a simple pulse system, with a step-wise periodically-varying parameter, to a step input excitation can be obtained in a similar manner in terms of the system transfer functions (3.131):

$$\left. \begin{aligned} z[n, \varepsilon] &= x_0 k_0 \left\{ 1 - \frac{1 - e^{-\beta\,(1-\gamma)}}{1 - e^{-\beta_{av}}} e^{-\beta'\varepsilon} + \frac{1 - e^{\beta\,\gamma}}{1 - e^{-\beta_{av}}} e^{-\beta_{av}(n+1)}\, e^{-\beta\,\varepsilon} \right\}, \\ &\qquad 0 \leqslant \varepsilon \leqslant \gamma, \\ z[n, \varepsilon] &= x_0 k_0 \left\{ \frac{1 - e^{-\beta\,\gamma}}{1 - e^{-\beta_{av}}} e^{-\beta''(\varepsilon-\gamma)} + \frac{e^{-\beta'\gamma} - 1}{1 - e^{-\beta_{av}}} e^{-\beta_{av}(n+1)}\, e^{-\beta''(\varepsilon-\gamma)} \right\}, \\ &\qquad \gamma \leqslant \varepsilon \leqslant 1, \end{aligned} \right\} \tag{3.163}$$

where

$$k_0 = k_p\, k \quad \text{and} \quad \beta_{av} = \beta'\,\gamma + \beta''(\varepsilon - \gamma)\,.$$

Harmonic excitation. Consider the case when the applied excitation is harmonic (Fig. 3.35*a*). The corresponding lattice function equals (Fig. 3.35*b*)

$$x[n] = x_m \cos(\bar{\omega}\, n + \varphi)\,,$$

or, in complex form,

$$\mathbf{x}[n] = x_m\, e^{j(\bar{\omega} n + \varphi)}\,,$$

where $\bar{\omega} = \omega\, T$ is the relative frequency, and ψ is the phase. In this case the "areas" of the instantaneous pulses acting on the linear part of the sytem vary according to a harmonic law. The image of the input variable, according to (2,29) for $a = j\bar{\omega}$, equals

$$\mathbf{X}^*(q) = x_m e^{j\psi} D\left\{e^{j\bar{\omega}n}\right\} = x_m e^{j\psi} \frac{e^q}{e^q - e^{j\bar{\omega}}} \,.$$

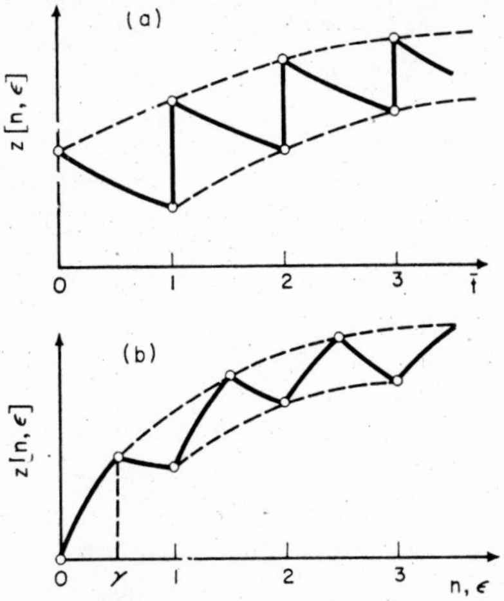

FIG. 3.34 Variation of $z[n, \varepsilon]$ in a simple pulse system when the input is a train of (*a*) instantaneous pulses, (*b*) rectangular pulses

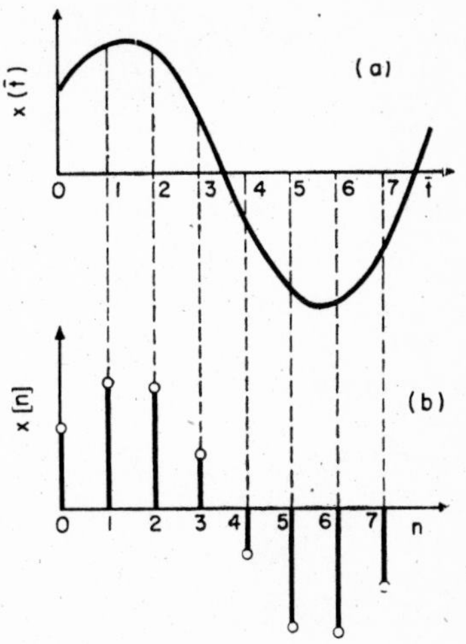

FIG. 3.35. A harmonic excitation (*a*) and the corresponding lattice function(*b*)

Using the equation of the pulse system (3.142), the image of the output quantity becomes

$$\mathbf{Z}^*(q, \varepsilon) = x_m e^{j\psi} \sum_{\nu=1}^{l} c'_{\nu 0} \frac{e^q}{e^q - e^{q_\nu}} \, \frac{e^q}{e^q - e^{j\bar{\omega}}} \, e^{q_\nu \varepsilon} \,. \tag{3.164}$$

Using the transformation

$$\frac{e^q}{e^q - e^{q_\nu})\,(e^q - e^{j\bar{\omega}})} \, e^q \overset{\cdot}{\underset{\cdot}{\longrightarrow}} \frac{1}{e^{j\bar{\omega}} - e^{q_\nu}} \left(e^{j\bar{\omega}(n+1)} - e^{q_\nu(n+1)}\right), \tag{3.165}$$

which follows by applying the real-translation theorem (Theorem 2) to (2.79), we obtain on transforming from images to originals

$$\mathbf{z}\,[n, \varepsilon] = x_m \left\{ \sum_{\nu=1}^{l} c'_{\nu 0} \frac{e^{j\bar{\omega}}}{e^{j\bar{\omega}} - e^{q_\nu}} \, e^{q_\nu \varepsilon} \, e^{j(\bar{\omega}n + \psi)} - \sum_{\nu=1} \frac{c_{\nu 0}}{e^{j\bar{\omega}} - e^{q_\nu}} \, e^{q_\nu(n+1+\varepsilon)} \right\}. \tag{3.166}$$

Noting, that for $q = j\bar{\omega}$ the pulse-system transfer function $K^*(q, \varepsilon)$ (3.49) equals

$$K^*(j\,\bar{\omega}, \varepsilon) = \sum_{\nu=1}^{l} c'_{\nu 0} \frac{e^{j\bar{\omega}}}{e^{j\bar{\omega}} - e^{q_\nu}} e^{q_\nu \varepsilon},$$

we can finally write $\mathbf{z}[n, \varepsilon]$ in the form

$$\mathbf{z}[n, \varepsilon] = x_m \left\{ K^*(j\,\bar{\omega}, \varepsilon)\, e^{j(\bar{\omega}n+\psi)} - \sum_{\nu=1}^{l} \frac{c'_{\nu 0}}{e^{j\bar{\omega}} - e^{q_\nu}} e^{q_\nu(n+1+\varepsilon)} \right\}. \quad (3.167)$$

As before, the second part of the expression characterises the transient process, which tends to zero as time increases (i.e. as n increases) provided the real parts of the poles of $K^*(q, \varepsilon)$, and therefore also of $K(q)$, are negative.

The steady-state response of the pulse system is characterised by the first part of expression (3.167)

$$\mathbf{z}_s[n, \varepsilon] = K^*(j\,\bar{\omega}, \varepsilon)\, x_m\, e^{j(\bar{\omega}n+\psi)}. \quad (3.168)$$

It follows from this expression *that the steady state response is given by multiplying the input variable* $x_m\, e^{j(\bar{\omega}n+\psi)}$ *by the pulse-system transfer function for* $q = j\,\bar{\omega}$.

The quantity $K^*(j\,\bar{\omega}, \varepsilon)$ is called the *frequency characteristic or amplitude-phase characteristic of the pulse system.* It can be written in exponential form

$$K^*(j\,\bar{\omega}, \varepsilon) = |K^*(\bar{\omega}, \varepsilon)|\, e^{j\theta^*(\bar{\omega}, \varepsilon)},$$

where $|K^*(\bar{\omega}, \varepsilon)|$ is the modulus, and $\theta^*(\bar{\omega}, \varepsilon)$ is the phase. Inserting this expression for $K^*(j\,\bar{\omega}, \varepsilon)$ in (3.168) we obtain

$$\mathbf{z}_s[n, \varepsilon] = x_m\, |K^*(\bar{\omega}, \varepsilon)|\, e^{j[\bar{\omega}n+\psi+\theta^*(\bar{\omega}, \varepsilon)]}, \quad (3.169)$$

or, in real form,

$$z_s[n, \varepsilon] = x_m\, |K^*(\bar{\omega}, \varepsilon)| \cos[\bar{\omega}\, n + \psi + \theta^*(\bar{\omega}, \varepsilon)]. \quad (3.170)$$

It follows from (3.170) that for a fixed ε, $z_s[n, \varepsilon]$ takes the form of a harmonic lattice function whose amplitude and phase differ from those of the input lattice function $x[n]$.

For a pulse system whose shaping element produces rectangular pulses, the expression for $\mathbf{z}[n, \varepsilon]$ can be written in the form

$$\mathbf{z}[n, \varepsilon] = x_m \left\{ K^*(j\,\bar{\omega}, \varepsilon)\, e^{j(\bar{\omega}n+\psi)} - \sum_{\nu=1}^{l} c_{\nu 0}\, e^{j\psi} \frac{1 - e^{-q_\nu \gamma}}{e^{j\bar{\omega}} - e^{q_\nu}} e^{q_\nu(n+1+\varepsilon)} \right\}, \quad (3.171)$$

where

$$K^*(j\bar{\omega}, \varepsilon) = \begin{cases} c_{00} + \sum_{\nu=1}^{l} c_{\nu 0} \dfrac{e^{j\bar{\omega}} - e^{q_\nu(1-\gamma)}}{e^{j\bar{\omega}} - e^{q_\nu}} e^{q_\nu \varepsilon}, & 0 \leqslant \varepsilon \leqslant \gamma, \\ \sum_{\nu=1}^{l} c_{\nu 0} \dfrac{(e^{q_\nu \gamma} - 1) e^{j\bar{\omega}}}{e^{j\bar{\omega}} - e^{q_\nu}} e^{q_\nu(\varepsilon-\gamma)}, & \gamma \leqslant \varepsilon \leqslant 1. \end{cases} \quad (3.172)$$

In particular, for $\gamma = 1$ we have

$$\mathbf{z}[n, \varepsilon] = x_m \left\{ K^*(j\bar{\omega}, \varepsilon) e^{j(\bar{\omega}n+\psi)} - \sum_{\nu=1}^{l} c_{\nu 0} e^{j\psi} \frac{e^{q_\nu} - 1}{e^{j\bar{\omega}} - e^{q_\nu}} e^{q_\nu(n+\varepsilon)} \right\}, \quad (3.173)$$

where

$$K^*(j\bar{\omega}, \varepsilon) = c_{00} + \sum_{\nu=1}^{l} c_{\nu 0} \frac{e^{j\bar{\omega}} - 1}{e^{j\bar{\omega}} - e^{q_\nu}} e^{q_\nu \varepsilon}. \quad (3.174)$$

Example. For a simple pulse system (Fig. 3.8) with a harmonic excitation

$$\mathbf{x}[x] = x_m e^{j\bar{\omega}n}$$

we obtain from (3.167) the following expression for the output

$$\mathbf{z}[n, \varepsilon] = x_m \left\{ K^*(j\bar{\omega}, \varepsilon) e^{j\bar{\omega}n} - \frac{k_0}{e^{j\bar{\omega}} - e^{-\beta}} e^{-\beta(n+1+\varepsilon)} \right\},$$

where

$k_0 = k_p/T$ and

$$\left. \begin{aligned} K^*(j\bar{\omega}, \varepsilon) &= \frac{k_0 e^{j\bar{\omega}}}{e^{j\bar{\omega}} - e^{-\beta}} e^{-\beta\varepsilon} = \frac{k_0 e^{-\beta\varepsilon} e^{j(\bar{\omega}+\psi)}}{\sqrt{(1 - 2e^{-\beta}\cos\bar{\omega} + e^{-2\beta})}}, \\ \psi &= -\arctan\frac{\sin\bar{\omega}}{\cos\bar{\omega} - e^{-\beta}}. \end{aligned} \right\} \quad (3.175)$$

For $x[n] = x_m \cos\bar{\omega}n$ we have

$$z[n, \varepsilon] = x_m |K^*(\bar{\omega}, \varepsilon)| \cos[\bar{\omega}n + \theta^*(\bar{\omega}, \varepsilon)] - \frac{k_0 e^{-\beta(n+1+\varepsilon)}}{\sqrt{(1 - 2e^{-\beta}\cos\bar{\omega} + e^{-2\beta})}} \cos\psi.$$

The variation of $\mathbf{z}[n, \varepsilon]$ for $\bar{\omega} = \pi/2$, $\beta = 0{\cdot}5$, $k_0 = 1$ is shown in Fig. 3.36*a*. For a simple pulse system in which rectangular pulses are formed, we have from (3.171) and (3.172)

$$\mathbf{z}[n, \varepsilon] = x_m \left\{ K^*(j\bar{\omega}, \varepsilon) e^{j\bar{\omega}n} + k_p \frac{1 - e^{\beta\gamma}}{e^{j\bar{\omega}} - e^{-\beta}} e^{-\beta(n+1+\varepsilon)} \right\} \quad (3.176)$$

where

$$K^*(j\bar{\omega}, \varepsilon) = \begin{cases} k_p \left[1 - \dfrac{e^{j\bar{\omega}} - e^{-\beta(1-\gamma)}}{e^{j\bar{\omega}} - e^{-\beta}} e^{-\beta\varepsilon} \right], & 0 \leqslant \varepsilon \leqslant \gamma, \\ k_p \dfrac{(1 - e^{-\beta\gamma}) e^{j\bar{\omega}}}{e^{j\bar{\omega}} - e^{-\beta}} e^{-\beta(\varepsilon-\gamma)}, & \gamma \leqslant \varepsilon \leqslant 1. \end{cases} \quad (3.177)$$

The qualitative variation of $z[n, \varepsilon] = \operatorname{Re} \mathbf{z}[n, \varepsilon]$ is sketched in Fig. 3.36*b*.

The response of a simple pulse system with step-wise periodically varying parameters to a harmonic excitation can be formed using the transfer functions (3.131):

$$\left.\begin{aligned} \mathbf{z}[n,\varepsilon] &= x_m k_0 \left\{\left[1 - \frac{e^{j\bar{\omega}} - e^{-\beta''(1-\gamma)}}{e^{j\bar{\omega}} - e^{-\beta_{av}}} e^{-\beta'\varepsilon}\right] e^{j\bar{\omega}n} + \right. \\ &\left. + \frac{1 - e^{\beta'\gamma}}{e^{j\bar{\omega}} - e^{-\beta_{av}}} e^{-\beta_{av}(n+1)} e^{-\beta'\varepsilon}\right\}, \qquad 0 \leqslant \varepsilon \leqslant \gamma, \\ \mathbf{z}[n,\varepsilon] &= x_m k_0 \left\{\left[\frac{(1 - e^{-\beta'\gamma}) e^{j\bar{\omega}}}{e^{j\bar{\omega}} - e^{-\beta_{av}}} e^{\beta''(\varepsilon-\gamma)}\right] e^{j\bar{\omega}n} + \right. \\ &\left. + \frac{e^{-\beta'\gamma} - 1}{e^{j\bar{\omega}} - e^{-\beta_{av}}} e^{-\beta_{av}(n+1)} e^{-\beta''(\varepsilon-\gamma)}\right\}, \qquad \gamma \leqslant \varepsilon \leqslant 1, \end{aligned}\right\} \quad (3.178)$$

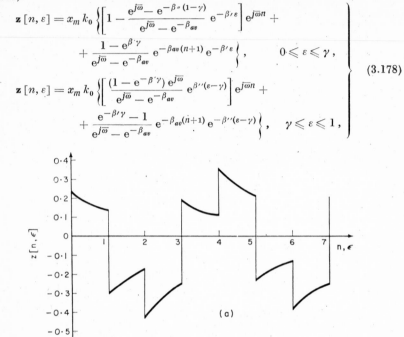

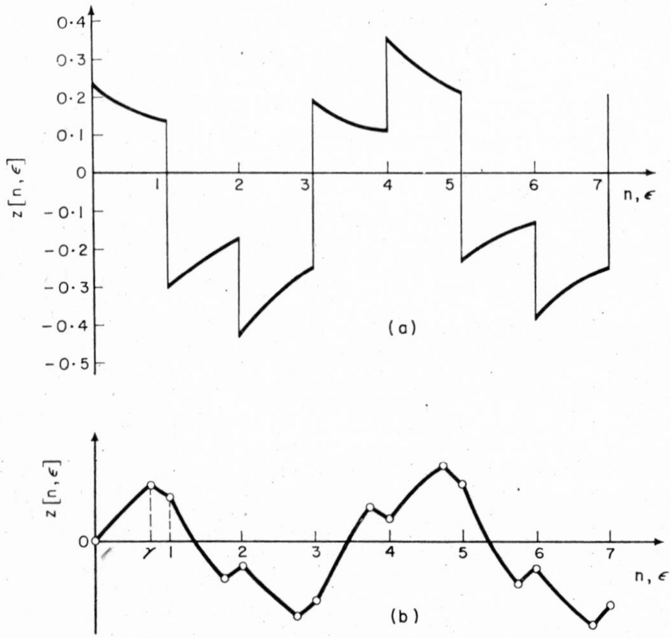

FIG. 3.36. Variation of $z\,[n, \varepsilon]$ in a simple pulse system for a harmonic excitation; case of (*a*) instantaneous pulses, and (*b*) rectangular pulses.

where

$$k_0 = k_p\, k \quad \text{and} \quad \beta_{av} = \beta'\,\gamma + \beta''(1-\gamma)\,.$$

Ramp excitation. In concluding we examine the case when the input excitation varies according to a linear law (Fig. 3.37*a*). The corresponding lattice function (Fig. 3.37*b*) equals

$$x\,[n] = x_0\, n\,.$$

The image of the input quantity, according to (2.56), equals

$$X^*(q) = x_0 D\{n\} = x_0 \frac{e^q}{(e^q - 1)^2}.$$

Consequently, the pulse-system equation in this case becomes

$$Z^*(q, \varepsilon) = x_0 \sum_{\nu=1}^{l} c_{\nu 0} \frac{e^q}{e^q - e^{q_\nu}} \frac{e^q}{(e^q - 1)^2} e^{q_\nu \varepsilon}.$$

Since

$$\frac{e^q}{(e^q - e^{q_\nu})(e^q - 1)^2} e^q \doteq \frac{n+1}{1 - e^{q_\nu}} - \frac{1 - e^{q_\nu(n+1)}}{(1 - e^{q_\nu})^2}, \qquad (3.179)$$

which follows on applying the real-translation theorem to (2.80), we can easily find the original of $z^*(q, \varepsilon)$:

$$z[n, \varepsilon] = x_0 \left\{ \sum_{\nu=1}^{l} \frac{c'_{\nu 0}}{1 - e^{q_\nu}} \left[n - \frac{e^{q_\nu}}{1 - e^{q_\nu}} \right] e^{q_\nu \varepsilon} + \sum_{\nu=1}^{l} \frac{c'_{\nu 0}}{(1 - e^{q_\nu})^2} e^{q_\nu(n+1+\varepsilon)} \right\}. \qquad (3.180)$$

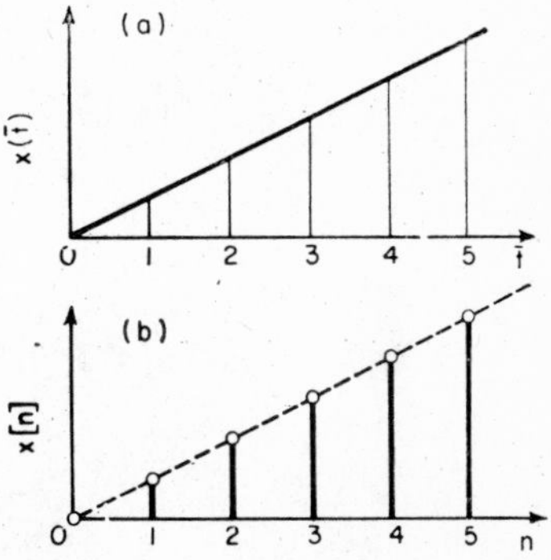

FIG. 3.37. Linear excitation (*a*) and the corresponding lattice function (*b*).

Expression (3.180) consists of two parts. The first part varies linearly with n and corresponds to the steady-state process; the second as before, characterises the transient process.

For a pulse system whose shaping element produces rectangular pulses, we can easily show that the output is given by

$$\left.\begin{aligned} z[n, \varepsilon] &= x_0 \left\{ c_{00} n + \sum_{\nu=1}^{l} \frac{c_{\nu 0}}{1 - e^{q_\nu}} \left[(1 - e^{q_\nu(1-\gamma)}) n - \right.\right. \\ &\quad \left.\left. - \frac{e^{q_\nu}(1 - e^{-q_\nu \gamma})}{1 - e^{q_\nu}} \right] e^{q_\nu \varepsilon} + \sum_{\nu=1}^{l} c_{\nu 0} \frac{1 - e^{-q_\nu \gamma}}{(1 - e^{q_\nu})^2} e^{q_\nu(n+1+\varepsilon)} \right\}, \\ &\qquad\qquad\qquad 0 \leqslant \varepsilon \leqslant \gamma, \\ z[n, \varepsilon] &= x_0 \left\{ \sum_{\nu=1}^{l} c_{\nu 0} \frac{1 - e^{-q_\nu \gamma}}{1 - e^{q_\nu}} \left(n - \frac{e^{q_\nu}}{1 - e^{q_\nu}} \right) e^{q_\nu \varepsilon} + \right. \\ &\quad \left. + \sum_{\nu=1}^{l} c_{\nu 0} \frac{1 - e^{-q_\nu \gamma}}{(1 - e^{q_\nu})^2} e^{q_\nu(n+1+\varepsilon)} \right\}, \qquad \gamma \leqslant \varepsilon \leqslant 1. \end{aligned}\right\} \qquad (3.181)$$

EXAMPLE. For the simple pulse system of Fig. 3.8. we obtain, from (3.180), the following expression for the output

$$z[n,\varepsilon]=x_0\left\{\frac{k_0}{1-e^{-\beta}}\left(n-\frac{e^{-\beta}}{1-e^{-\beta}}\right)e^{-\beta\varepsilon}+\frac{k_0}{(1-e^{-\beta})^2}e^{-\beta(n+1+\varepsilon)}\right\}. \qquad (3.182)$$

The variation of $z[n, \varepsilon]$ is sketched in Fig. 3.38*a*.

If the pulse-system shaping element produces rectangular pulses, we have from (3.181):

$$\left.\begin{aligned}
z[n,\varepsilon]&=x_0k_p\left\{n-\frac{1}{1-e^{-\beta}}\left[(1-e^{-\beta(1-\gamma)})\,n-\frac{e^{-\beta}(1-e^{\beta\gamma})}{1-e^{-\beta}}\right]e^{-\beta\varepsilon}-\right.\\
&\qquad\left.-\frac{1-e^{\beta\gamma}}{(1-e^{-\beta})^2}e^{-\beta(n+1+\varepsilon)}\right\}, \qquad 0\leqslant\varepsilon\leqslant\gamma,\\
z[n,\varepsilon]&=x_0k_p\left\{\frac{e^{\beta\gamma}-1}{1-e^{-\beta}}\left(n-\frac{e^{-\beta}}{1-e^{-\beta}}\right)e^{-\beta\varepsilon}-\right.\\
&\qquad\left.-\frac{1-e^{\beta\gamma}}{(1-e^{-\beta})^2}e^{-\beta(n+1+\varepsilon)}\right\}, \qquad \gamma\leqslant\varepsilon\leqslant 1.
\end{aligned}\right\} \qquad (3.183)$$

The nature of this response is sketched in Fig. 3.38*b*.

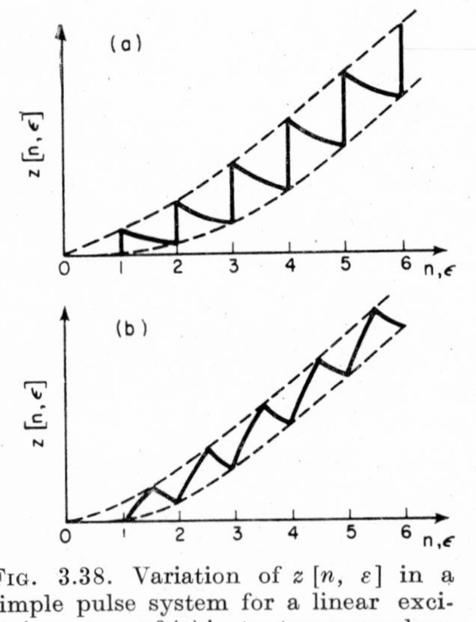

FIG. 3.38. Variation of $z[n, \varepsilon]$ in a simple pulse system for a linear excitation; case of (*a*) instantaneous pulses, and (*b*) rectangular pulses.

When deriving the above expressions for the responses of pulse systems we did not require the inversion and expansion formulae since the transmission coefficients of the pulse systems, and consequently the images of the output variables, took the form of a sum of simple images the originals of which could be found without difficulty.

We note that the formulae obtained in this section are analogous to the well-known Heaviside formulae in the theory of transients in continuous systems.

3.6. Pulse and frequency characteristics of open-loop pulse systems

The properties of a pulse system, like those of a conventional continuous system, can be completely characterised by its pulse and frequency characteristics. The *pulse characteristic* of an open-loop pulse